A VARIETY
OF SHORT PLAYS

A VARIETY OF SHORT PLAYS

edited by *John C. Schweitzer*

ENGLISH DEPARTMENT
RYE HIGH SCHOOL, RYE, NEW YORK

Charles Scribner's Sons　　New York

Printed in the United States of America
SBN 684-51555-5
Library of Congress Catalog Card Number 66-18179

CONTENTS

TO THE READER

As you read the plays in this collection, you may find yourself identifying with characters whose experiences in some way resemble your own. Perhaps it will be with John Taplow in *The Browning Version*, anxious about his scholastic future, or with Shirley in *Native Dancer*, anticipating her first important audition. Examine the plays closely, and you will observe that the playwright has dramatized these experiences at the expense of other matters he might easily have included. What are John Taplow's hobbies? Who are his favorite authors? Is he a good ball player? How did Shirley meet Max?

Although these are things you may imagine, you do not learn them from reading the plays. It was never the playwright's intention that you should. In order to capture and sustain your interest in what he has to say, he must concentrate upon a limited range of human experience, dramatizing only those situations that most clearly illustrate his point. This point is the underlying idea or *theme* of the play, and all details of the play's construction are carefully organized around it.

In the full-length play the playwright may show how each of several situations contributes to his theme; in the briefer play he seldom has the time to do so. Since most short plays run no longer than thirty minutes of actual playing time when performed on stage, the playwright who chooses this form must generally confine himself to a single situation.

A typical example of a single situation is Eugene O'Neill's *Ile*. There is only one main setting, and a small cast of characters. The action is continuous. From the beginning of the play, you are aware that Captain Keeney is a deeply troubled man, tormented by the conflict between pride in his record as a whaling captain and his obligations to those around him. The ice, the almost perpetual stillness, the movements and mannerisms of his wife and the crew all highlight Keeney's dilemma. The result is what Edgar Allan Poe termed *singleness of effect* in writing. He happened to be speaking of the short story, but singleness of effect is just as indispensable to the successful short play. Were *Ile* a full-length play, you might have started on that voyage with Captain Keeney earlier and traveled with him farther, participating along the way in experiences missing from the play in its existing one-act form.

However, just because these plays are short, they are not necessarily easy reading. Although the plays in this collection have been selected for their enjoyment and "readability," every one of them will require your close, critical attention. A playwright differs from a short story writer or a novelist in that he cannot tell you what the characters are thinking. He is restricted in his presentation to what the characters *hear,* and *do,* and *say.* For the writer of the short play, such restrictions pose a special burden.

If the writer is to reveal what the characters are like, and at the same time remain brief and to the point, he must rely upon small details to help communicate his meaning. By slight gestures indicated in his stage directions, by specifications for stage properties and for lighting, he often gives you important clues to character and theme.

In addition to noting such clues, you should note the relationship between one part of the play and another. First, you must ask yourself, "What is this play all about?" In the short play the author will usually provide the answer very quickly, by giving background information that explains the situation in which the characters are presently involved. This explanation is called the *exposition.* It will come chiefly from the dialogue, but it may also come from the opening description of the setting, or from stage "business"—action without dialogue. Study the beginnings of such plays as *Ile* and *The Browning Version* for good examples of how a playwright uses setting and stage business to introduce his story.

As the action of the play moves forward, you will not only learn more about the characters and their relationships, but you will also discover the nature of their problem. Whatever the problem, it will always involve some kind of conflict. It may be a conflict of ideas, or a conflict between men, or a conflict between man and nature.

The portion of the play that presents the conflict and shows the first step toward a solution is called the *rising action*. During the rising action there is often a dramatic turning point, or *crisis*, as a character attempts to resolve the conflict, but is unsuccessful. A typical crisis is the moment in *Sammy* when the hero realizes that his own brother will not lend him the money he needs to avert disaster. There may be several such turning points, even in the short play, before the major turning point occurs.

This major turning point represents the moment in the play when the conflict is at last resolved. It is called the *climax*. In most short plays the climax is followed quite swiftly by the *falling action* or *dénouement*, a French word that means "the unraveling." At this point you see how the solution to the conflict affects the main characters, and gain an inkling of what their future may hold.

There is no rule, of course, which states that a playwright is obligated to present the kind of orderly, step-like development to his story that this structural outline suggests. Characters do not always solve their problems or change as a result of their experiences. Sometimes the playwright is more interested in showing you the reasons for these failures than he is in intensifying the conflict or in building suspense. Both *To Bobolink for Her Spirit* and *The Man With the Heart in the Highlands*, for example, lack a strong rising action and a distinguishable climax; yet in their revelation of character they are among the most meaningful plays in the present collection. You must be prepared for such variations in play construction, however infrequently they may occur.

Finally, it is important to evaluate the play as a whole by asking yourself: How successfully has the author carried out his purpose? Are the characters true-to-life? Do they behave in a manner that is understandable, considering the circumstances of the play and their own personalities? Does the solution to the problem arise naturally out of the events that preceded it?

In summary, then, most short plays have the following characteristics: (1) emphasis upon a single situation, (2) restricted use of characters and setting, (3) unity of effect, (4) continuity of action, and (5) brevity of form. Because the short play embodies many of the same principles of play construction as the full-length play, without the latter's greater complexity of design, it provides an ideal opportunity to become acquainted with the technique of the drama.

These plays are brief enough to be read in a single sitting, and thoroughly discussed in a single class session.

ABOUT THE SELECTIONS AND THE STUDY MATERIAL

This collection indicates the wide range of topics that writers have found appropriate for short plays. Representing the talents of twenty authors of different backgrounds and nationalities, these plays vary markedly in mood, in setting, and in theme. There are fantasies and farces, comedies and tragedies, melodramas and historical dramas, including some notable examples from the sound stages and studios of radio and television.

Sometimes, as has already been suggested, you may share an actual experience with the character of a play. More often the similarity will be one of outlook. Undoubtedly you have never served as a teacher of Latin in a boy's preparatory school (*The Browning Version*), sailed the Arctic seas in search of whale oil (*Ile*), or listened to the click of the telegraph as you awaited news of your men in battle (*The Thinking Heart*), but surely you have at one time or another put your courage to the test and attempted to meet a trying situation with resourcefulness and dignity.

Although you may seek your own identity in the plays that you read, if you are a truly observant reader you will not stop there. You will go on to examine critically the lives of characters whose behavior and point of view differ from your own. Further, you will enrich your pleasure in reading a play by comparing it with others that you have already read. Do the characters have anything in common? Are there similarities in the themes? Is the conflict in one developed more effectively than the conflict in another?

The study material has been arranged to lead you into a discussion of just such questions as these. At the beginning of each play there is a brief biography of the playwright and a statement suggesting the play's theme. At the end of the play there are questions for discussion and topics for writing, designed to bring the issues of the play into meaningful focus. The comparative reading questions listed separately at the end of the study material will challenge your depth and range of understanding. Here you have an opportunity to express yourself on matters which may not have been thoroughly explored in class discussion. A glossary has been provided for your reference, and explanatory notes appear for the plays where necessary, but there has been no attempt to overwhelm you with technical terms. Unfamiliar terms are italicized the first time they appear to indicate that they are defined in the glossary.

While the plays may be read in almost any order that is desired, they have been carefully arranged on the basis of story difficulty. Those toward the end of the text are, for the most part, the longer and the more challenging selections. They may be easier to understand if you first gain practice in playreading by studying the brief comedies and melodramas that appear at the beginning of the text.

The primary purpose of this study material is, of course, to help you to understand the plays. Its final purpose, however, is to help you to enjoy them. Approach your study in the manner that has been suggested, and you will find that no other form of literature offers you a more enjoyable reading experience than the short play.

PERSONAL ACKNOWLEDGMENTS

I wish to thank my wife, Barbara, my family, and the staff of Charles Scribner's Sons, especially Miss Ellen Ehrlich, Mr. Paul L. Millane, and Miss Sandra Thompson, for their cooperation in the many phases of planning and preparing this work.

I also wish to thank Mrs. Sarah Lalli of the White Plains, New York, Public Library, Miss Phyllis Paccadolmi of the public library in Ridgefield, Connecticut, and Mr. David K. Seplow for their help in locating needed materials.

A VARIETY
OF SHORT PLAYS

THE $99,000 ANSWER

Leonard Stern and Sydney Zelinka

CHARACTERS

Ralph Kramden
Alice Kramden
Ed Norton
Trixie Norton
Announcer
MC
Parker
Mother
Garrity
Mrs. Manicotti

The $99,000 Answer was first presented on "The Honeymooners" program by Jackie Gleason Enterprises, Inc. on CBS-TV, under the direction of Frank Satenstein, on January 28, 1956.

Leonard Stern and Sydney Zelinka
(1922-   )   (1911-   )

Both Leonard Stern and Sydney Zelinka were born and educated in New York, and achieved recognition as radio and motion picture script writers before turning to television. Over the past several years they have contributed to many of the nation's major television comedy shows, including the highly successful "Sergeant Bilko" and the Jackie Gleason "Honeymooners" series. Stern, who is now an executive with Talent Associates—Paramount, Ltd., has also had experience as a television producer. Zelinka has written several shows for Sid Caesar as well as "TV Specials" for various other comedy stars.

For their collaboration on "The $99,000 Answer" Stern and Zelinka earned the Writer's Guild Award for "Best Situation Comedy" script of 1956. A spoof of the television quiz shows popular during the 1950's, the play appeared originally on "The Honeymooners" program.

THE $99,000 ANSWER

As curtains part camera holds on establishing shot of stage setting for $99,000 Answer Show. Big Banner says "$99,000 Answer." Should be standard quiz show set of type used on audience participation shows. Center stage are MC and a male contestant. Contestant is bright-looking, conservatively dressed man in his middle forties. Music Playoff.

ANNOUNCER'S VOICE   Now back to Herb Norris and the $99,000 Answer . . . the show that gives away ninety-nine thousand dollars!

MC   Well, Mr. Parker, you have successfully gone over the $4,750 hurdle and now it is time to make up your mind whether you are willing to go for the $9,500 answer.

PARKER   I am, Mr. Norris. (*Audience reaction.*)

MC   Good. I wish you luck, Mr. Parker. If you complete the $9,500 answer you will then be eligible to come back next week and try to clear the last hurdle for the $99,000 answer. Mr. Parker, are you ready?

PARKER   I'm ready, Mr. Norris.

MC   Fine, this question for your $9,500 answer was prepared by an expert in the field of banking and finance . . . Professor Walter Newman. Your question has to do with something you see and handle every day—a dollar bill. Now, disregarding the serial number, tell me how many times the figure "ONE" appears on a dollar bill, either in numeral form or spelled out. I'll repeat that. How many times does the figure one appear on a dollar bill, either in numeral form or spelled out! Give me the total and then tell me how many there are . . . you have fifteen seconds to give the $9,500 answer. . . . Your time is up! What is your answer?

MUSIC OUT

PARKER   The total number is twenty-five.

MC   That's correct!

PARKER   Sixteen times for the word "ONE" and nine times for the numeral "ONE."

MC   You're absolutely right!

LIGHTS UP—MUSIC—APPLAUSE—

MC   Mr. Parker, you've won yourself $9,500 of those one-dollar bills and you are now eligible to come back next week when you have the choice of taking the $9,500 or going for the last hurdle and $99,000! Good-bye—Good luck. (*Applause, music playoff as* PARKER *exits.*) And now, who is our next guest? (*A shot of a petrified* KRAMDEN *being led from wings by a lovely young girl. Over this shot,* ANNOUNCER'S *voice speaks.*)

ANNOUNCER'S VOICE   Herb, here's our next guest ready to leap the first hurdle on his way to the $99,000 answer . . . from Brooklyn, New York . . . Mr. Ralph Kramden! (*Applause.* RALPH *is now standing downstage with* MC.)

MC   How do you do, Mr. Kramden. (*As* MC *extends hand,* RALPH *grabs for it as though it were a life preserver and continues to shake it in his nervousness.*)

RALPH   Buh—Buh— (MC *sizing up situation and anxious to get his hand back.*)

MC   Mr. Kramden, there's nothing for you to be nervous about. We're all your friends and everybody's rooting for you. (RALPH *nods with weak smile but keeps shaking* MC's *hand*) Just relax, Mr. Kramden. (RALPH *nods but keeps shaking hand*) It's certainly been nice shaking hands with you, Mr. Kramden. (RALPH *suddenly comes to his senses.*)

RALPH   Oh, buh, buh . . . buh . . . (RALPH *lets go of* MC's *hand and for a moment is at a loss as to what to do with his free hand.*)

MC   What kind of work do you do, Mr. Kramden?

RALPH   I'm a brus diver.

MC   A brus diver??

RALPH   Yeah. I brive a dus.

MC   Oh, you drive a bus!

RALPH   That's what I said, I'm a dus briver!

MC   Mr. Kramden, I can understand you being nervous, but it will be to your advantage to relax and calm yourself. Just remember we're all friends and I'm here to help you. (RALPH *smiles appreciatively*) Are you married, Mr. Kramden? (RALPH *nods "yes"*) What's your wife's name?

RALPH   Kramden.

MC   (*Helpfully*)   Her first name.

RALPH   Her—oh!—Alice!

MC   And you're from Brooklyn . . . have you lived in Brooklyn all your life?

RALPH   Er—not yet.

MC   (*Amused*)   I see . . . Mr. Kramden, I've always had great respect for the bus drivers of New York. It's been a constant source of wonderment to me how you men who have those huge buses to handle, and all the responsibilities that go with it, can remain as courteous and considerate as you do.

RALPH   Thank you, sir.

MC   Of course there always are exceptions to the rule—like what happened to me the other day. It was raining and I was waiting on Madison Avenue for a bus. Finally a bus came along and I signaled the driver. Not only did that driver ignore my signal, but he drove right by me through a puddle and splashed mud all over me!

RALPH Was that you?

MC (*Good-naturedly*) Well. I hope you win some money . . . I've got a cleaning bill for you . . . Now, Mr. Kramden, it's time to choose your category from our list of subjects. (*Girl holds up cardboard for* RALPH *to look at; it has fifteen categories*) Take your time in picking your category because all your answers will be based on the category you decide upon.

RALPH I think I'll take popular songs.

MC Very well, popular songs.

ANNOUNCER'S VOICE I'm sorry to interrupt, Herb, but our time is up.

MC Mr. Kramden, I'm sorry but if you come back next week, you'll get your chance to reach the first hurdle and work your way up to the $99,000 answer . . . Can you be here?

RALPH Yeah . . . Sure . . . Yes, sir!

MC Thank you for being with us on the $99,000 answer. We look forward to seeing you next week. Good night. And good night, everyone.

MUSIC—PLAYOFF—DISSOLVE

As curtains part camera holds on establishing shot of KRAMDEN *kitchen.* ALICE *is in process of removing her coat. Door opens, a breathless* TRIXIE *enters.*

TRIXIE Alice! Oh, Alice! I couldn't wait until you got home. Ralph looked wonderful on television!

ALICE Trix, it was so exciting.

TRIXIE I'll bet. (TRIXIE *looks around*) Isn't Ralph here?

ALICE He decided to stay downstairs. He's waiting for people to go by and recognize him.

TRIXIE Who can recognize him at this hour? It's dark out. (ALICE *takes* TRIXIE *to window.*)

ALICE He thought of that. (*Points out window*) There he is standing under the street light with his hat off!

TRIXIE Well, on second thought, I don't know if I'd act any different, if I was on a big television program and I was seen by millions of people.

ALICE Don't get me wrong, Trix. I'm real proud that Ralph's on the show. The only thing is that he gets over-enthused—runs away with himself. He can build himself way up to a let down and then he'll feel miserable.

TRIXIE   Yeah.

ALICE   Here he's acting like he's already given the 99,000-dollar answer and he hasn't even been asked the first question!

TRIXIE   Gee, wouldn't it be great if Ralph won 99,000 dollars?

ALICE   Take it easy, Trix. Let's be practical. Even Ralph knows he's no expert. The first two questions usually aren't so tough. If he can answer those and walk away with six hundred dollars, I'll be more than happy.

TRIXIE   You're right. Six hundred dollars can come in mighty handy . . . but just between us, Alice, you'd better hint to Ralph to always face the camera. When he stands in profile—brother! He's the biggest thing on television! (TRIXIE *goes to door as* ALICE *laughs good-naturedly.*)

ALICE   How about Ed, did he see the show?

TRIXIE   Yeah. He watched it with the boys over at the bowling alley. He'll probably stop in and see Ralph on his way upstairs. Night, Alice. See you tomorrow.

ALICE   Night, Trix. (TRIXIE *goes out.* TRIXIE *closes door behind her.* ALICE *picks up coat and carries it into bedroom.* RALPH *comes in. He's carrying large piece of cardboard. The blank side is visible.* ALICE *comes out of bedroom.*)

RALPH   Well, Alice, I've finally learned a lesson. This house is filled with nothing but jealous people.

ALICE   What are you talking about?

RALPH   There wasn't one person in this house, not one, waiting downstairs to congratulate me! They won't admit they saw me on the program.

ALICE   Ralph, don't talk that way. Norton watched it over at the bowling alley with all your friends and Trixie was just here to say she saw you.

RALPH   (*Brightens*)   Oh, she saw me. How'd she like me? How'd she think I was?

ALICE   She says you're the biggest thing on television!

RALPH   She said that? Nice girl, Trixie. And that Norton's a good guy too. They're real, true friends. Alice, they're gonna be with me when I celebrate my big night.

ALICE   What big night?

RALPH   When I win the 99,000 dollars! (ALICE *is struck speechless by* RALPH's *crazy confidence*) Yessiree, Alice. Soon we'll be livin' on Park Avenue. And just you wait and see how different this furniture'll look in a Park Avenue apartment! (ALICE *has to flag him down.*)

ALICE   Ralph, aren't you being a little too ambitious? You've heard some of the questions . . . they get awfully tough after the first two.

RALPH   Why do you think I picked popular songs as my category? I know all about them songs.

ALICE   But, Ralph, you're not an expert.

RALPH   Oh, no? I was interested in songs even when I was a little kid. And when I grew up I didn't waste my time like the other guys. While they were bumming around street corners and pool rooms . . . *I* spent every night of the week up at Roseland!

ALICE   Ralph, I'll be very proud of you if you just answer the first two questions and come home with six hundred dollars.

RALPH   Six hundred dollars! That's pennies!

ALICE   Ralph, I'm only talking common sense.

RALPH   Common sense? It's common sense to blow the opportunity of a lifetime? Look, I'll explain it to you real simple. (*He illustrates by putting imaginary piles of money on table*) Right over here is six hundred dollars. Over here is ninety-nine thousand dollars. I have a choice of taking either one of the two. Now my intelligence tells me that I gotta take the ninety-nine thousand. But if you're foolish enough to think I'm wrong, just tell me because I got an open mind!

ALICE   Well, you better close it before the rest of your brains fall out! . . . Stop dreaming, Ralph. They don't hand you that ninety-nine thousand. You've got to answer questions. And they're tough questions!

RALPH   Oh, so that's what you've been leading up to. Your husband's too dumb to answer questions. A twelve-year-old little girl can come on another program and win $16,000 but it comes out now you don't think I'm as smart as a twelve-year-old kid. Well, for your information, I can answer the toughest question they can think up because it stands to reason I gotta be smarter than any twelve-year-old kid!

ALICE   Spell Antidisestablishmentarianism. (RALPH *stares at* ALICE *for a split second.*)

RALPH   I can spell it. I can spell it, all right.

ALICE   Well, go ahead.

RALPH   Why should I? I'll spell it when you can give me sixteen thousand dollars for spelling it.

ALICE   Sixteen thousand for spelling it? I'll give you thirty-two thousand dollars if you can *say* it!

RALPH   (*Reacts*)   All right. All right, I will . . . some day.

ALICE   Ralph, I don't doubt you know a lot about popular songs. Let's even say you know *everything* about them. There's still one thing you're overlooking. That when you're on a television show, under pressure, with millions of people looking at you and with big money at stake, you're liable to get nervous and forget what you know. Any person could do that.

RALPH   Not this person. When I'm under pressure I'm at my best. I never get nervous.

ALICE   Oh, that's right, I forgot. You're always calm. You have to be in the work you do. You're a man who *brives a dus*. (RALPH *grunts*.)

RALPH   Alice, nothing you say is gonna make me change my mind. I'm gonna win that $99,000 and to make sure I do I ain't gonna leave a stone unturned. I'm staying home every night this week. I'm gonna study all the books on songs and songwriters. I'm gonna study every piece of sheet music. I'm gonna buy phonograph records. And that ain't all. I'm gonna rent a piano so that Norton can come down and play the tunes until I'm sure that I can recognize every one of them.

ALICE   Ralph, that's gonna cost a fortune. It'll take every cent we have saved. We'll have nothing in the bank.

RALPH   We'll have $99,000 in the bank . . . you ain't talking me out of it, Alice. I'm going for that pot of gold!

ALICE   Just go for the gold—you've already got the pot! (ALICE *turns and exits into bedroom, slamming door behind her.* RALPH *shouts at closed door.*)

> As curtains part, camera holds on establishing shot of KRAM-DEN *kitchen. Changes have been wrought. There's a piano upstage right, a portable hand-crank Victrola is strategically placed and piles of sheet music and records stacked all over the place. There's a knock on door.* ALICE *comes out of bedroom in robe and slippers. She goes to door and opens it.*

ALICE   Mother, what are you doing here at this hour?

MOTHER   (*Hands* ALICE *a package*)   Here's the dress material that you wanted.

ALICE   Oh, you didn't have to make a special trip for that, Mother.

MOTHER   I didn't. We went to a movie in the neighborhood, so it wasn't out of the way at all.

ALICE   Sit down. Have a cup of coffee.

MOTHER   I can't. Your father's waiting in the car. He's double parked. (MOTHER *looks around and takes the place in*) How's the brain doing?

ALICE   What a week! The piano and phonograph have been going every night until three in the morning. He's been fighting out the window with Mr. Garrity upstairs. Strangers have been stopping in to give him advice. He's gotten letters. Staying home from work without salary, paying for all this stuff? He'll have to win the $99,000 to cover expenses.

MOTHER   Where is he now?

ALICE   He's down at Mrs. Manicotti's. She's helping him brush up on all the popular songs that have been taken from Italian classics. This boy isn't missing a trick.

MOTHER   I've got to go. I'll keep my fingers crossed for Ralph tomorrow night.

ALICE   Thanks. Say hello to Pop. (*As* ALICE's *mother goes to door, it opens and* RALPH *comes in.*)

RALPH   (*Sees* ALICE's *mother. His enthusiasm disappears immediately*)   Alice, I was perfect. I . . . Oh, hello, Mother.

MOTHER   Hello, Ralph. Well, tomorrow's your big night. Alice and I were talking about it and there's just one thing I want to say . . .

RALPH   Save your breath! I know what you're gonna say and I ain't gonna do it! I ain't quittin' at six hundred bucks. I might've known you'd both get together to work on me. Well, Mrs. Buttinsky, you're wasting your time 'cause I'm goin' all the way.

MOTHER   But, Ralph, before you interrupted me, I was about to say I hoped you'd go for the $99,000 answer. (RALPH *is taken aback by* MOTHER's *statement.*)

RALPH   Oh . . . oh . . . you hear that, Alice? Why don't you listen to your mother once in a while? She's a smart woman. (*Pleased.*)

MOTHER   As a matter of fact, I can't wait for you to answer that question . . . want to see the expression on your face when you miss it. (MOTHER *hurries out and slams door.*)

RALPH   That does it! That does it! When we move to Park Avenue, I ain't givin' her our new address!

ALICE   Ralph, I must be crazy to even argue with you about this.

You've got us living on Park Avenue, winning $99,000—Ralph, you haven't even answered the first question!

RALPH   There you go, tearing me down and upsetting me at a time like this. Mrs. Edward R. Murrow wouldn't act this way!

ALICE   What's Mrs. Edward R. Murrow got to do with this?

RALPH   Her husband's got a television show, too. (ALICE *looks at him as though this is the end. She's heard everything.*)

ALICE   I'm going to bed. (ALICE *goes into bedroom. Closes door.* RALPH *yells at closed door.*)

RALPH   (*Shouts*) The truth hurts! (RALPH *crosses to piano and riffs through songs on top. Door opens and* NORTON *enters, singing happily. He is carrying an armful of sheet music.*)

NORTON   (*Singing*) "Give me land, lots of land, deedle, deedle, deedle, dee—don't deedle dee . . ."

RALPH   "Don't fence me in" . . . written by Cole Porter . . . from the picture *Hollywood Canteen*, produced by Warner Brothers in 1944.

NORTON   When that master of ceremonies gets to you, Ralph, he's gonna run out of hurdles! How'd you do at Mrs. Manicotti's?

RALPH   I left her speechless. She kept trying to stick me, but I knew the English name for every song she sang in Italian.

NORTON   I picked up some more movie songs to try out on you.

RALPH   Well, come on, play them. I want to see if I know them.

NORTON   Okay, okay. (*He puts sheet music on rack; hand routine, loosening of fingers, etc.*)

RALPH   Will you come on! This is the last night I got (NORTON *starts to play Swanee River and picks up.* RALPH *shoves him*) There you go again. You can't play a song without starting with that. (*Hums "Swanee River"*) Why do you have to do that?

NORTON   If I've explained it once, I've explained it a hundred times. It's the only way I can play the piano. A baseball pitcher's gotta warm up before he pitches—I gotta warm up before I play! . . . I hope I don't have to explain again! You ready?

RALPH   Yeah. (NORTON *plays "Swanee River" and pick up into "Shuffle Off to Buffalo"*) "Shuffle Off to Buffalo" by Warren and Dubin from *Forty-Second Street*. 1932.

NORTON   Perfect. Now hear this. (NORTON *plays "Swanee River" and pick up into "Too Marvelous for Words."*)

RALPH   "Too Marvelous for Words" by Johnny Mercer and Richard Whiting from *Ready, Willing and Able*, 1937.

NORTON Right again. This is a tricky one, Ralph. Goes back a way. (RALPH *sings.* NORTON *plays Swanee and pick up into "Melancholy Serenade" fast tempo. It is interrupted by loud pounding at door.* RALPH *goes to door. It's* GARRITY.)

GARRITY Shut up in here. You're driving everyone crazy!

RALPH Oh, so it's you, Garrity. You're jealous, Garrity. You're jealous because tomorrow my picture's gonna be on the front page of every newspaper.

GARRITY So will mine . . . for killing you! (GARRITY *leaves, slamming door behind him.* ALICE *appears in doorway.*)

ALICE Ralph! (RALPH *opens door and shouts down hall after* GARRITY.)

RALPH Ya satisfied, loud mouth! Now you woke up my wife! (*As* RALPH *comes back from door,* ALICE *addresses* NORTON.)

ALICE Ed, I realize I can't talk to Ralph because he's stubborn and unreasonable. I've always had respect for your sense of fair play, so I appeal to you. It's late and people want to go to sleep. I think you ought to stop playing the piano. I'm sure you agree with me because you've always been fair and considerate—a reasonable man! (NORTON *caught between the devil and the deep blue sea looks from one to the other.*)

RALPH Don't let her soft soap you. You're just as unreasonable as I am. Go ahead and play the piano!

ALICE If you touch that piano again, I'll lose all my respect for you!

RALPH Play that piano or our friendship is over! (*Poor* ED. *He looks from one to the other.*)

NORTON If I play the piano I lose your respect. If I don't play the piano I lose your friendship. (*He looks heavenward, arms extended and speaks beseechingly*) Why, oh, why was I blessed with this musical talent? (*There's a knock on door.*)

ALICE I wouldn't be surprised if that's the police. (ALICE *opens door.* MRS. MANICOTTI *enters*) Mrs. Manicotti! (MRS. MANICOTTI, *a woman with a purpose, looks right at* RALPH *and blasts out in opera style. Tune is "Come Back to Sorrento."*)

MRS. MANICOTTI Guarda il mare come bello, spira tanto sentimento . . .

RALPH (*Proudly*) "Come Back to Sorrento" written by Ernesto Dicurtis in 1898.

MRS. MANICOTTI　I give up. (*Throws her hands up in the air and goes. Closes door.*)

ALICE　The whole house has gone crazy!

RALPH　Crazy? She's crazy because she helps me and roots for me? That's more than I can say for you!

ALICE　I've been trying to help you by being sensible. If you had listened to me you could have avoided all this pressure you're putting on yourself.

RALPH　For the last time, I'm going for $99,000!

ALICE　For the last time, I'd be very proud of you if you won six hundred.

RALPH　Six hundred bucks is peanuts! Peanuts! What am I gonna do with peanuts?

GARRITY'S VOICE　Eat them—like any other elephant! (RALPH *charges to window and opens it.*)

RALPH (*To* GARRITY)　Garrity, when I move to Park Avenue, you'll be singing a different tune.

GARRITY'S VOICE　Yeah. "Happy Days Are Here Again" written by Yellen and Ager, 1929! (RALPH *slams down window, infuriated. He glares at* ALICE *and* NORTON.)

RALPH　Start playing, Norton. (NORTON *starts playing "Swanee River" intro.*)

RALPH　Oh . . . No! (. . . *and sinks in despair.*)

DISSOLVE

As curtains part camera holds on establishing shot of $99,000 set. Same as in scene one. As music dissolves, MC *starts entrance.*

ANNOUNCER'S VOICE　. . . And now—the star of our show—Herb Norris! (*Audience applause.*)

MC　Thank you, and welcome to America's most exciting quiz show—the $99,000 answer. Tom, who is our first guest?

ANNOUNCER'S VOICE　Herb, our next guest ready to leap the first hurdle on his way to the $99,000 answer is our bus driver from Brooklyn, Mr. Ralph Kramden! (*Applause.* RALPH *is led down ramp by girl.*)

MC　Hello, Mr. Kramden. Nice to see you again.

RALPH　Thank you.

MC Last week we just had time enough to get as far as picking your category—you picked popular songs.

RALPH That's right, sir.

MC Well, you had a whole week to prepare yourself. Did you do much studying?

RALPH Oh, just a little.

MC You mean just in your spare time.

RALPH Yes, sir.

MC Well, let's get on with our little competition. (*Girl brings questions to* HERB.) I have here your first question. Now, Mr. Kramden, you know how the $99,000 answer works. We start with the first question, which is our lowest hurdle. You get that right and get $100. Then you go over our second hurdle which is worth $600. After that our hurdles become higher and our questions naturally a little harder. Our third hurdle is worth $6,187.50, and if you answer that right, you will have a total of $12,375. Then we keep doubling until you finally get to the $99,000 hurdle. Any time you feel like stopping you can do so and keep whatever you have won. Of course if you miss, you go home empty-handed. Is that clear, Mr. Kramden?

RALPH Yes, sir. But if it's all right with you I'd like to make a statement.

MC Certainly. Go right ahead.

RALPH I've made up my mind I'm going for the $99,000 (*Audience applause.*)

MC Mr. Kramden, you don't have to make that decision now. You can decide as you go along.

RALPH I know but I've already made up my mind.

MC Have you discussed this at home? Have you talked it over with your wife?

RALPH Yeah . . . but I'm goin' for it anyway! Making up my mind now's gonna save me a lot of headaches.

MC That's quite a decision to come to. You certainly must know your popular songs.

RALPH Yes, sir. And this way everything's settled. I know, you know and everybody lookin' in knows I ain't stoppin' until I've won the $99,000!

MC I wish you the best of luck and here's your first question for $100. (*He reads from card*) Tell me, Mr. Kramden, who is the composer of "Swanee River"?

RALPH   "Swanee River"?

MC (*Off to piano player*)   José—a few bars of "Swanee River," please. (*Music off. Scene on piano only. "Swanee River."* RALPH *looks as if he's never heard of it.* RALPH *does eye bulge.*)

RALPH   That's Swanee River?

MC   Yes. Now who wrote it? (RALPH *is speechless*) Your time is almost up. Who wrote it? Make a stab at it. Take a guess!

RALPH   Ed Norton?

MC   Oh, I'm terribly sorry, Mr. Kramden, the right answer is Stephen Foster. But at least you have the satisfaction of knowing you have been a good contestant and a good sport. Good-bye, Mr. Kramden.

RALPH (*Looks lost at him*)   Buh . . . buh . . . (*As jovial as possible,* MC *wants* RALPH *to leave.*)

MC   Well, Mr. Kramden . . . I'll be seeing you. (RALPH *half dazed automatically answers what he thinks of as a song title.*)

RALPH   "I'll Be Seeing You." A hit song written in 1938 by Irving Kale and Sammy Fain!

MC   But, Mr. Kramden . . . it's all over now.

RALPH   "It's All Over Now" words and music by Bazzy Simon. 1927.

MC   Good Night, Mr. Kramden, Good Night. (MC *motions off to* GIRL *assistant to come and help.*)

RALPH   There are two good nights. "Good Night, Irene" written by Lomax and Leadbetter and "Good Night, Sweetheart" by Rudy Vallee and Ray Noble and . . . (*The* GIRL *now has* RALPH *by arm.*)

GIRL   Please. This way, sir. Please.

RALPH (*As he is being led off*)   "Please" sung by Bing Crosby in *Big Broadcast of 1933.* By Robins and Ranger. (*As they lead poor* RALPH *off camera.*)

BLACKOUT

DISCUSSION

1. Why do the authors begin the play with Mr. Parker's performance as a quiz contestant, instead of immediately introducing Ralph Kramden?
2. Cite evidences of Ralph's nervousness, in scene one. How does the behavior of the master of ceremonies heighten the comic effect?

3. From her brief conversation with Trixie, what can you tell about Alice's outlook? How does it differ from Ralph's? Is Alice's appraisal of Ralph, beginning "Don't get me wrong, Trix . . ." necessary to your understanding of the play?

4. Is Ralph a recognizable *type* of person?

5. How do the authors indicate a lapse of time between the first scene of the play and the second? What is accomplished?

6. Alice tells Ralph, "I've been trying to help you by being sensible." Why have Alice's attempts to help Ralph failed?

7. How do the authors sustain your interest in the final scene, despite the fact that in certain respects it is similar to the first? What makes the final scene amusing?

8. Do you feel that Alice's attitude toward Ralph will change as a result of his quiz show experience? Will the experience change Ralph? Justify your reasoning.

9. Often, when a central character in a play fails to attain the goal for which he has striven, you feel sorry for the character and disappointed in his failure. Do you experience either of these reactions at the end of *The $99,000 Answer*? Why?

TOPICS FOR WRITING

Exaggeration for comic effect
Television quiz shows: a commentary on American values
The $99,000 Answer as a Farce.

THE MONKEY'S PAW

W. W. Jacobs
Dramatized by Louis N. Parker

CHARACTERS

Mr. White
Mrs. White
Herbert
Sergeant-Major Morris
Mr. Sampson

William Wymark Jacobs (1863-1943)

William Wymark Jacobs was born in London in 1863. His father was a wharf manager, so that Jacobs became familiar early in life with the atmosphere of the docks and with the comings and goings of ships. Although he held a civil service job for a number of years, he never enjoyed this work, preferring to spend his time writing stories and sketches. His humorous accounts of life in dock towns and of the misadventures of sailors ashore established his reputation as a writer, but he is best known today for a single horror story, The Monkey's Paw. *So convincingly does Jacobs portray the emotions of his characters, in this story, that if you are a typical reader you will never stop to question the credibility of the plot or its outcome.*

Louis N. Parker's short play adaptation of The Monkey's Paw *retains the qualities that made the original version a favorite among readers: simplicity of language, fast-moving action, and an atmosphere of suspense and terror that has never been surpassed in fiction.*

THE MONKEY'S PAW

Scene   *The living-room of an old-fashioned cottage on the outskirts of Fulham. Set corner-wise in the left angle at the back a deep window; further front, three or four steps lead up to a door. Further forward a dresser, with plates, glasses, etc. At back an alcove with the street door fully visible. On the inside of the street door, a wire letter-box. On the right a cupboard, then a fireplace. In the center a round table. Against the wall, an old-fashioned piano. A comfortable arm-*

*chair each side of the fireplace. Other chairs. On the mantel-
piece a clock, old china figures, etc. An air of comfort
pervades the room.*

Scene One

At the rise of the curtain, MRS. WHITE, *a pleasant-looking old
woman, is seated in the armchair below the fire, attending to
a kettle which is steaming on the fire, and keeping a laughing
eye on* MR. WHITE *and* HERBERT. *These two are seated at the
right angle of the table nearest the fire with a chess-board
between them.* MR. WHITE *is evidently losing. His hair is
ruffled; his spectacles are high up on his forehead.* HERBERT,
*a fine young fellow, is looking with satisfaction at the move
he has just made.* MR. WHITE *makes several attempts to move,
but thinks better of them. There is a shaded lamp on the
table. The door is tightly shut. The curtains of the window
are drawn; but every now and then the wind is heard whis-
tling outside.*

MR. WHITE (*moving at last, and triumphant*)   There, Herbert, my
boy! Got you, I think.

HERBERT   Oh, you're a deep 'un, Dad, aren't you?

MRS. WHITE   Mean to say he's beaten you at last?

HERBERT   Lor, no! Why, he's overlooked—

MR. WHITE (*very excited*)   I see it! Lemme have that back!

HERBERT   Not much. Rules of the game!

MR. WHITE (*disgusted*)   I don't hold with them scientific rules.
You turn what ought to be an innocent relaxation—

MRS. WHITE   Don't talk so much, Father. You put him off—

HERBERT (*laughing*)   Not he!

MR. WHITE (*trying to distract his attention*)   Hark at the wind.

HERBERT (*drily*)   Ah! I'm listening. Check.

MR. WHITE (*still trying to distract him*)   I should hardly think
Sergeant-Major Morris'd come tonight.

HERBERT   Mate. (*Rises.*)

MR. WHITE (*with an outbreak of disgust and sweeping the chess-
men off the board*)   That's the worst of living so far out. Your friends

can't come for a quiet chat, and you addle your brains over a confounded—

HERBERT   Now, Father! Morris'll turn up all right.

MR. WHITE (*still in a temper*)   Lover's Lane, Fulham! Ho! Of all the beastly, slushy, out-o'-the-way places to live in——! Pathway's a bog, and the road's a torrent. (*To* MRS. WHITE, *who has risen, and is at his side*). What's the County Council thinking of, that's what I want to know? Because this is the only house in the road it doesn't matter if nobody can get near it, I s'pose.

MRS. WHITE   Never mind, dear. Perhaps you'll win tomorrow. (*She moves to back of table.*)

MR. WHITE   Perhaps I'll—perhaps I'll——! What d'you mean? (*Bursts out laughing*) There! You always know what's going on inside o' me, don't you, Mother?

MRS. WHITE   Ought to, after thirty years, John. (*She goes to dresser, and busies herself wiping tumblers on tray there. He rises, goes to fireplace and lights pipe.*)

HERBERT   And it's not such a bad place, Dad, after all. One of the few old-fashioned houses left near London. None o' your stucco villas. Home-like, I call it. And so do you, or you wouldn't ha' bought it. (*Rolls a cigarette.*)

MR. WHITE (*growling*)   Nice job I made o' that, too! With two hundred pounds owin' on it.

HERBERT (*on back of chair*)   Why, I shall work that off in no time, Dad. Matter o' three years, with the rise promised me.

MR. WHITE   If you don't get married.

HERBERT   Not me. Not that sort.

MRS. WHITE   I wish you would, Herbert. A good, steady, lad——
    (*She brings the tray with a bottle of whisky, glasses, a lemon,
    spoons, buns, and a knife to the table.*)

HERBERT   Lots o' time, Mother. Sufficient for the day—as the sayin' goes. Just now my dynamos don't leave me any time for love-making. Jealous they are, I tell you!

MR. WHITE (*chuckling*)   I lay awake o' night often, and think: If Herbert took a nap, and let his what-d'you-call-ums—dynamos, run down, all Fulham would be in darkness. Lord! what a joke!

HERBERT   Joke! And me with the sack! Pretty idea of a joke you've got, I don't think. (*Knock at outer door.*)

MRS. WHITE   Hark! (*Knock repeated, louder.*)

MR. WHITE (*going toward door*) That's him. That's the Sergeant-Major. (*He unlocks door, back.*)

HERBERT (*removes chess-board*) Wonder what yarn he's got for us tonight. (*Places chess-board on piano.*)

MRS. WHITE (*goes up right, busies herself putting the other armchair nearer fire, etc.*) Don't let the door slam, John!

(MR. WHITE *opens the door a little, struggling with it. Wind.* SERGEANT-MAJOR MORRIS, *a veteran with a distinct military appearance—left arm gone—dressed as a commissionaire, is seen to enter.* MR. WHITE *helps him off with his coat, which he hangs up in the outer hall.*)

MR. WHITE (*at the door*) Slip in quick! It's as much as I can do to hold it against the wind.

SERGEANT Awful! Awful! (*Busy taking off his cloak, etc.*) And a mile up the road—by the cemetery—it's worse. Enough to blow the hair off your head.

MR. WHITE Give me your stick.

SERGEANT If 'twasn't I knew what a welcome I'd get——

MR. WHITE (*preceding him into the room*) Sergeant-Major Morris!

MRS. WHITE Tut! tut! So cold you must be! Come to the fire; do'ee, now.

SERGEANT How are you, marm? (*To* HERBERT) How's yourself, laddie? Not on duty yet, eh? Day-week, eh?

HERBERT No, sir. Night week. But there's half an hour yet.

SERGEANT (*sitting in the armchair above the fire, toward which* MRS. WHITE *is motioning him.* MR. WHITE *mixes grog for* MORRIS) Thank'ee kindly, marm. That's good—hah! That's a sight better than the trenches at Chitral. That's better than settin' in a puddle with the rain pourin' down in buckets and the natives takin' pot-shots at you.

MRS. WHITE Didn't you have no umbrellas? (*Corner below fire, kneels before it, stirs it, etc.*)

SERGEANT Umbrell——? Ho! ho! That's good! Eh, White? That's good. Did ye hear what she said? Umbrellas!— And goloshes! And hot-water bottles!—Ho, yes! No offense, marm, but it's easy to see you was never a soldier.

HERBERT (*rather hurt*) Mother spoke out o' kindness, sir.

SERGEANT And well I know it; and no offense intended. No,

marm, 'ardship, 'ardship is the soldier's lot. Starvation, fever, and get yourself shot. That's a bit o' my own.

MRS. WHITE   You don't look to've taken much harm—except—— (*Indicates his empty sleeve. She takes kettle to table, then returns to fire.*)

SERGEANT (*showing a medal hidden under his coat*)   And that I got this for. No, marm. Tough. Thomas Morris is tough. (MR. WHITE *is holding a glass of grog under the* SERGEANT's *nose*) And sober. What's this now?

MR. WHITE   Put your nose in it; you'll see.

SERGEANT   Whisky? And hot? And sugar? And a slice o' lemon? No. I said I'd never—but seein' the sort o' night. Well! (*Waving the glass at them*) Here's another thousand a year!

MR. WHITE (*also with a glass*)   Same to you, and many of 'em.

SERGEANT (*to* HERBERT, *who has no glass*)   What? Not you?

HERBERT (*laughing and sitting across chair*)   Oh! 'tisn't for want of being sociable. But my work don't go with it. Not if 'twas ever so little. I've got to keep a cool head, a steady eye, and a still hand. The fly-wheel might gobble me up.

MRS. WHITE   Don't, Herbert. (*Sits in armchair below fire.*)

HERBERT (*laughing*)   No fear, Mother.

SERGEANT   Ah! You electricians!—Sort o' magicians, you are. Light! says you—and light it is. And, power! says you—and the trams go whizzin'. And, knowledge! says you—and words go 'ummin' to the ends o' the world. It fair beats me—and I've seen a bit in my time, too.

HERBERT (*nudges his father*)   Your Indian magic? All a fake, Governor. The fakir's fake.

SERGEANT   Fake, you call it? I tell you, I've *seen* it.

HERBERT (*nudging his father with his foot*)   Oh, come, now! Such as what? Come, now!

SERGEANT   I've seen a cove with no more clothes on than a babby, (*to* MRS. WHITE) if you know what I mean—take an empty basket— empty, mind!—as empty as—as this here glass——

MR. WHITE   Hand it over, Morris. (*Hands it to* HERBERT, *who goes quickly behind table and fills it.*)

SERGEANT   Which was not my intentions, but used for illustration.

HERBERT (*while mixing*)   Oh, I've seen the basket trick; and I've read how it was done. Why, I could do it myself, with a bit o' practice. Ladle out something stronger. (HERBERT *brings him the glass.*)

SERGEANT   Stronger?—What do you say to an old fakir chuckin' a rope up in the air—in the *air*, mind you!—and swarming up it, same as if it was 'ooked on—and vanishing clean out o' sight?—I've seen *that*. (HERBERT *goes to table, plunges a knife into a bun and offers it to the* SERGEANT *with exaggerated politeness.*)

SERGEANT   (*eyeing it with disgust*)   Bun—? What for?

HERBERT   That yarn takes it. (MR. *and* MRS. WHITE *delighted.*)

SERGEANT   Mean to say you doubt my word?

MRS. WHITE   No, no! He's only taking you off.—You shouldn't, Herbert.

MR. WHITE   Herbert always was one for a bit o' fun!

> (HERBERT *puts bun back on table, comes round in front, and moving the chair out of the way, sits cross-legged on the floor at his father's side.*)

SERGEANT   But it's true. Why, if I chose, I could tell you things— But there! You don't get no more yarns out o' *me*.

MR. WHITE   Nonsense, old friend. (*Puts down his glass*) You're not going to get shirty about a bit o' fun. (*Moves his chair nearer* MORRIS's) What was that you started telling me the other day about a monkey's paw, or something? (*Nudges* HERBERT, *and winks at* MRS. WHITE.)

SERGEANT   (*gravely*)   Nothing. Leastways, nothing worth hearing.

MRS. WHITE   (*with astonished curiosity*)   Monkey's *paw*——?

MR. WHITE   Ah—you was tellin' me——

SERGEANT   Nothing. Don't go on about it. (*Puts his empty glass to his lips—then stares at it*) What? Empty again? There! When I begin thinkin' o' the paw, it makes me that absent-minded——

MR. WHITE   (*rises and fills glass*)   You said you always carried it on you.

SERGEANT   So I do, for fear o' what might happen (*Sunk in thought*) Ay!—ay!

MR. WHITE   (*handing him his glass refilled*)   There. (*Sits again in same chair.*)

MRS. WHITE   What's it for?

SERGEANT   You wouldn't believe me, if I was to tell you.

HERBERT   *I* will, every word.

SERGEANT   Magic, then! Don't you laugh!

HERBERT   I'm not. Got it on you now?

SERGEANT Of course.

HERBERT Let's see it. (*Seeing the* SERGEANT *embarrassed with his glass,* MRS. WHITE *rises, takes it from him, places it on mantelpiece and remains standing.*)

SERGEANT Oh, it's nothing to look at. (*Hunting in his pocket*) Just an ordinary—little paw—dried to a mummy. (*Produces it and holds it toward* MRS. WHITE) Here.

MRS. WHITE (*who has leant forward eagerly to see it, starts back with a little cry of disgust*) Oh!

HERBERT Give us a look. (MORRIS *passes the paw to* MR. WHITE, *from whom* HERBERT *takes it*) Why, it's all dried up!

SERGEANT I said so. (*Wind.*)

MRS. WHITE (*with a slight shudder*) Hark at the wind! (*Sits again in her old place.*)

MR. WHITE (*taking the paw from* HERBERT) And what might there be special about it?

SERGEANT (*impressively*) That there paw has had a spell put upon it!

MR. WHITE No? (*In great alarm he thrusts the paw back into* MORRIS's *hand.*)

SERGEANT (*pensively, holding the paw in the palm of his hand*) Ah! By an old fakir. He was a very holy man. He'd sat all doubled up in one spot, goin' on for fifteen year; thinkin' o' things. And he wanted to show that fate ruled people. That everything was cut and dried from the beginning, as you might say. That there warn't no gettin' away from it. And that, if you tried to, you caught it hot. (*Pauses solemnly*) So he put a spell on this bit of a paw. It might ha' been anything else, but he took the first thing that came handy. Ah! He put a spell on it, and made it so that three people (*looking at them and with deep meaning*) could each have three wishes.

(*All but* MRS. WHITE *laugh rather nervously.*)

MRS. WHITE Ssh! Don't!

SERGEANT (*more gravely*) But——! But, mark you, though the wishes was granted, those three people would have cause to wish they *hadn't* been.

MR. WHITE But how *could* the wishes be granted?

SERGEANT He didn't say. It would all happen so natural, you might think it a coincidence if so disposed.

HERBERT Why haven't you tried it, sir?

SERGEANT (*gravely, after a pause*) I have.

HERBERT (*eagerly* You've had your three wishes?

SERGEANT (*gravely*) Yes.

MRS. WHITE Were they granted?

SERGEANT (*staring at the fire*) They were.

(*A pause.*)

MR. WHITE Has anybody else wished?

SERGEANT Yes. The first owner had his three wish——(*Lost in recollection*) Yes, oh, yes, he had his three wishes all right. I don't know what his first two were, (*very impressively*) but the third was for death. (*All shudder*) That's how I got the paw.

(*A pause.*)

HERBERT (*cheerfully*) Well! Seems to me you've only got to wish for things that *can't* have any bad luck about 'em——(*Rises.*)

SERGEANT (*shaking his head*) Ah!

MR. WHITE (*tentatively*) Morris—if you've had your three wishes—it's no good to you, now—what do you keep it for?

SERGEANT (*still holding the paw; looking at it*) Fancy, I s'pose. I did have some idea of selling it, but I don't think I will. It's done mischief enough already. Besides, people won't buy. Some of 'em think it's a fairy tale. And some want to try it first, and pay after. (*Nervous laugh from the others.*)

MRS. WHITE If you could have another three wishes, would you?

SERGEANT (*slowly—weighing the paw in his hand and looking at it*) I don't know—I don't know——(*Suddenly, with violence, flinging it in the fire*) No! I'm damned if I would!

(*Movement from all.*)

MR. WHITE (*rises and quickly snatches it out of the fire*) What are you doing? (WHITE *goes to the fireplace.*)

SERGEANT (*rising and following him and trying to prevent him*) Let it burn! Let the infernal thing burn!

MRS. WHITE (*rises*) Let it burn, Father!

MR. WHITE (*wiping it on his coatsleeve*) No. If you don't want it, give it to me.

SERGEANT (*violently*) I won't! I won't! My hands are clear of it. I threw it on the fire. If you keep it, don't blame me, whatever happens. Here! Pitch it back again.

MR. WHITE (*stubbornly*) I'm going to keep it. What do you say, Herbert?

HERBERT (*laughing*) I say, keep it if you want to. Stuff and nonsense, anyhow.

MR. WHITE (*looking at the paw thoughtfully*) Stuff and nonsense. Yes. I wonder—(*casually*) I wish——(*He was going to say some ordinary thing, like "I wish I were certain."*)

SERGEANT (*misunderstanding him; violently*) Stop! Mind what you're doing. That's not the way.

MR. WHITE What *is* the way?

MRS. WHITE (*moving away to back of table, and beginning to put the tumblers straight, and the chairs in their places*) Oh, don't have anything to do with it, John. (*Takes glasses on tray to dresser, busies herself there, rinsing them in a bowl of water on the dresser, and wiping them with a cloth.*)

SERGEANT That's what I say, marm. But if I warn't to tell him, he might go wishing something he didn't mean to. You hold it in your right hand, and wish aloud. But I warn you! I warn you!

MRS. WHITE Sounds like the Arabian Nights. Don't you think you might wish me four pair o' hands?

MR. WHITE (*laughing*) Right you are, Mother!— I wish——

SERGEANT (*pulling his arm down*) Stop it! If you must wish, wish for something sensible. Look here! I can't stand this. Gets on my nerves. Where's my coat? (*Goes into alcove.*)

    (MR. WHITE *crosses to fireplace and carefully puts the paw on mantelpiece. He is absorbed in it to the end of the tableau.*)

HERBERT I'm coming your way, to the works, in a minute. Won't you wait? (*Helps* MORRIS *with his coat.*)

SERGEANT (*putting on his coat*) No. I'm all shook up. I want fresh air. I don't want to be here when you wish. And wish you will as soon's my back's turned. I know. I know. But I've warned you, mind.

MR. WHITE (*helping him into his coat*) All right, Morris. Don't you fret about us. (*Gives him money*) Here.

SERGEANT (*refusing it*) No, I won't——

MR. WHITE (*forcing it into his hand*) Yes, you will. (*Opens door.*)

SERGEANT (*turning to the room*) Well, good night all. (*To* WHITE) Put it in the fire.

ALL Good night.

    (*Exit* SERGEANT. MR. WHITE *closes door, comes toward fireplace, absorbed in the paw.*)

HERBERT If there's no more in this than there is in his other stories, we shan't make much out of it.

MRS. WHITE (*to* WHITE)   Did you give him anything for it, Father?

MR. WHITE   A trifle. He didn't want it, but I made him take it.

MRS. WHITE   There, now! You shouldn't. Throwing your money about.

MR. WHITE (*looking at the paw which he has picked up again*)   I wonder——

HERBERT   What?

MR. WHITE   I wonder, whether we hadn't better chuck it on the fire?

HERBERT (*laughing*)   Likely! Why! we're all going to be rich and famous, and happy.

MRS. WHITE   Throw it on the fire, indeed, when you've given money for it! So like you, Father.

HERBERT   Wish to be an Emperor, Father, to begin with. Then you can't be henpecked!

MRS. WHITE (*going for him front of table with a duster*)   You young——! (*Follows him to back of table.*)

HERBERT (*running away from her, hiding behind table*)   Steady with that duster, Mother!

MR. WHITE   Be quiet, there! (HERBERT *catches* MRS. WHITE *in his arms and kisses her*) I wonder——(*He has the paw in his hand*) I don't know what to wish for, and that's a fact. (*He looks about him with a happy smile*) I seem to've got all I want.

HERBERT (*with his hands on the old man's shoulders*)   Old Dad! If you'd only cleared the debt on the house, you'd be quite happy, wouldn't you? (*Laughing*) Well—go ahead!—wish for the two hundred pounds: that'll just do it.

MR. WHITE (*half laughing*)   Shall I?

HERBERT   Go on! Here!—I'll play slow music. (*Goes to piano.*)

MRS. WHITE   Don't 'ee, John. Don't have nothing to do with it!

HERBERT   Now, Dad! (*Plays.*)

MR. WHITE   I will! (*Holds up the paw, as if half ashamed*) I wish for two hundred pounds. (*Crash on the piano. At the same instant* MR. WHITE *utters a cry and lets the paw drop.*)

MRS. WHITE *and* HERBERT   What's the matter?

MR. WHITE (*gazing with horror at the paw*)   It moved! As I wished, it twisted in my hand like a snake.

HERBERT (*goes down and picks the paw up*)   Nonsense, Dad. Why, it's as stiff as a bone. (*Lays it on the mantelpiece.*)

MRS. WHITE Must have been your fancy, Father.

HERBERT (*laughing*) Well——? (*Looking round the room.*) I don't see the money; and I bet I never shall.

MR. WHITE (*relieved*) Thank God, there's no harm done! But it gave me a shock.

HERBERT Half-past eleven. I must get along. I'm on at midnight. (*Fetches his coat, etc.*) We've had quite a merry evening.

MRS. WHITE I'm off to bed. Don't be late for breakfast, Herbert.

HERBERT I shall walk home as usual. Does me good. I shall be with you about nine. Don't wait, though.

MRS. WHITE You know your father never waits.

HERBERT Good night, Mother.

(*Kisses her. She lights candle on dresser, goes up stairs and exit.*)

HERBERT (*coming to his father, who is sunk in thought*) Good night, Dad. You'll find the cash tied up in the middle of the bed.

MR. WHITE (*staring, seizes* HERBERT's *hand*) It moved, Herbert.

HERBERT Ah! And a monkey hanging by his tail from the bed-post, watching you count the golden sovereigns.

MR. WHITE (*accompanying him to the door*) I wish you wouldn't joke, my boy.

HERBERT All right, Dad. (*Opens door*) Lord! What weather! Good night. (*Exit.*)

(*The old man shakes his head, closes the door, locks it, puts the chain up, slips the lower bolt, has some difficulty with the upper bolt.*)

MR. WHITE This bolt's stiff again! I must get Herbert to look to it in the morning. (*Comes into the room, puts out the lamp, crosses toward steps; but is irresistibly attracted toward fireplace. Sits down and stares into the fire. His expression changes: he sees something horrible.*)

MR. WHITE (*with involuntary cry*) Mother! Mother!

MRS. WHITE (*appearing at the door at the top of the steps with candle*) What's the matter?

MR. WHITE (*mastering himself. Rises*) Nothing—I—haha!—I saw faces in the fire.

MRS. WHITE Come along. (*She takes his arm and draws him to-*

*ward the steps. He looks back frightened toward fireplace as they reach
the first step.)*

T A B L E A U   C U R T A I N

Scene Two

*Bright sunshine. The table, which has been moved nearer the
window, is laid for breakfast.* MRS. WHITE *busy about the
table.* MR. WHITE *standing in the window looking off. The
inner door is open, showing the outer door.*

MR. WHITE   What a morning Herbert's got for walking home!

MRS. WHITE   What's o'clock? (*Looks at clock on mantelpiece*)
Quarter to nine, I declare. He's off at eight. (*Crosses to fire.*)

MR. WHITE   Takes him half an hour to change and wash. He's
just by the cemetery now.

MRS. WHITE   He'll be here in ten minutes.

MR. WHITE (*coming to the table*)   What's for breakfast?

MRS. WHITE   Sausages. (*At the mantelpiece*) Why, if here isn't
that dirty monkey's paw! (*Picks it up, looks at it with disgust, puts it
back. Takes sausages in dish from before fire and places them on table*)
Silly thing! The idea of us listening to such nonsense!

MR. WHITE (*goes up to window again*)   Ay—the Sergeant-Major
and his yarns! I suppose all old soldiers are alike——

MRS. WHITE   Come on, Father. Herbert hates us to wait. (*They
both sit and begin breakfast.*)

MRS. WHITE   How could wishes be granted, nowadays?

MR. WHITE   Ah! Been thinking about it all night, have you?

MRS. WHITE   You kept me awake, with your tossing and tum-
bling——

MR. WHITE   Ay, I had a bad night.

MRS. WHITE   It was the storm, I expect. How it blew!

MR. WHITE   I didn't hear it. I was asleep and not asleep, if you
know what I mean.

MRS. WHITE   And all that rubbish about its making you unhappy
if your wish *was* granted; How could two hundred pounds hurt you,
eh, Father?

MR. WHITE   Might drop on my head in a lump. Don't see any other
way. And I'd try to bear that. Though, mind you, Morris said it would

all happen so naturally that you might take it for a coincidence, if so disposed.

MRS. WHITE   Well—it hasn't happened. That's all I know. And it isn't going to. (*A letter is seen to drop in the letter-box*) And how you can sit there and talk about it——(*Sharp postman's knock; she jumps to her feet*) What's that?

MR. WHITE   Postman, o' course.

MRS. WHITE (*seeing the letter from a distance; in an awed whisper*) He's brought a letter, John!

MR. WHITE (*laughing*)   What did you think he'd bring? Ton o' coals?

MRS. WHITE   John—! John—! Suppose——?

MR. WHITE   Suppose what?

MRS. WHITE   Suppose it was two hundred pounds!

MR. WHITE (*suppressing his excitement*)   Eh!—Here! Don't talk nonsense. Why don't you fetch it?

MRS. WHITE (*crosses and takes letter out of the box*)   It's thick, John—(*feels it*)—and—and it's got something crisp inside it. (*Takes letter to* WHITE.)

MR. WHITE   Who—who's it for?

MRS. WHITE   You.

MR. WHITE   Hand it over then. (*Feeling and examining it with ill-concealed excitement*) The idea! What a superstitious old woman you are! Where are my specs?

MRS. WHITE   Let me open it.

MR. WHITE   Don't you touch it. Where are my specs?

MRS. WHITE   Don't let sudden wealth sour your temper, John.

MR. WHITE   *Will* you find my specs?

MRS. WHITE (*taking them off mantelpiece*)   Here, John, here. (*As he opens the letter*) Take care! Don't tear it!

MR. WHITE   Tear what?

MRS. WHITE   If it was banknotes, John!

MR. WHITE (*taking a thick, formal document out of the envelope and a crisp-looking slip*)   You've gone dotty.—You've made me nervous. (*Reads*) "Sir,—Enclosed please find receipt for interest on the mortgage of £200 on your house, duly received." (*They look at each other.* MR. WHITE *sits down to finish his breakfast silently.* MRS. WHITE *goes to the window.*)

MRS. WHITE   That comes of listening to tipsy old soldiers.

MR. WHITE (*pettish*)   What does?

MRS. WHITE   You thought there was banknotes in it.

MR. WHITE (*injured*)   I didn't! I said all along——

MRS. WHITE   How Herbert will laugh, when I tell him!

MR. WHITE (*with gruff good-humor*)   You're not going to tell him. You're going to keep your mouth shut. That's what you're going to do. Why, I should never hear the last of it.

MRS. WHITE   Serve you right. I shall tell him. You know you like his fun. See how he joked you last night when you said the paw moved. (*She is looking through the window.*)

MR. WHITE   So it did. It did move. That I'll swear to.

MRS. WHITE (*abstractedly; she is watching something outside*) You thought it did.

MR. WHITE   I say it did. There was no thinking about it. You saw how it upset me, didn't you? (*She doesn't answer*) *Didn't* you?—Why don't you listen? (*Turns round*) What is it?

MRS. WHITE   Nothing.

MR. WHITE (*turns back to his breakfast*)   Do you see Herbert coming?

MRS. WHITE   No.

MR. WHITE   He's about due. What *is* it?

MRS. WHITE   Nothing. Only a man. Looks like a gentleman. Leastways, he's in black, and he's got a top-hat on.

MR. WHITE   What about him? (*He is not interested; goes on eating.*)

MRS. WHITE   He stood at the garden-gate as if he wanted to come in. But he couldn't seem to make up his mind.

MR. WHITE   Oh, go on! You're full o' fancies.

MRS. WHITE   He's going—no; he's coming back.

MR. WHITE   Don't let him see you peeping.

MRS. WHITE (*with increasing excitement*)   He's looking at the house. He's got his hand on the latch. No. He turns away again. (*Eagerly*) John! He looks like a sort of a lawyer.

MR. WHITE   What of it?

MRS. WHITE   Oh, you'll only laugh again. But suppose—suppose he's coming about the two hundred——

MR. WHITE   You're not to mention it again! You're a foolish old woman. Come and eat your breakfast. (*Eagerly*) Where is he now?

MRS. WHITE   Gone down the road. He has turned back. He seems to've made up his mind. Here he comes! Oh, John, and me all untidy! (*Crosses to fire. There is a knock.*)

MR. WHITE (*to* MRS. WHITE *who is hastily smoothing her hair*) What's it matter? He's made a mistake. Come to the wrong house. (*Goes to fireplace.* MRS. WHITE *opens the door.* MR. SAMPSON, *dressed from head to foot in solemn black, with a top-hat, stands in the doorway.*)

SAMPSON (*outside*) Is this Mr. White's?

MRS. WHITE Come in, sir. Please step in. (*She shows him into the room. He is awkward and nervous*) You must overlook our being so untidy; and the room all anyhow; and John in his garden-coat. (*To* MR. WHITE, *reproachfully*) Oh, John.

SAMPSON (*to* MR. WHITE) Morning. My name is Sampson.

MRS. WHITE (*offering a chair*) Won't you please be seated?

(SAMPSON *stands quite still.*)

SAMPSON Ah—thank you—no, I think not—I think not. (*Pause.*)

MR. WHITE (*awkwardly, trying to help him*) Fine weather for the time o' year.

SAMPSON Ah—yes—yes——(*Pause; he makes a renewed effort*) My name is Sampson—I've come——

MRS. WHITE Perhaps you was wishful to see Herbert; he'll be home in a minute. (*Pointing*) Here's his breakfast waiting——

SAMPSON (*interrupting her hastily*) No, no! (*Pause*) I've come from the electrical works——

MRS. WHITE Why, you might have come *with* him.

(MR. WHITE *sees something is wrong, tenderly puts his hand on her arm.*)

SAMPSON No—no—I've—come—*alone*.

MRS. WHITE (*with a little anxiety*) Is anything the matter?

SAMPSON I was asked to call——

MRS. WHITE (*abruptly*) Herbert! Has anything happened? Is he hurt? Is he hurt?

MR. WHITE (*soothing her*) There, there, Mother. Don't you jump to conclusions. Let the gentleman speak. You've not brought bad news, I'm sure, sir.

SAMPSON I'm—sorry——

MRS. WHITE Is he hurt? (SAMPSON *bows*) Badly?

SAMPSON Very badly. (*Turns away.*)

MRS. WHITE (*with a cry*) John—! (*She instinctively moves toward* WHITE.)

MR. WHITE Is he in pain?

SAMPSON He is not in pain.

MRS. WHITE   Oh, thank God! Thank God for that! Thank——(*She looks in a startled fashion at* MR. WHITE—*realizes what* SAMPSON *means, catches his arm and tries to turn him toward her*) Do you mean——?

(SAMPSON *avoids her look; she gropes for her husband: he takes her two hands in his, and gently lets her sink into the armchair above the fireplace, then he stands on her right, between her and* SAMPSON.)

MR. WHITE (*hoarsely*)   Go on, sir.

SAMPSON   He was telling his mates a story. Something that had happened here last night. He was laughing, and wasn't noticing and—and—(*hushed*) the machinery caught him——

(*A little cry from* MRS. WHITE, *her face shows her horror and agony.*)

MR. WHITE (*vague, holding* MRS. WHITE's *hand*)   The machinery caught him—yes—and him the only child—it's hard, sir—very hard——

SAMPSON (*subdued*)   The Company wished me to convey their sincere sympathy with you in your great loss——

MR. WHITE (*staring blankly*)   Our—great—loss——!

SAMPSON   I was to say further—(*as if apologizing*) I am only their servant—I am only obeying orders——

MR. WHITE   Our—great—loss——

SAMPSON (*laying an envelope on the table and edging toward the door*)   I was to say, the Company disclaim all responsibility, but, in consideration of your son's services, they wish to present you with a certain sum as compensation. (*Gets to door.*)

MR. WHITE   Our—great—loss——(*Suddenly, with horror*) How —how much?

SAMPSON (*in the doorway*)   Two hundred pounds. (*Exit.*)

(MRS. WHITE *gives a cry. The old man takes no heed of her, smiles faintly, puts out his hands like a sightless man, and drops, a senseless heap, to the floor.* MRS. WHITE *stares at him blankly and her hands go out helplessly toward him.*)

TABLEAU CURTAIN

Scene Three

Night. On the table a candle is flickering at its last gasp. The room looks neglected. MR. WHITE *is dozing fitfully in the armchair.* MRS. WHITE *is in the window peering through the blind.* MR. WHITE *starts, wakes, looks around him.*

MR. WHITE (*fretfully*) Jenny—Jenny.

MRS. WHITE (*in the window*) Yes.

MR. WHITE Where are you?

MRS. WHITE At the window.

MR. WHITE What are you doing?

MRS. WHITE Looking up the road.

MR. WHITE (*falling back*) What's the use, Jenny? What's the use?

MRS. WHITE That's where the cemetery is; that's where we've laid him.

MR. WHITE Ay—ay—a week today—what o'clock is it?

MRS. WHITE I don't know.

MR. WHITE We don't take much account of time now, Jenny, do we?

MRS. WHITE Why should we? He don't come home. He'll never come home again. There's nothing to think about

MR. WHITE Or to talk about. (*Pause*) Come away from the window; you'll get cold.

MRS. WHITE It's colder where *he* is.

MR. WHITE Ay—gone for ever——

MRS. WHITE And taken all our hopes with him——

MR. WHITE And all our *wishes*——

MRS. WHITE Ay, and all our——(*With a sudden cry*) John! (*She comes quickly to him; he rises.*)

MR. WHITE Jenny! For God's sake! What's the matter?

MRS. WHITE (*with dreadful eagerness*) The *paw!* The monkey's paw!

MR. WHITE (*bewildered*) Where? Where is it? What's wrong with it?

MRS. WHITE I want it! You haven't done away with it?

MR. WHITE I haven't seen it—since—why?

MRS. WHITE   I want it! Find it! Find it!

MR.. WHITE (*groping on the mantelpiece*)   Here! Here it is! What do you want of it? (*He leaves it there.*)

MRS. WHITE   Why didn't I think of it? Why didn't *you* think of it?

MR. WHITE   Think of what?

MRS. WHITE   The *other two* wishes!

MR. WHITE (*with horror*)   What?

MRS. WHITE   We've only had one.

MR. WHITE (*tragically*)   Wasn't that enough?

MRS. WHITE   No! We'll have one more. (WHITE *crosses.* MRS. WHITE *takes the paw and follows him*) Take it. Take it quickly. And wish——

MR. WHITE (*avoiding the paw*)   Wish what?

MRS. WHITE   Oh, John! John! Wish our boy alive again!

MR. WHITE   Good God! Are you mad?

MRS. WHITE   Take it. Take it and wish. (*With a paroxysm of grief*) Oh, my boy! My boy!

MR. WHITE   Get to bed. Get to sleep. You don't know what you're saying.

MRS. WHITE   We had the first wish granted—why not the second?

MR. WHITE (*hushed*)   He's been dead ten days, and—Jenny! Jenny! I only knew him by his clothing—if you wasn't allowed to see him then—how could you bear to see him *now?*

MRS. WHITE   I don't care. Bring him back.

MR. WHITE (*shrinking from the paw*)   I daren't touch it!

MRS. WHITE (*thrusting it in his hand*)   Here! Here! Wish!

MR. WHITE (*trembling*)   Jenny!

MRS. WHITE (*fiercely*)   Wish. (*She goes on frantically whispering* "*Wish.*")

MR. WHITE (*shuddering but overcome by her insistence*)   I—I—wish—my—son—alive again. (*He drops it with a cry. The candle goes out. Utter darkness. He sinks into a chair.* MRS. WHITE *hurries to the window and draws the blind back. She stands in the moonlight. Pause.*)

MRS. WHITE (*drearily*)   Nothing.

MR. WHITE   Thank God! Thank God!

MRS. WHITE   Nothing at all. Along the whole length of the road not a living thing. (*Closes blind*) And nothing, nothing, nothing left in our lives, John.

MR. WHITE   Except each other, Jenny—and memories.

MRS. WHITE (*coming back slowly to the fireplace*)   We're too old. We were only alive in him. We can't begin again. We can't feel anything now, John, but emptiness and darkness. (*She sinks into arm-chair.*)

MR. WHITE 'Tisn't for long, Jenny. There's that to look forward to.

MRS. WHITE Every minute's long, now.

MR. WHITE (*rising*) I can't bear the darkness!

MRS. WHITE It's dreary—dreary.

MR. WHITE (*goes to dresser*) Where's the candle? (*Finds it and brings it to table*) And the matches? Where are the matches? We mustn't sit in the dark. 'Tisn't wholesome. (*Lights match; the other candlestick is close to him*) There. (*Turning with the lighted match toward* MRS. WHITE, *who is rocking and moaning*) Don't take on so, Mother.

MRS. WHITE I'm a mother no longer.

MR. WHITE (*lights candle*) There now; there now. Go on up to bed. Go on, now—I'm a-coming.

MRS. WHITE Whether I'm here or in bed, or wherever I am, I'm with my boy, I'm with——

(*A low single knock at the street door.*)

MRS. WHITE (*starting*) What's that!

MR. WHITE (*mastering his horror*) A rat. The house is full of 'em. (*A louder single knock; she starts up. He catches her by the arm*) Stop! What are you going to do?

MRS. WHITE (*wildly*) It's my boy! It's Herbert! I forgot it was a mile away! What are you holding me for? I must open the door!

(*The knocking continues in single knocks at irregular inter-vals, constantly growing louder and more insistent.*)

MR. WHITE (*still holding her*) For God's sake!

MRS. WHITE (*struggling*) Let me go!

MR. WHITE Don't open the door! (*He drags her away.*)

MRS. WHITE Let me go!

MR. WHITE Think what you might see!

MRS. WHITE (*struggling fiercely*) Do you think I fear the child I bore! Let me go! (*She wrenches herself loose and rushes to the door which she tears open*) I'm coming, Herbert! I'm coming!

MR. WHITE (*cowering in the extreme corner, left front*) Don't 'ee do it! Don't 'ee do it!

(MRS. WHITE *is at work on the outer door, where the knocking still continues. She slips the chain, slips the lower bolt, unlocks the door.*)

MR. WHITE (*suddenly*)   The paw! Where's the monkey's paw?
(*He gets on his knees and feels along the floor for it.*)

MRS. WHITE (*tugging at the top bolt*)   John! the top bolt's stuck.
I can't move it. Come and help. Quick!

MR. WHITE (*wildly groping*)   The paw! There's a wish left.

> (*The knocking is now loud, and in groups of increasing length
> between the speeches.*)

MRS. WHITE   D'ye hear him? John! Your child's knocking!

MR. WHITE   Where is it? Where did it fall?

MRS. WHITE (*tugging desperately at the bolt*)   Help! Help! Will
you keep your child from his home?

MR. WHITE   Where did it fall? I can't find it—I can't find——

> (*The knocking is now tempestuous, and there are blows upon
> the door as of a body beating against it.*)

MRS. WHITE   Herbert! Herbert! My boy! Wait! Your mother's
opening to you! Ah! It's moving! It's moving!

MR. WHITE   God forbid! (*Finds the paw*) Ah!

MRS. WHITE (*slipping the bolt*)   Herbert!

MR. WHITE (*has raised himself to his knees; he holds the paw high*)
I wish him dead. (*The knocking stops abruptly.*) I wish him dead and
at peace!

MRS. WHITE (*flinging the door open simultaneously*)   Herb——

> (*A flood of moonlight. Emptiness. The old man sways in
> prayer on his knees. The old woman lies half swooning, wail-
> ing against the doorpost.*)

CURTAIN

DISCUSSION

1. Note the playwright's use of *dialogue* to introduce facts that are
    essential to the development of the *plot*. Explain the importance
    to the plot of each of the following statements:
    (a) Mr. White: "Pathway's a bog, and the road's a torrent . . .

Because this is the only house in the road it doesn't matter if nobody can get near it, I s'pose."

(b) Herbert: "I shall walk home as usual . . . I shall be with you about nine . . ."

(c) Sergeant-Major Morris: "It would all happen so natural, you might think it a coincidence if so disposed."

(d) Mr. White: "This bolt's stiff again. I must get Herbert to look to it in the morning."

2. Examine the exchange of comments between Herbert and his father during the chess game with which the play begins. How do these comments *foreshadow* the *conflict*?

3. Before relating the story of the monkey's paw, how does the sergeant arouse the curiosity of his listeners? What are their reactions to his story?

4. Do you think that when the sergeant first came to the White household he had any intention of giving up the paw? Explain.

5. Although Sergeant Morris never reveals the content of his own three wishes, how is it clear from his behavior what his experience with the paw must have been?

6. What is Mr. White's state of mind as he makes the first wish? Why is it noteworthy that he could not, at first, think of anything to wish for? By the end of scene one, Mr. White's state of mind has changed considerably. How? Why?

7. Account for the ease with which the Whites dismiss their fears of the previous evening, as scene two begins.

8. How does the playwright keep you guessing as to the outcome of the first wish?

9. How are the circumstances of Herbert's death grimly *ironic*? Does Herbert's death convince you of the power of the paw? Does it convince the Whites? Explain.

10. By what means does the playwright create an *atmosphere* of mounting suspense at the end of the play?

11. Contrast the atmosphere within the White household at the end of the play to the atmosphere at the very beginning. What irony does this contrast serve to sharpen?

12. Why does the playwright refer with such frequency to the sound of the wind?

TOPICS FOR WRITING

In adapting *The Monkey's Paw* for stage presentation, Louis N. Parker divided the story into three distinct scenes. Read the original story

and discuss whether or not you feel that the playwright has
    (a) heightened or diminshed its dramatic intensity
    (b) maintained its unity of effect
as a result of these scene divisions. State your reasons.
A character study of Mrs. White (or) of Mr. White
The playwright's use of atmosphere

NOTES

p. 23 cove (British slang): a guy, a fellow

MY CLIENT CURLEY

(Based on an Unpublished Short Story by Lucille Fletcher Herrmann.)

Norman Corwin

CHARACTERS

Announcer	Man
Agent	Woman
Fatso	Spokesman
Stinky	Conductor
Bidder	Musician
Child	AP Representative
Girl	Eleanor Roosevelt
Disney	Philatelist
First Lepidopterist	Police Radio
Second Lepidopterist	Winchell
Third Lepidopterist	"Find-Curleyites"
Editorial Writer	Waiter
Defender	Shipper
Knell	

First produced on the Columbia Workshop, March 7, 1940, under the direction of the author. Everett Sloane was the Agent, and Kingsley Colton was Stinky. The role of the agent later provided Fred Allen with his first "straight" dramatic role when he appeared in a slightly shortened version of the play on "The Campbell Playhouse," April 11, 1941. George Zachary directed. The play was produced over a South African network later that year.

Norman Corwin (1910-   )

Norman Corwin is considered one of the masters of the radio play. His contributions to this medium have been acknowledged by the American Academy of Arts and Letters, and his works have appeared in numerous textbooks and anthologies.

Corwin's best known play is My Client Curley. It is based on an unpublished story by Lucille Fletcher, the author of another play in this collection. While Corwin retained the general outline of the original story, he considerably expanded the theme. In its present form, My Client Curley offers a thought-provoking commentary on American values.

MY CLIENT CURLEY

ANNOUNCER Ladies and gentlemen: In the following play, any similarity to caterpillars, living or dead, is purely coincidental.

Music: Symphonic treatment of "Yes, Sir, That's My Baby" up and out, under:

AGENT There are some things a man doesn't like to talk about because they're . . . (*Breaks off.*) Well, I'll just tell this story about

my client Curley, and then I'll go back to the agent business and try
to forget it. But if I should get a lump in my throat while I'm telling
it, I hope you'll understand, because this whole thing was so recent,
I still feel pretty upset about it.

To make a long story short, I'm out walking one day in the suburbs
where I live, when my attention is attracted by two kids sitting on the
side of the road and one of them is playing a harmonica.

Harmonica in, well off mike, after "the side of the road."

They're bent over, watching something on the ground, and I, being
curious, go over to see what it is.

Fade in harmonica, playing "Yes, Sir, That's My Baby."

AGENT   Hiya, boys, what you got there?

Harmonica stops abruptly.

FATSO   We got a trained caterpillar.
AGENT   What's trained about it?
STINKY   He dances.
AGENT   (*laughing*)   I don't believe it.
STINKY   He sure does!
FATSO   (*the business brains*)   Give us a nickel and we'll show you.
AGENT   (*good-naturedly*)   Oh, a racket, eh? All right, I'm a sucker.
Here's two nickels.
FATSO   Thanks, Mister. Okay, play, Stinky.

Harmonica begins tune.

AGENT   (*fascinated. After a moment:*)   Well, what do you know!
(*To* STINKY.)   Now stop.

Harmonica out.

AGENT   I'll be darned! Stops right when you do.
FATSO   (*proudly*)   Sure. That's the way Stinky trained him, didn't
ya, Stinky?
STINKY   Aw, it was nothin'.

AGENT (*still incredulous*) Play some more, Stinky.

Harmonica starts and plays through briefly to finish.

AGENT (*laughing with delight*) Lies right down when you're finished!

STINKY Sure, he's talented, ain't he? (*To* CURLEY, *affectionately.*) Come on up on my finger, Curley. Th—a-at's a boy!

AGENT Does Curley dance to any kind of music?

FATSO Nope. Only "Yes, Sir, That's My Baby."

AGENT You mean to tell me he dances to only *one* tune?

STINKY That's right. I tried lots more, but I guess he only likes that one.

AGENT Well, why is that, do you suppose?

STINKY Feller I know says he got a real musical ear.

FATSO I guess that's what those two branches are on his head, huh? Musical ears.

AGENT No, that's his antennae.

STINKY Antenna? (*Laughs.*) He ain't no radio set! (*Vastly amused by his own joke, he laughs again.*)

FATSO (*Joins in laughter.*)

AGENT Say!

FATSO What?

AGENT I wonder if he's got any snake blood in him? You know there are some snakes who dance.

FATSO No kiddin'?

AGENT Here, let me take your harmonica a minute.

STINKY Okay, Sure.

AGENT Curley may be related to one of them Asiatic snakes or something. Lemme play it a minute.

Harmonica plays "Hoochie Koochie" (danse de ventre).

AGENT (*stopping*) Nope. Won't budge. I guess it's an American caterpillar, all right.

STINKY Oh, sure.

AGENT (*all business*) Look, fellers; I'll make you a proposition. How would you like to sell Curley?

FATSO (*the commercial-minded*) How much?

STINKY (*the sustaining-minded*) Wait a minute. I own Curley, and I don't wanna sell him.

AGENT Why not, Stinky?

STINKY (*ashamed to confess he loves the thing*) Well, because I—well—just *because!*

FATSO (*interpreting*) Know why he don't wanna sell?

AGENT Why?

FATSO On account of he's stuck on him.

STINKY Aw, shut up, Fatso!

AGENT You mean you like Curley so much you don't want to part with him?

STINKY I just don't want to sell him, that's all. Not even for a dollar. (*Afterthought.*) Not even for two dollars!

AGENT Well, of course I don't think anybody'd ever offer you *that* much money.

STINKY I don't care. He's my pet, and I want to keep him. I trained him from a pup.

AGENT Now look, kiddo; I think you're a very bright and sensitive boy, and because of that, I'm going to make you an immediate cash payment of *five dollars* for Curley!

FATSO Hey! *Five bucks!* Holy smackerels! Whadda ya say, Stinky? Huh?

STINKY (*almost in tears*) Well—gosh—I dunno.

FATSO Take it, I'm tellin' ya! Now you can buy a bike!

STINKY (*deserted by Fatso and now a martyr to his affection for* CURLEY) Well, that sure is a lot of money—but, y'see—I *like* Curley, and I guess Curley likes me, too; and when we're alone I talk to him, and he understands me. (*Warming up; finding reasons to support his refusal to sell.*) Curley likes me around. He's very intelligent, even though he don't look so smart.

AGENT Oh, he looks smart, all right.

STINKY (*deadly serious*) You know—if somebody took him away from me—Curley would die.

AGENT Think so?

STINKY Sure. He's only human, ain't he? He would absolutely die.

AGENT Listen to me, Stinky. I'm going to talk to you man to man. This caterpillar you've got is very valuable. He's worth a lot of money—'way more than five dollars, maybe.

FATSO No kiddin'?

AGENT Now this is what we're gonna do. Stinky, you're gonna *stay* with Curley and I'm gonna manage both of you. Curley will be my client!

FATSO   What's that mean?

STINKY   What's a client?

AGENT   Well, you wouldn't understand very well. That's something I'll have to explain to your parents, because I've got to get their signatures on a long-term contract with options. You're a minor under the law, you see.

STINKY (*apprehensive of the terminology*)   I didn't do anything wrong, did I?

Music: Transitional cue, orchestra with harmonica.

AGENT   That was how it began. I get Curley under my management, and take him and Stinky with me. The first thing I do is start out after some publicity, and *say*—do those reporters eat it up! Front page, with pictures! Pictures of Curley and pictures of Stinky and pictures of me; pictures of my client dancing on a leaf, curling around the mayor's finger, climbing up a pretty model's leg, sitting in a tiny box at the opera. And *headlines!* Headlines, like in the *Times* . . .

TIMES   Swing Caterpillar Sways to Strains of "Yes, Sir, That's My Baby"; Fred Astaire of Insect World Demonstrates Almost Human Sense of Rhythm.

Music: Motif.

AGENT   The *Post* . . .

POST   Curley in Custody of Stinky, Young Svengali of Caterpillars.

Music: Motif.

AGENT   The *Brooklyn Eagle* . . .

BROOKLYN EAGLE   Insect Phenomenon Learned to Truck in Truck Garden, Manager Avers.

Music: Motif.

AGENT   The *World-Telegram* . . .

WORLD-TELEGRAM   The Curley Crawl Becomes New National Dance Sensation.

Music: Motif.

AGENT   The *Daily News* . . .
NEWS   BUG CUTS RUG! *Story on page 2.*

Music: Finale treatment of motif.

AGENT   And sure enough, with all that publicity, things really begin to happen. First, Bill Robinson introduces the Curley Capers at the Cotton Club!

Music: Effect of solo tap dancing.

AGENT   Then Raymond Scott writes a song called "The Caterpillar Creep."

Music: "Caterpillar Creep."

AGENT   Then half a dozen agencies bid for the rights to syndicate a comic strip.
BIDDER   Four hundred twenty-nine papers, five days a week, making a grand total of . . .
AGENT   Other companies pay me royalties for Curley balloons and spaghetti and dolls and toys and picture books and decorations on the outside of drinking glasses.
CHILD (*whining*)   Maw, buy me the glass with Curley's picture on it!
AGENT   And to make a long story short, I get a vaudeville offer; the money begins to roll in; I hire an expensive suite and a secretary . . .
GIRL   Curley Enterprises. Good afternoon!
AGENT   I buy Stinky a bike and a new suit of clothes.
STINKY   Gee, thanks!
AGENT   The publicity begins to pile up, and at the height of the excitement, I get a wire from Hollywood!
DISNEY (*on filter*)   Offer ten thousand for Curley appearance in feature length cartoon. Propose using live character for first time among cartoon characters. Appreciate immediate answer. Would like to rush story and production. Cordially, Walt Disney.
AGENT   Mm. Oh—er—Miss Neilson!

GIRL Yes?

AGENT Take a wire to Walt Disney, Hollywood, California.

GIRL Yes, sir.

AGENT Curley price one hundred thousand.

GIRL Is that all?

AGENT Do you think I should ask for more?

GIRL No, I mean is there any more to the wire?

Phone rings. Receiver off.

GIRL Curley Enterprises . . . Just a moment, please. (*To Agent.*) *Time Magazine* on the line. Will you take it on the table phone?

AGENT (*going off*) All right.

Sound of phone receiver off, and following conversation is background all the way through to end of scene.

AGENT Hello? Yes? This is him. . . . Yes. . . . Well, you see . . . Yuh. . . . Uhuh. . . . No, I discovered him in the boy's possession. . . . That's right. . . .

No. . . . No. . . . Yes, sure. . . . No, he hasn't yet. . . . Right. . . . I keep him right here. . . . Stinky looks after him most of the time. . . . Yes. . . . What? . . . No. . . . Oh, no. . . . I beg your pardon. . . . Oh, by all means. . . . From the very first, yes . . . that's right . . . that's right . . . Hm? . . . Not yet. . . . Probably not for another week or two. . . . Absolutely. . . . Well, we tried all kinds of tunes . . . no, sir . . . Which . . . which . . . are you referring to . . . No. . . . I don't. . . . Hm? . . . Yes. . . .

Second phone rings; perspective with the girl.

GIRL Curley Enterprises. . . . Well, he's busy on another line. Who? . . . Oh, yes. He wanted me to tell you to order a special airmail daily shipment of willow leaves from Florida. (*Third phone rings.*) Wait a minute, will you? (*Fourth phone rings; alternates with third. Finally the flustered* GIRL *can stand it no longer, and she shouts to Agent:*)

You better hire some more secretaries!

Music: Sock cue. Rides over ringing phones and conversation.

AGENT   Well, things are going in great shape and Curley is making us a bundle of dough, when all of a sudden I get three visitors I didn't figure on.

FIRST LEPIDOPTERIST   We have been reading about your wonderful specimen in the papers, and we have come to ask permission to examine it.

AGENT   Examine it? What for?

SECOND LEPIDOPTERIST   We are lepidopterists.

AGENT   Lepidopterists? But Curley's a caterpillar, not a leopard.

THIRD LEPIDOPTERIST   Ah, no, my dear man—lepidopterology is a branch of entomology dealing with the insect order of which your —er—shall we say client—is a member.

AGENT   Well, I'm sure Curley doesn't want to be examined by nobody.

FIRST LEPIDOPTERIST   Oh, come, come! If this caterpillar is as remarkable as the newspapers say, then you certainly owe science the courtesy of permitting an examination.

SECOND LEPIDOPTERIST   Exactly.

THIRD LEPIDOPTERIST   It would be nothing short of criminal to withhold such knowledge from science.

AGENT   (*grudgingly*)   Well—if you want to put it that way, I suppose—

FIRST LEPIDOPTERIST   It will take no more than two minutes.

AGENT   Oh—I suppose it's all right. Come with me, please.

> *Steps, as of group passing from one room to another. Door opens, closes.*

AGENT   Hello, Stinky.

STINKY   Hello.

AGENT   This is Master Stinky, gentlemen—discoverer and trainer of my client. He guards Curley all the time.

ALL   (*Ad-lib greetings.*)

AGENT   Well, there he is in that box. Please be careful how you handle him.

SECOND LEPIDOPTERIST   Aaahhh—here you are!

THIRD LEPIDOPTERIST   My! Muscular little fellow, isn't he?

FIRST LEPIDOPTERIST   Mm-hm. (*Examining.*) Normal mandible . . . unusually conspicuous first maxillae . . .

SECOND LEPIDOPTERIST I say, watch out there, Doctor, he's trying to bite you!

THIRD LEPIDOPTERIST Ha! Never been attacked by a caterpillar before! Astounding!

FIRST LEPIDOPTERIST See here, Doctor—just notice this remarkable elongation of the abdominal feet.

SECOND LEPIDOPTERIST Yes, quite. And doesn't this feature make you think of the Aglais antiopa?

THIRD LEPIDOPTERIST Incredible!

FIRST LEPIDOPTERIST Look here! Isn't *this* remarkable! I've never seen such ocelli except in the Melanargia galathea. And the chitinization . . .!

AGENT No kidding?

SECOND LEPIDOPTERIST (*to* AGENT) Well, sir! Congratulations! This is a remarkable specimen, even before we test its reactions to musical stimuli.

AGENT Gosh, thanks.

THIRD LEPIDOPTERIST It is of the ordinary genus Papilio rutulus, mind you, but it has the most extraordinary features . . .

AGENT Thanks very much.

FIRST LEPIDOPTERIST But—ahum—we feel that the specimen would be much more valuable to society if you, instead of exhibiting it for commercial purposes, were to—uh—lend or donate it to the Museum of Natural History, where it could be further studied by the leading entomologists of the world. . . .

AGENT But I . . .

SECOND LEPIDOPTERIST Yes, and when it dies, we can dissect it, and . . .

STINKY (*terrified by the thought*) No! No! They're not gonna take him away! (*Crying.*) Don't let them take Curley! (*Keeps protesting and crying under:*)

THIRD LEPIDOPTERIST Don't cry, my boy, we're not going to hurt him . . .

FIRST LEPIDOPTERIST (*ignoring the commotion*) An insect like this occurs probably once in a million years—and surely, for the sake of a few dollars, you're not going to risk injuring him by overwork!

AGENT (*rising above mercenary motives*) Are you accusing me of sacrificing Curley's health for *profits?* (*Scornfully.*) Why, that's ridiculous! Curley is . . .

*Knocking on door. All noise stops, including Stinky's pro-
testation.*

AGENT Yes—come in.

Door opens.

GIRL Just got another wire from the coast! Disney's raised his
offer to twenty thousand!

AGENT (*heatedly*) Twenty! Tell him a hundred thousand or
nothing!

Music: Sock cue up; then down behind:

AGENT Well, the papers get hold of the lepidopterists' story,
and there's another pile of publicity. It gets to be a moral issue, with
preachers delivering sermons, and all like that. I'm attacked editorially
for exploiting caterpillar labor. . . .

EDITORIAL (*fade on*) . . . of the shameless exploitation of a little
unsuspecting insect, by a mercenary agent who has turned to his own
greedy personal advantage a natural phenomenon which belongs nowhere else but in a museum. The public at large is to be condemned
for encouraging this veritable slave-trader to continue (*fading*) his
career of rank exhibitionism, unabashed and in the full glare of wide
publicity. . . .

AGENT But on the other hand, I am defended as an individualist
who refuses to submit to regimentation!

DEFENDER A man owns a clever bug. He has the right to manage
that bug. There is no *question* about his status as manager of that bug.
Yet he is asked to release his client for scientific purposes. He refuses.
He has a right to refuse. Nobody denies that right. Yet in certain quarters he is attacked merely because he insists upon his constitutional
guarantees. We say it is consoling to find a man, in this day of reckless
encroachment upon the individual, who will stand up and fight for his
rights. We wish him well. We stand behind him, foursquare, our feet
firmly implanted in the soil from which his bug has sprung, to support
his defiance (*fading*) of those who would turn back the progress . . .

AGENT The American Legion and the Daughters of the American
Revolution send Curley an engraved silverplated twig and a miniature
flag to put on top of his box. The foreign correspondents get busy and

cable stories to their papers. In Madrid, the Spanish *Gráfico* comes out with a dirty dig.

GRAFICO   Más los norte-americanos no deben olvidar que la danza española es la mejor de todar y que si la oruga del Señor Stinky tuviese un poquitin de buen oído para la música, reconoceria los irresistibles ritmos de la jota, y no se limitaria a tocar "Yes, Sir, That's My Baby." Es un insulto a los paises Latinos que esse insecto . . .

AGENT   How do you like that for nerve? That's the Latin mind for ya! But darned if the Curley motif ain't reflected, as they say, in the latest Paris fashions. Caterpillar doodads on hats and coats and scarfs and all like that. *Le Temps*—that's a newspaper in Paris—comes out with a swell plug.

LE TEMPS   Tous ceux qui aiment la nature, de même que ceux qui s'intéressent aux aspects les plus subtiles de la danse et de la musique, se rejouiront avec notre république sœur, les États-Unis, de la découverte faite récemment par un garçon qui s'appelle Stinky . . . la découverte d'une chenille dansante que le monde connaît affectuesement sous le nom de Curley. Et c'est remarquable de constater que cet insecte ne consent à danser que si l'on joue l'air justement célèbre: "Oui, Monsieur, C'est Mon Bébé!"

AGENT   And you know what? My clipping service sends me some encouraging comment from Shanghai, which I get my laundryman to translate.

CHINESE

六日上海電
聲音之道與性情通
其感人亦微矣哉故一曲
雍門鬼神歌泣感連海上
禽鳥移人從未有不定中
聲而可言正樂不嫻妙技
而可嘵知音者也音樂名
家士丁記君無所不能復
無所不精允文允武担任
各劇無不盡量拍演亦
現身術界不可多得之才

AGENT   The Maharajah of Lahore sends Curley some willow leaves from the sacred willow trees of the temple.

STINKY   Gee, look, a package from a place named Lakeshore with a lot of funny-looking stamps.

AGENT   Lahore, not Lakeshore.

STINKY   C'n I have the stamps?

AGENT   Yeah—here y'are. . . . I sign Curley up for a super-special movie short, and it sweeps the box office of the country in spite of terrible weather, including blizzards and rainstorms. *Variety* reports:

VARIETY   Bliz and Driz Fail to Fizzle Biz as Bug Biffs B.O. from N.Y. to L.A.

AGENT   *Life Magazine* runs a Margaret Bourke-White picture of Curley on the cover, with the caption:

LIFE   Curley.

AGENT   CBS does a pickup direct from Curley's box, bringing the sound of Curley eating dinner.

KNELL   This is Jack Knell speaking to you from the headquarters of Curley Enterprises, where we have a microphone buried among willow leaves, to pick up the sound of the world's leading insect dancer, busy (*fading*) eating dinner after a hard day's work of exhibiting his talents to the press. . . .

AGENT   The *New Yorker* comes out with a cartoon showing Martha Graham nibbling willow leaves. . . .

MAN   (*laughing*)   Did you see this cartoon in the *New Yorker?*

WOMAN   Lemme see. (*Silence.*) Well, what's funny about that?

MAN   For Heaven's sake, don't you get the point?

WOMAN   No.

MAN   Well, don't you know who Martha Graham is?

WOMAN   Yes.

MAN   And you know who Curley is, of course?

WOMAN   The caterpillar.

MAN   Yes. . . . Well, now, (*fading*) you see, Curley lives on willow leaves, and . . .

AGENT   Walt Disney raises his bid to fifty thousand, but I still hold out for a hundred thousand; Grover Whalen invites Curley to do an English country dance on the cover of the Magna Carta at the World's Fair; and, to make a long story short, everything's going along hunky-dory until one day some *more* public-spirited guys get ahold of Curley—only this time they're not scientists, but musicians.

SPOKESMAN (*fading on*) And therefore, in the interests of music, we of the committee feel that you would be rendering an invaluable service to musical knowledge if you would permit us to test the effect of *classical* music on your client.

AGENT But what good will that do anybody?

SPOKESMAN Why, it may open up an entirely new field of psychology in relation to music. The world knows very little about musical instincts of animals, and nothing at all about insects'. Now . . .

AGENT But you're wasting your time. Curley dances to only one tune.

SPOKESMAN Have you *tried* other tunes?

AGENT Why, sure. Tell him what you've played, Stinky.

STINKY I played "It Ain't Gonna Rain No More," "My Country, 'Tis of Thee," "The Beer Barrel Polka," "Shine on, Harvest Moon," "The Music Goes Round and . . ."

SPOKESMAN Ah, but no *classical* music!

AGENT Sure we did. I myself played "Ah, Sweet Mystery of Life," by Victor Herbert.

SPOKESMAN (*condescendingly*) But you haven't tried any symphonies, have you?

AGENT (*straight*) Disney's trying to get us for a Silly Symphony right now. His latest offer . . .

SPOKESMAN No; I'm afraid you don't understand. Let me explain what we propose to do. (*Fading.*) We get Curley in a studio with an orchestra and go through a careful series of tests, using selected symphonic music of dance-like tempo. Now, by the choice of representative works, we can quickly establish . . .

    Rap of baton.

CONDUCTOR All right! I know you're tired, gentlemen; we've now been through sixty-seven pieces already. But let's try a few more, and then we'll quit until tomorrow.

MUSICIAN Has the caterpillar moved at all?

CONDUCTOR So far he hasn't budged once, but maybe we'll get him with the Habañera from *Carmen.*

    Baton rapping for attention.
    Music: Habañera for about twelve measures. Then:

CONDUCTOR (*perfunctorily; this is the sixty-eighth time he's had to stop almost at the beginning*) Stop . . .stop.

Music: Out.

CONDUCTOR All right, try Number 69—*Rosamunde* Ballet.

Music: Same business as before.

CONDUCTOR Stop.

Music: Out.

CONDUCTOR Next, Number 70—Strauss's "Perpetuum Mobile."

Music: Same business as before. Fade under:

AGENT For two and a half days this went on, and finally, after the two hundred second try, something happened that really made the papers sit up and take notice all over again. The Associated Press next day carried this story. . . .

Fade in news printer. Establish, and take down for:

ASSOCIATED PRESS Curley, the terpsichorean caterpillar, today staggered scientists and musicians when he suddenly went into a stately dance upon hearing the second movement of Beethoven's Eighth Symphony. The movement, marked Allegretto Scherzando, was the two hundred third musical sampling performed in an effort to determine whether the super-caterpillar could, or would, dance to anything besides the song, "Yes, Sir, That's My Baby." The insect further astonished observers by dancing in a contrapuntal manner to an arrangement of melodies from both the song and the movement.

Scientists are unable to explain the phenomenon. (*Fade in Allegretto Scherzando movement after "unable."*) The management of the caterpillar announced meanwhile that Curley will appear as the lead in a ballet entitled "Extravaganza for Insects Only," by William Saroyan, and that Curley will also be seen soon in a dance recital at Carnegie Hall.

Music: Up full and down, under:

AGENT   Well, then things really begin to break for us. Mrs. Roosevelt writes about it in her column, "My Day."

ELEANOR   It is not often that a creature smaller than one's little finger can completely captivate the imagination of millions. Yet such is the remarkable truth about the caterpillar named Curley, and only today I was telling the President that (*fading*) it has been many years since the country has become so interested in . . .

AGENT   There's talk among stamp collectors of issuing a special Curley stamp.

PHILATELIST   And since the Curley stamp would be the only insect subject in existence, its value to philately would naturally (*fading*) assume prodigious proportions . . .

AGENT   Scientific societies offer to investigate Curley's genius— and would you believe that the annual convention of the American Lepidopterological and Entomological Academy even invites Stinky to lecture before it:

STINKY   (*echo—hesitantly; scared; obviously no speechmaker*) Er—so I says to my mother, "Ma, can I have a penny? I want to buy a piece of candy," so my mother says yes, so she gives me the penny— er—so on my way to the store, I see a caterpillar—uh—crossing the road—er—um—so I stopped to watch it, see? So then (*fading*) I picked it up, and then I started to whistle a song—uh—and it happened to be—er—"Yes, Sir, That's My Baby." . . .

AGENT   And all this time the money keeps coming in. We're getting along fine, although it costs a lot to keep up my expensive offices and staff of secretaries, but I'm figuring on getting the big dough—the hundred thousand from Disney, and then retiring, see? Well, to make a long story short, there are a couple of exchanges of telegrams and phone calls, with me holding out for my price, and then one night Disney wires.

DISNEY   (*filter*) Will meet your price of hundred thousand. Please fly out with Curley next plane.

AGENT   Wow! Am I excited! I rush into the next room, where Stinky and Curley are sleeping.

Door.

AGENT   Stinky! Wake up! We're rich! We're practically millionaires!

STINKY (*sleepily*) What's the matter?

AGENT (*excitedly*) Come on, kid! Get your clothes on! Hurry! You're gonna take a long airplane ride with me and Curley! And, boy, I'm gonna buy Curley the juiciest willow leaf he ever ate in his life! . . . Now lemme tell the news to Curley. (*As if opening Curley's box.*) Here you are, little fella, here you . . . (*Freezes; then panicky.*) Where is he? Why isn't he in his box? Where's Curley? *Curley!*

STINKY (*refusing to believe*) I put him to bed all right. Ain't he in his box?

AGENT Quick! Look all around the room. Under the carpet, under the bed, on the walls—everywhere—And be careful where you walk!

STINKY (*half calling, half crying*) Curley! Come back! Curley! Where are you, Curley?

AGENT Curley! Curley, listen . . . (*Sings "Yes, Sir," in a croaking, terror-stricken voice.*)

STINKY (*Joins in the general desultory singing, interspersed with cries for Curley.*)

AGENT Curley! I love you! Where are you?

STINKY Curley, don't leave us!

AGENT A hundred thousand bucks, Curley! (*Sings vehemently; breaks off when he gets an idea.*) Here, Stinky! Take this flashlight and look for him along the corridor and ask the manager to let you look at the bottom of the elevator shaft. Meanwhile I'll phone the police!

STINKY (*Goes off half singing, half crying.*)

Phone receiver jiggles.

AGENT Operator! Operator! Get me the police headquarters! Operator!

Siren.

POLICE RADIO (*filter*) Calling all cars. Calling all cars. Be on the lookout for a dancing caterpillar. Be on the lookout for a dancing caterpillar. C-A—T-E—R-P-I—L-L—A-R—caterpillar. That is all!

Code.

WINCHELL Flash! The Federal Bureau of Investigation will neither deny nor confirm rumors that Curley, the hundred-thousand-dollar caterpillar, was *kidnapped!*

Single chime.

ANNOUNCER Ladies and gentlemen, we have been requested by the civic authorities to make the following announcement. Whenever you hear the song "Yes, Sir, That's My Baby" will you please watch very carefully, wherever you may be, for a dancing catepillar in your vicinity. This announcement is (*fading*) in reference to Curley, the famous caterpillar whose recent career has . . .

AGENT The whole country searches in vain; nobody's seen Curley. The police throw out a dragnet. Posses are formed. Radio stations play "Yes, Sir, That's My Baby" at intervals throughout the day, and ask all listeners to be on the lookout; Curley fans from all over send in money for a Find-Curley Fund.

FIND-CURLEYITE (*orating—slight echo*) And I am privileged, as president of the Find-Curley Club, to announce to the members that the Find-Curley Fund has reached the impressive and staggering total of twelve thousand, three hundred eighty-five dollars and fourteen cents, with the entire South yet to be heard from!

CAST (*Great applause.*)

FIND-CURLEYITE And I am positive that every mother's son of you—yes, and every father's daughter—will pledge his or her heart and hand to the one main and permanent objective—that Curley may be found!

CAST (*Even greater applause.*)

AGENT But nobody finds Curley. And now that he's gone, I begin to realize how much I love that bug. I begin to understand why it was Stinky couldn't bear to sell him to me, 'way back in those happy days. I can't bear thinking of willow leaves. I find myself hating all birds and looking suspiciously at cats. And I take to drinking.

Light background of sound.

WAITER What will it be for you, sir?
AGENT A triple zombie.
WAITER Are you sure you . . .

AGENT   *A triple zombie!*
WAITER   Yes, sir. . . .

Background sound out.

AGENT   And even Stinky tries to drink his way out of his grief. . . .

Background sound in.

WAITER   And what will it be for you, young man?
STINKY   A cup of coffee—and make it *black!*
WAITER   Are you sure you want . . .
STINKY   *Black coffee!*
WAITER   Yes, sir. . . .

Background sound out.

AGENT   Meanwhile, sympathizers from all over the world, including Scandinavian countries, send me caterpillars, hoping maybe they have found Curley and are eligible for a reward offered by the Find-Curley Fund!
SHIPPER   Mister, here's another barrel of caterpillars from Australia, Where shall I put it?
AGENT   Give it to the Zoo.
SHIPPER   Which zoo, Mister?
AGENT   Any zoo, any zoo—so long as you get it out of here!
SHIPPER   Okay, Mister.

Door closes.

AGENT   Days go by. Weeks go by. I send Stinky home.
STINKY   (*tearfully*) Good-bye.
AGENT   Good-bye, Stinky. Well, at least you got a nice suit of clothes on you, and a fine automobile and a chauffeur to drive you home.
STINKY   I would rather have Curley back again.
AGENT   Yes, I know. Well—good-bye.
STINKY   G'bye.
AGENT   G'bye.
STINKY   G'bye. (*Pause.*)

AGENT   And then one day I'm sitting in my place, playing sadly on the piano with one finger, as is my want.

Music: One-finger plunking of "Yes, Sir" on piano.

AGENT   All of a sudden, out from under the music rack creeps—Curley!

Music: Piano stops.

AGENT   Only he's changed. He's different. He's not dancing any more. He—he's a—a *butterfly!*

Music: Orchestra sneaks in with Beethoven movement, softly.

AGENT   (*to* CURLEY, *tenderly*)   Curley! Hello, Curley . . . you're a big boy now, ain't you? . . . (*Low, narrating.*) He flutters his wings a little when I say that, and I stroke his antennae, which are now very long and beautiful. I see he's getting restless for the outdoors, where he no doubt hears the call of his mate; so I sing a farewell to him.

Music: Orchestra stops.

AGENT   (*sings softly "Yes, Sir"*)   He flutters around my head, and then flies over to a picture of Stinky on the bureau, and then flutters back to me . . . and after one long look at me, he flies out of the window, never more to come back again.

Music: Sneak in slow reprise combining both the Beethoven and "Yes, Sir" themes, and hold under:

AGENT   To make a long story short, I sit down, and I feel like crying. In fact, I do cry. (*Pause.*) Yes, who would ever think that a grown man would ever cry about a caterpillar? But I did, and I'm not ashamed to admit it.

Music: Up briefly, then down again for:

AGENT   Well . . . that's the story of my client Curley.

Music: Up to finish.

DISCUSSION

1. How does Corwin establish the humorous tone of his story?
2. How do the introductory passages reveal the character of the agent? Does his behavior later in the play confirm your first impressions?
3. What can you tell about Stinky and Fatso from their reactions to the agent's offers? Why is the part of Fatso restricted to the opening scene of the play?
4. Several times during the course of the play, the agent states his intention to "mak(e) a long story short." Discuss some of the techniques by which this purpose is accomplished.
5. Although *My Client Curley* contains elements of *fantasy*, you find yourself accepting the story as somehow believable. Account for this.
6. Does the inclusion of technical jargon and slang add to your enjoyment of the play, or detract from it? Why?
7. Why does the story of Curley seem like an immediate experience, despite the fact that it is told by the agent some time after it actually occurred?
8. Had the story been told from the point of view of Stinky, rather than from that of the agent, how might it have differed?
9. Are the many shifts of scene and the long cast of characters an asset, in this short play, or a liability? Why?

TOPICS FOR WRITING

Using *My Client Curley* as an example, discuss the advantages and the limitations of the radio play as a dramatic form.

Much of the appeal of *My Client Curley* lies in the author's skillful use of *satire*. Referring to the play for examples, explain the nature and purpose of this kind of humor.

SORRY, WRONG NUMBER

Lucille Fletcher

SORRY, WRONG NUMBER

CHARACTERS

Mrs. Stevenson
1st Operator
1st Man
2nd Man
Chief Operator
2nd Operator
3rd Operator
4th Operator
5th Operator
Information
Hospital Receptionist
Western Union
Sergeant Duffy
A Lunch Room Counter Attendant

Lucille Fletcher (1913-   )

Lucille Fletcher is well-known for her suspenseful dramas, for her many contributions to popular magazines, and, in recent years, for her mystery novels. Miss Fletcher was born in Brooklyn, and graduated in 1933 from Vassar College. She is a member of Phi Beta Kappa honorary society.

Originally a radio play, Sorry, Wrong Number *has enjoyed further success as a stage play, a novel, and a television production. Miss Fletcher claims that her idea for the play was inspired by the thought of being alone in an isolated room, unable to communicate with anyone.*

An unpublished story written by Miss Fletcher was adapted for the radio by Norman Corwin, and appears in this collection under the title, My Client Curley.

SORRY, WRONG NUMBER

SCENE *As curtain rises, we see a divided stage, only the center part of which is lighted and furnished as* MRS. STEVENSON's *bedroom. Expensive, rather fussy furnishings. A large bed, on which* MRS. STEVENSON, *clad in bed-jacket, is lying. A night-table close by, with phone, lighted lamp, and pill bottles. A mantel, with clock,* R. *A closed door,* R. *A window, with curtains closed, rear. The set is lit by one lamp on night-*

*table. It is enclosed by three flats. Beyond this central set,
the stage, on either side, is in darkness.*

MRS. STEVENSON *is dialling a number on phone, as curtain
rises. She listens to phone, slams down receiver in irritation.
As she does so, we hear sound of a train roaring by in the
distance. She reaches for her pill bottle, pours herself a glass
of water, shakes out pill, swallows it, then reaches for phone
again, dials number nervously.* SOUND: *Number being dialled
on phone: Busy signal.*

MRS. STEVENSON (*a querulous, self-centered neurotic*) Oh—dear!
(*Slams down receiver. Dials* OPERATOR). (SCENE: *A spotlight,* L. *of side
flat, picks up out of peripheral darkness, figure of* 1ST OPERATOR, *sitting
with headphones at small table. If spotlight not available, use flashlight,
clicked on by* 1ST OPERATOR, *illumining her face.*)

OPERATOR Your call, please?

MRS. STEVENSON Operator? I have been dialling Murray Hill
4-0098 now for the last three-quarters of an hour, and the line is always busy. But I don't see how it *could* be busy that long. Will you try
it for me, please?

OPERATOR Murray Hill 4-0098? One moment, please. (SCENE: *She
makes gesture of plugging in call through a switchboard.*)

MRS. STEVENSON I don't see how it could be busy all this time.
It's my husband's office. He's working late tonight, and I'm all alone
here in the house. My health is very poor—and I've been feeling so
nervous all day. . . .

OPERATOR Ringing Murray Hill 4-0098. . . . (SOUND: *Phone buzz.
It rings three times. Receiver is picked up at other end*). (SCENE: *Spotlight picks up figure of a heavy-set man, seated at desk with phone
on* R. *side of dark periphery of stage. He is wearing a hat. Picks up
phone, which rings three times.*)

MAN Hello.

MRS. STEVENSON Hello . . . ? (*a little puzzled*). Hello. Is Mr.
Stevenson there?

MAN (*into phone, as though he had not heard*) Hello. . . .
(*Louder*). Hello. (SCENE: *Spotlight on* L. *now moves from* OPERATOR
to another man, GEORGE. *A killer type, also wearing hat, but standing
as in a phone booth. A three-sided screen may be used to suggest this.*)

2ND MAN (*slow heavy quality, faintly foreign accent*) Hello.

1ST MAN Hello. George?

GEORGE Yes, sir.

MRS. STEVENSON (*louder and more imperious, to phone*) Hello. Who's this? What number am I calling, please?

1ST MAN We have heard from our client. He says the coast is clear for tonight.

GEORGE Yes, sir.

1ST MAN Where are you now?

GEORGE In a phone booth.

1ST MAN Okay. You know the address. At eleven o'clock the private patrolman goes around to the bar on Second Avenue for a beer. Be sure that all the lights downstairs are out. There should be only one light visible from the street. At eleven-fifteen a subway train crosses the bridge. It makes a noise in case her window is open, and she should scream.

MRS. STEVENSON (*shocked*) Oh—HELLO! What number is this, please?

GEORGE Okay, I understand

1ST MAN Make it quick. As little blood as possible. Our client does not wish to make her suffer long.

GEORGE A knife okay, sir?

1ST MAN Yes. A knife will be okay. And remember—remove the rings and bracelets, and the jewelry in the bureau drawer. Our client wishes it to look like simple robbery.

GEORGE Okay—I get—(SCENE: *Spotlight suddenly goes out on* GEORGE.) (SOUND: *A bland buzzing signal*). (SCENE: *Spotlight goes off on* 1ST MAN.)

MRS. STEVENSON (*clicking phone*) Oh . . . ! (*Bland buzzing signal continues. She hangs up*). How awful! How unspeakably . . . (SCENE: *She lies back on her pillows, overcome for a few seconds, then suddenly pulls herself together, reaches for phone*). (SOUND: *Dialling. Phone buzz*). (SCENE: *Spotlight goes on at* 1ST OPERATOR's *switchboard.* 1ST *and* 2ND MAN *exit as unobtrusively as possible, in darkness.*)

OPERATOR Your call, please?

MRS. STEVENSON (*unnerved and breathless, into phone*) Operator. I—I've just been cut off.

OPERATOR I'm sorry, madam. What number were you calling?

MRS. STEVENSON Why—it was supposed to be Murray Hill 4-0098, but it wasn't. Some wires must have crossed—I was cut into a wrong

number—and—I've just heard the most dreadful thing—a—a murder
—and—(*Imperiously*). Operator, you'll simply have to retrace that
call at once.

OPERATOR   I beg your pardon, madam—I don't quite—

MRS. STEVENSON   Oh—I know it was a wrong number, and I had
no business listening—but these two men—they were cold-blooded
fiends—and they were going to murder somebody—some poor innocent woman—who was all alone—in a house near a bridge. And we've
got to stop them—we've got to—

OPERATOR (*patiently*)   What number were you calling, madam?

MRS. STEVENSON   That doesn't matter. This was a *wrong* number.
And *you* dialled it. And we've got to find out what it was—immediately!

OPERATOR   But—madam——

MRS. STEVENSON   Oh—why are you so stupid? Look—it was obviously a case of some little slip of the finger. I told you to try Murray
Hill 4-0098 for me—you dialled it but your finger must have slipped—
and I was connected with some other number—and I could hear them,
but they couldn't hear me. Now, I simply fail to see why you couldn't
make that same mistake again—on purpose—why you couldn't *try*
to dial Murray Hill 4-0098 in the same careless sort of way. . . .

OPERATOR (*quickly*)   Murray Hill 4-0098? I will try to get it for
you, madam.

MRS. STEVENSON (*sarcastically*)   *Thank* you. (SCENE: *She bridles,
adjusts herself on her pillows, reaches for handkerchief, wipes forehead, glancing uneasily for a moment toward window, while still holding phone*). (*Sound of ringing: Busy signal.*)

OPERATOR   I am sorry. Murray Hill 4-0098 is busy.

MRS. STEVENSON (*frantically clicking receiver*)   Operator. Operator.

OPERATOR   Yes, Madam.

MRS. STEVENSON (*angrily*)   You *didn't* try to get that wrong
number at all. I asked explicitly. And all you did was dial correctly.

OPERATOR   I am sorry. What number were you calling?

MRS. STEVENSON   Can't you, for once, forget what number I was
calling, and do something specific? Now I want to trace that call. It's
my civic duty—it's *your* civic duty—to trace that call . . . and to appre-
hend those dangerous killers—and if *you* won't . . .

OPERATOR (*glancing around wearily*)   I will connect you with the
Chief Operator.

MRS. STEVENSON *Please! (Sound of ringing).* (SCENE: OPERATOR *puts hand over mouthpiece of phone, gestures into darkness. A half whisper:*

OPERATOR Miss Curtis. Will you pick up on 17, please? (MISS CURTIS, *Chief Operator, enters. Middle-aged, efficient type, pleasant. Wearing headphones.*)

MISS CURTIS Yes, dear. What's the trouble?

OPERATOR Somebody wanting a call traced. I can't make head nor tail of it. . . .

MISS CURTIS (*sitting down at desk, as* OPERATOR *gets up*) Sure, dear. 17? (*She makes gesture of plugging in her headphone, coolly and professionally*). This is the Chief Operator.

MRS. STEVENSON Chief Operator? I want you to trace a call. A telephone call. Immediately. I don't know where it came from, or who was making it, but it's absolutely necessary that it be tracked down. Because it was about a murder. Yes, a terrible, cold-blooded murder of a poor innocent woman—tonight—at eleven-fifteen.

CHIEF OPERATOR I see.

MRS. STEVENSON (*high-strung, demanding*) Can you trace it for me? Can you track down those men?

CHIEF OPERATOR It depends, madam.

MRS. STEVENSON Depends on what?

CHIEF OPERATOR It depends on whether the call is still going on. If it's a live call, we can trace it on the equipment. If it's been disconnected, we can't.

MRS. STEVENSON Disconnected?

CHIEF OPERATOR If the parties have stopped talking to each other.

MRS. STEVENSON Oh—but—but of course they must have stopped talking to each other by *now*. That was at least five minutes ago—and they didn't sound like the type who would make a long call.

CHIEF OPERATOR Well, I can try tracing it. (SCENE: *She takes pencil out of her hair-do*). Now—what is your name, madam?

MRS. STEVENSON Mrs. Stevenson. Mrs. Elbert Stevenson. But— listen——

CHIEF OPERATOR (*writing it down*) And your telephone number?

MRS. STEVENSON (*more irritated*) Plaza 4-2295. But if you go on wasting all this time—— (SCENE: *She glances at clock on mantel.*)

CHIEF OPERATOR And what is your reason for wanting this call traced?

MRS. STEVENSON My reason? Well—for Heaven's sake—isn't it

obvious? I overhear two men—they're killers—they're planning to murder this woman—it's a matter for the police.

CHIEF OPERATOR Have you told the police?

MRS. STEVENSON No. How could I?

CHIEF OPERATOR You're making this check into a private call purely as a private individual?

MRS. STEVENSON Yes. But meanwhile——

CHIEF OPERATOR Well, Mrs. Stevenson—I seriously doubt whether we could make this check for you at this time just on your say-so as a private individual. We'd have to have something more official.

MRS. STEVENSON Oh—for Heaven's sake! You mean to tell me I can't report a murder without getting tied up in all this redtape? Why —its perfectly idiotic. All right, then. I *will* call the police. (*She slams down receiver*). (SCENE: *Spotlight goes off on two* OPERATORS). Ridiculous! (*Sound of dialling*). (SCENE: MRS. STEVENSON *dials numbers on phone, as two* OPERATORS *exit unobtrusively in darkness.*) (*On* R. *of stage, spotlight picks up a* 2ND OPERATOR, *seated like first, with headphones at table* [*same one vacated by* 1ST MAN].)

2ND OPERATOR Your call, please?

MRS. STEVENSON (*very annoyed*) The Police Department—*please.*

2ND OPERATOR Ringing the Police Department. (*Ring twice. Phone is picked up*). (SCENE: L. *stage, at table vacated by* 1ST *and* CHIEF OPERATOR, *spotlight now picks up* SERGEANT DUFFY, *seated in a relaxed position. Just entering beside him is a young man in cap and apron, carrying a large brown paper parcel, delivery boy for a local lunch counter. Phone is ringing.*)

YOUNG MAN Here's your lunch, Sarge. They didn't have no jelly doughnuts, so I give you French crullers. Okay, Sarge?

S. DUFFY French crullers. I got ulcers. Whyn't you make it apple pie? (*Picks up phone, which has rung twice*). Police department. Precinct 43. Duffy speaking. (SCENE: LUNCH ROOM ATTENDANT, *anxiously.* We dont' have no apple pie, either, Sarge—)

MRS. STEVENSON Police Department? Oh. This is Mrs. Stevenson —Mrs. Elbert Smythe Stevenson of 53 North Sutton Place. I'm calling up to report a murder. (SCENE: DUFFY *has been examining lunch, but double-takes suddenly on above.*)

DUFFY Eh?

MRS. STEVENSON I mean—the murder hasn't been committed yet. I just overheard plans for it over the telephone . . . over a wrong number that the operator gave me. (SCENE: DUFFY *relaxes, sighs, starts taking lunch from bag*). I've been trying to trace down the call myself, but everybody is so stupid—and I guess in the end you're the only people who could *do* anything.

DUFFY (*not too impressed*). (SCENE: ATTENDANT, *who exits*)   Yes, ma'am.

MRS. STEVENSON (*trying to impress him*)   It was a perfectly *definite* murder. I heard their plans distinctly. (SCENE: DUFFY *begins to eat sandwich, phone at his ear*). Two men were talking, and they were going to murder some woman at eleven-fifteen tonight—she lived in a house near a bridge.

DUFFY   Yes, ma'am.

MRS. STEVENSON   And there was a private patrolman on the street. He was going to go around for a beer on Second Avenue. And there was some third man—a client, who was paying to have this poor woman murdered—they were going to take her rings and bracelets—and use a knife . . . well, it's unnerved me dreadfully—and I'm not well. . . .

DUFFY   I see. (SCENE: *Having finished sandwich, he wipes mouth with paper napkin*). When was all this, ma'am?

MRS. STEVENSON   About eight minutes ago. Oh . . . (*Relieved*). Then you *can* do something? You *do* understand—

DUFFY   And what is your name, ma'am? (SCENE: *He reaches for pad.*)

MRS. STEVENSON (*impatiently*)   Mrs. Stevenson. Mrs. Elbert Stevenson.

DUFFY   And your address?

MRS. STEVENSON   53 North Sutton Place. *That's* near a bridge. The Queensboro Bridge, you know—and *we* have a private patrolman on *our* street—and Second Avenue——

DUFFY   And what was that number you were calling?

MRS. STEVENSON   Murray Hill 4-0098. (SCENE: DUFFY *writes it down.*) But—that wasn't the number I overheard. I mean Murray Hill 4-0098 is my husband's office. (SCENE: DUFFY, *in exasperation, holds pencil poised.*) He's working late tonight, and I was trying to reach him to ask him to come home. I'm an invalid, you know—and it's the maid's night off—and I *hate* to be alone—even though he says I'm perfectly safe as long as I have the telephone right beside my bed.

DUFFY (*stolidly*). (SCENE: *He has put pencil down, pushes pad away*) Well—we'll look into it, Mrs. Stevenson—and see if we can check it with the telephone company.

MRS. STEVENSON (*getting impatient*) But the telephone company said they couldn't check the call if the parties had stopped talking. I've already taken care of *that.*

DUFFY Oh—yes? (SCENE: *He yawns slightly.*)

MRS. STEVENSON (*high-handed*) Personally I feel you ought to do something far more immediate and drastic than just check the call. What good does checking the call do, if they've stopped talking? By the time you track it down, they'll already have committed the murder.

DUFFY (SCENE: *He reaches for paper cup of coffee*) Well—we'll take care of it, lady. Don't worry. (SCENE: *He begins to take off paper top of coffee container.*)

MRS. STEVENSON I'd say the whole thing calls for a search—a complete and thorough search of the whole city. (SCENE: DUFFY *puts down phone for a moment, to work on cup, as her voice continues*). I'm very near a bridge, and I'm not far from Second Avenue. And I know *I'd* feel a whole lot better if you sent around a radio car to *this* neighborhood at once.

DUFFY (SCENE: *Picks up phone again, drinks coffee*) And what makes you think the murder's going to be committed in your neighborhood, ma'am?

MRS. STEVENSON Oh—I don't know. The coincidence is so horrible. Second Avenue—the patrolman—the bridge . . .

DUFFY (SCENE: *He sips coffee*) Second Avenue is a very long street, ma'am. And do you happen to know how many bridges there are in the city of New York alone? Not to mention Brooklyn, Staten Island, Queens, and the Bronx? And how do you know there isn't some little house out on Staten Island—on some little Second Avenue you never heard about? (SCENE: *A long gulp of coffee*). How do you know they were even talking about New York at all?

MRS. STEVENSON But I heard the call on the New York dialling system.

DUFFY How do you know it wasn't a long distance call you overheard? Telephones are funny things. (SCENE: *He sets down coffee*). Look, lady, why don't you look at it this way? Supposing you hadn't broken in on that telephone call? Supposing you'd got your husband the way you always do? Would this murder have made any difference to you then?

MRS. STEVENSON I suppose not. But it's so inhuman—so cold-blooded . . .

DUFFY A lot of murders are committed in this city every day, ma'am. If we could do something to stop 'em, we would. But a clue of this kind that's so vague isn't much more use to us than no clue at all.

MRS. STEVENSON But, surely——

DUFFY Unless, of course, you have some reason for thinking this call is phoney—and that someone may be planning to murder *you?*

MRS. STEVENSON *Me?* Oh—no—I hardly think so. I—I mean—why should anybody? I'm alone all day and night—I see nobody except my maid Eloise—she's a big two-hundred-pounder—she's too lazy to bring up my breakfast tray—and the only other person is my husband Elbert—he's crazy about me—adores me—waits on me hand and foot—he's scarcely left my side since I took sick twelve years ago—

DUFFY Well—then—there's nothing for you to worry about, is there? (SCENE: LUNCH COUNTER ATTENDANT *has entered. He is carrying a piece of apple pie on a plate. Points it out to* DUFFY *triumphantly*). And now—if you'll just leave the rest of this to us——

MRS. STEVENSON But what will you *do?* It's so late—it's nearly eleven o'clock.

DUFFY (*firmly*). (SCENE: *He nods to* ATTENDANT, *pleased*) We'll take care of it, lady.

MRS. STEVENSON Will you broadcast it all over the city? And send out squads? And warn your radio cars to watch out—especially in suspicious neighborhoods like mine? (SCENE: ATTENDANT, *in triumph, has put pie down in front of* DUFFY. *Takes fork out of his pocket, stands at attention, waiting.*)

DUFFY (*more firmly*) Lady, I *said* we'd take care of it. (SCENE: *Glances at pie*). Just now I've got a couple of other matters here on my desk that require my immediate——

MRS. STEVENSON Oh! (*She slams down receiver hard*). Idiot. (SCENE: DUFFY, *listening at phone, hangs up. Shrugs. Winks at* ATTEND-ANT *as though to say,* "What a crazy character!" *Attacks his pie as spotlight fades out*). (MRS. STEVENSON, *in bed, looking at phone nervously*). Now—why did I do that?—Now—he'll think I *am* a fool. (SCENE: *She sits there tensely, then throws herself back against pillows, lies there a moment, whimpering with self-pity*). Oh—why doesn't Elbert come home? *Why* doesn't he? (SCENE: *We hear sound of train roaring by in the distance. She sits up reaching for phone). (Sound of dialling operator).* (SCENE: *Spotlight picks up* 2ND OPERATOR, *seated* R.)

OPERATOR   Your call, please?

MRS. STEVENSON   Operator—for Heaven's sake—will you ring that Murray Hill 4-0098 number again? I can't think what's keeping him so long.

OPERATOR   Ringing Murray Hill 4-0098. (*Rings. Busy signal*). The line is busy. Shall I——

MRS. STEVENSON   (*nastily*)   I can hear it. You don't have to tell me. I know it's busy. (*Slams down receiver*). (SCENE: *Spotlight fades off on* 2ND OPERATOR). (SCENE: MRS. STEVENSON *sinks back against pillows again, whimpering to herself fretfully. She glances at clock, then turning, punches her pillows up, trying to make herself comfortable. But she isn't. Whimpers to herself as she squirms restlessly in bed*). If I could only get out of this bed for a little while. If I could get a breath of fresh air—or just lean out the window—and see the street. . . . (SCENE: *She sighs, reaches for pill bottle, shakes out a pill. As she does so:*) (*The phone rings. She darts for it instantly*). Hello. Elbert? Hello. Hello. Oh—what's the *matter* with this phone? HELLO? HELLO? (*Slams down the receiver*). (SCENE: *She stares at it, tensely*). (*The phone rings again. Once. She picks it up*). Hello? Hello. . . . O—for Heaven's sake—who *is* this? Hello. Hello. HELLO. (*Slams down receiver. Dials operator*). (SCENE: *Spotlight comes on* L., *showing* 3RD OPERATOR, *at spot vacated by* DUFFY.)

3RD OPERATOR   Your call, please?

MRS. STEVENSON   (*very annoyed and imperious*)   Hello. Operator. I don't know what's the matter with this telephone tonight, but it's positively driving me crazy. I've never seen such inefficient, miserable service. Now, look, I'm an invalid, and I'm very nervous, and I'm *not* supposed to be annoyed. But if this keeps on much longer . . .

3RD OPERATOR   (*a young sweet type*)   What seems to be the trouble, madam?

MRS. STEVENSON   Well—everything's wrong. The whole world could be murdered, for all you people care. And now—my phone keeps ringing. . . .

OPERATOR   Yes, madam?

MRS. STEVENSON   Ringing and ringing and ringing every five seconds or so, and when I pick it up, there's no one there.

OPERATOR   I am sorry, madam. If you will hang up, I will test it for you.

MRS. STEVENSON   I don't want you to test it for me. I want you to put through that call—whatever it is—at once.

OPERATOR (*gently*)   I am afraid that is not possible, madam.

MRS. STEVENSON (*storming*)   Not possible? And why—may I ask?

OPERATOR   The system is automatic, madam. If someone is trying to dial your number, there is no way to check whether the call is coming through the system or not—unless the person who is trying to reach you complains to his particular operator——

MRS. STEVENSON   Well, of all the stupid, complicated . . . ! And meanwhile *I've* got to sit here in my bed, *suffering* every time that phone rings—imagining everything. . . .

OPERATOR   I will try to check it for you, madam.

MRS. STEVENSON   Check it! Check it! That's all anybody can do. Of all the stupid, idiotic . . . ! (*She hangs up*). Oh—what's the use . . . (SCENE: 3RD OPERATOR *fades out of spotlight, as*) (*Instantly* MRS. STEVENSON'S *phone rings again. She picks up receiver. Wildly*). Hello. HELLO. Stop ringing, do you hear me? Answer me? What do you want? Do you realize you're driving me crazy? (SCENE: *Spotlight goes on* R. *We see a* MAN *in eye-shade and shirt-sleeves, at desk with phone and telegrams*). Stark, staring . . .

MAN (*dull flat voice*)   Hello. Is this Plaza 4-2295?

MRS. STEVENSON (*catching her breath*)   Yes. Yes. This is Plaza 4-2295.

WESTERN UNION   This is Western Union. I have a telegram here for Mrs. Elbert Stevenson. Is there anyone there to receive the message?

MRS. STEVENSON (*trying to calm herself*)   I am Mrs. Stevenson.

WESTERN UNION (*reading flatly*)   The telegram is as follows: "Mrs. Elbert Stevenson. 53 North Sutton Place, New York, New York. Darling. Terribly sorry. Tried to get you for last hour, but line busy. Leaving for Boston eleven p. m. tonight on urgent business. Back tomorrow afternoon. Keep happy. Love. Signed. Elbert."

MRS. STEVENSON (*breathlessly, aghast, to herself*)   Oh . . . no . . .

WESTERN UNION   That is all, madam. Do you wish us to deliver a copy of the message?

MRS. STEVENSON   No—no, thank you.

WESTERN UNION   Thank you, madam. Good night. (*He hangs up phone.*) (SCENE: *Spotlight on* WESTERN UNION *immediately out.*)

MRS. STEVENSON (*mechanically, to phone*)   Good night. (*She hangs up slowly. Suddenly bursting into*). No—no—it isn't true! He

couldn't do it! Not when he knows I'll be all alone. It's some trick—
some fiendish . . .

> (SCENE: *We hear sound of train roaring by outside. She half
> rises in bed, in panic, glaring toward curtains. Her move-
> ments are frenzied. She beats with her knuckles on bed, then
> suddenly stops, and reaches for phone*). (*She dials operator*).

> (SCENE: *Spotlight picks up* 4TH OPERATOR, *seated* L.)

OPERATOR (*coolly*)   Your call, please?

MRS. STEVENSON   Operator—try that Murray Hill 4-0098 number
for me just once more, please.

OPERATOR   Ringing Murray Hill 4-0098. (*Call goes through. We
hear ringing at other end. Ring after ring*). (SCENE: *If telephone noises
are not used audibly, have* OPERATOR *say after a brief pause: "They do
not answer."*)

MRS. STEVENSON   He's gone. Oh—Elbert, how could you? How
could you . . . ? (*She hangs up phone, sobbing pityingly to herself,
turning restlessly*). (SCENE: *Spotlight goes out on* 4TH OPERATOR). But
I can't be alone tonight. I can't. If I'm alone one more second . . .
(SCENE: *She runs hands wildly through hair*). I don't care what he
says—or what the expense is—I'm a sick woman—I'm entitled . . .
(SCENE: *With trembling fingers she picks up receiver again*). (*She
dials* INFORMATION). (SCENE: *The spotlight picks up* INFORMATION
OPERATOR, *seated* R.)

INFORMATION   This is Information.

MRS. STEVENSON   I want the telephone number of Henchley Hospital.

INFORMATION   Henchley Hospital? Do you have the address,
madam?

MRS. STEVENSON   No. It's somewhere in the 70's, though. It's a
very small, private and exclusive hospital where I had my appendix
out two years ago. Henchley. H-E-N-C——

INFORMATION   One moment, please.

MRS. STEVENSON   Please—hurry. And please—what *is* the time?

INFORMATION   I do not know, madam. You may find out the time
by dialling Meridian 7-1212.

MRS. STEVENSON (*irritated*)   Oh—for Heaven's sake! Couldn't
you——?

INFORMATION The number of Henchley Hospital is Butterfield 7-0105, madam.

MRS. STEVENSON Butterfield 7-0105. (*She hangs up before she finishes speaking, and immediately dials number as she repeats it*). (SCENE: *Spotlight goes out on* INFORMATION). (*Phone rings*). (SCENE: *Spotlight picks up* WOMAN *in nurse's uniform, seated at desk,* L.)

WOMAN (*middle-aged, solid, firm, practical*) Henchley Hospital, good evening.

MRS. STEVENSON Nurses' Registry.

WOMAN Who was it you wished to speak to, please?

MRS. STEVENSON (*high-handed*) I want the Nurses' Registry at once. I want a trained nurse. I want to hire her immediately. For the night.

WOMAN I see. And what is the nature of the case, madam?

MRS. STEVENSON Nerves. I'm very nervous. I need soothing—and companionship. My husband is away—and I'm——

WOMAN Have you been recommended to us by any doctor in particular, madam?

MRS. STEVENSON No. But I really don't see why all this catechizing is necessary. I want a trained nurse. I was a patient in your hospital two years ago. And after all, I *do* expect to *pay* this person——

WOMAN We quite understand that, madam. But registered nurses are very scarce just now—and our superintendent has asked us to send people out only on cases where the physician in charge feels it is absolutely necessary.

MRS. STEVENSON (*growing hysterical*) Well—it *is* absolutely necessary. I'm a sick woman. I—I'm very upset. Very. I'm alone in this house—and I'm an invalid—and tonight I overhead a telephone conversation that upset me dreadfully. About a murder—a poor woman who was going to be murdered at eleven-fifteen tonight—in fact, if someone doesn't come at once—I'm afraid I'll go out of my mind. . . . (*Almost off handle by now.*)

WOMAN (*calmly*) I see. Well—I'll speak to Miss Phillips as soon as she comes in. And what is your name, madam?

MRS. STEVENSON Miss Phillips. And when do you expect her in?

WOMAN I really don't know, madam. She went out to supper at eleven o'clock.

MRS. STEVENSON Eleven o'clock. But it's not eleven yet. (*She cries out*). Oh, my clock *has* stopped. I thought it was running down. What time is it? (SCENE: WOMAN *glances at wristwatch.*)

WOMAN   Just fourteen minutes past eleven. . . . (*Sound of phone receiver being lifted on same line as* MRS. STEVENSON's. *A click.*)

MRS. STEVENSON (*crying out*)   What's *that?*

WOMAN   What was what, madam?

MRS. STEVENSON   That—that click just now—in my own telephone? As though someone had lifted the receiver off the hook of the extension phone downstairs. . . .

WOMAN   I didn't hear it, madam. Now—about this . . .

MRS. STEVENSON (*scared*)   But I *did*. There's someone in this house. Someone downstairs in the kitchen. And they're listening to me now. They're . . . (SCENE: *She puts hand over her mouth*). (*Hangs up phone*). (SCENE: *She sits there, in terror, frozen, listening*). (*In a suffocated voice*). I won't pick it up, I won't let them hear me. I'll be quiet—and they'll think . . . (*With growing terror*). But if I don't call someone now—while they're still down there—there'll be no time. . . . (*She picks up receiver. Bland buzzing signal. She dials operator. Ring twice*).

> (SCENE: *On second ring, spotlight goes on* R. *We see* 5TH OPERATOR.)

OPERATOR (*fat and lethargic*).   Your call, please?

MRS. STEVENSON (*a desperate whisper*)   Operator—I—I'm in desperate trouble . . . I——

OPERATOR   I cannot hear you, madam. Please speak louder.

MRS. STEVENSON (*still whispering*)   I don't dare. I—there's someone listening. Can you hear me now?

OPERATOR   Your call, please? What number are you calling, madam?

MRS. STEVENSON (*desperately*)   You've got to hear me. Oh—please. You've got to help me. There's someone in this house. Someone who's going to murder me. And you've got to get in touch with the . . . (*Click of receiver being put down on* MRS. STEVENSON's *line. Bursting out wildly*). Oh—there it is . . . he's put it down . . . he's coming . . . (*She screams.*) he's coming up the stairs . . . (SCENE: *She thrashes in bed, phone cord catching in lamp wire, lamp topples, goes out. Darkness*). (*Hoarsely*). Give me the Police Department. . . . (SCENE: *We see on the dark* C. *stage, the shadow of door opening*). (*Screaming*). The police! . . . (SCENE: *On stage, swift rush of a shadow, advancing to bed—sound of her voice is choked out, as*)

OPERATOR Ringing the Police Department. (*Phone is rung. We hear sound of a train beginning to fade in. On second ring,* MRS. STEVENSON *screams again, but roaring of train drowns out her voice. For a few seconds we hear nothing but roaring of train, then dying away, phone at police headquarters ringing*). (SCENE: *Spotlight goes on* DUFFY, L. *stage.*)

DUFFY Police Department. Precinct 43. Duffy speaking. (*Pause*). (SCENE: *Nothing visible but darkness on* C. *stage*). Police Department. Duffy speaking. (SCENE: *A flashlight goes on, illuminating open phone to one side of* MRS. STEVENSON's *bed. Nearby, hanging down, is her lifeless hand. We see the second man,* GEORGE, *in black gloves, reach down and pick up phone. He is breathing hard.*)

GEORGE Sorry. Wrong number. (*Hangs up*). (SCENE: *He replaces receiver on hook quietly, exits, as* DUFFY *hangs up with a shrug, and* CURTAIN FALLS.)

DISCUSSION

1. Discuss the playwright's purpose in specifying each of the following: (a) a divided stage, (b) expensive, fussy furnishings, (c) darkness, save for a single bedroom light, (d) the sound of a train roaring by.
2. When do you first suspect that the overheard telephone conversation refers to Mrs. Stevenson? When does she? How has the playwright used *dramatic irony* to heighten the suspense?
3. From what you observe of Mrs. Stevenson's behavior, are her husband's motives for murder understandable? Explain.
4. Why is it consistent with her character that Mrs. Stevenson has never doubted her husband's affection?
5. How do the reactions of the policeman and the telephone operators underscore Mrs. Stevenson's growing anxiety?
6. How might your attitude toward the outcome of the story have differed, had the playwright established Mrs. Stevenson as a sympathetic character?
7. Could *Sorry, Wrong Number* be classified as a *melodrama*? Explain.

TOPICS FOR WRITING

A character study of Mrs. Stevenson
The trial of Mr. Stevenson

THE STILL ALARM

George S. Kaufman

CHARACTERS

Ed
Bob
The Bellboy
A Fireman
Another Fireman

George S. Kaufman (1889-1961)

A master of high comedy and stage technique, George S. Kaufman did most of his playwriting in collaboration with other authors. For two of these collaborations, Of Thee I Sing *and* You Can't Take It With You, *he received the Pulitzer Prize for Drama. Kaufman was born in 1889, and distinguished himself as a journalist before he began to write plays. His first play was* Dulcy, *written with Marc Connelly, and produced in 1921. Other playwrights with whom Kaufman collaborated were Edna Ferber and Moss Hart.*

The Still Alarm *is one of several short plays that Kaufman wrote without the benefit of a collaborator. Whether or not you discover the many possible meanings that underly this story, you will admire the author's ingenuity and enjoy his dry humor.*

THE STILL ALARM

VITAL NOTE: *It is important that the entire play should be acted calmly and politely, in the manner of an English drawing-room comedy. No actor ever raises his voice; every line must be read as though it were an invitation to a cup of tea. If this direction is disregarded, the play has no point at all. The Scene is a hotel bedroom. Two windows rear; door to the hall at the right, chair R.C. Bed between windows. 'Phone stand R., downstage end of bed. Dresser L.U. corner. Another door at left. Small table and chairs downstage L.C.*

*ED and BOB are on the stage. ED is getting into his over-
coat as the curtain rises. Both are at R. door.*

ED   Well, Bob, it's certainly been nice to see you again.

BOB   It was nice to see *you.*

ED   You come to town so seldom, I hardly ever get the chance
to——

BOB   Well, you know how it is. A business trip is always more or
less of a bore.

ED   Next time you've got to come out to the house.

BOB   I want to come out. I just had to stick around the hotel this
trip.

ED   Oh, I understand. Well, give my best to Edith.

BOB   (*remembering something*)   Oh, I say, Ed. Wait a minute.

ED   What's the matter?

BOB   I knew I wanted to show you something. (*Crosses L. to
table. Gets roll of blueprints from drawer*). Did you know I'm going
to build?

ED   (*follows to R. of table*)   A house?

BOB   You bet it's a house! (*Knock on R. door*). Come in! (*Spreads
plans*). I just got these yesterday.

ED   (*sits*)   Well, that's fine! (*The knock is repeated—louder. Both
men now give full attention to the door.*)

BOB   Come! Come in!

BELLBOY   (*enters R.*)   Mr. Barclay?

BOB   Well?

BELLBOY   I've a message from the clerk, sir. For Mr. Barclay
personally.

BOB   (*crosses to boy*)   I'm Mr. Barclay. What is the message?

BELLBOY   The hotel is on fire, sir.

BOB   What's that?

BELLBOY   The hotel is on fire.

ED   This hotel?

BELLBOY   Yes, sir.

BOB   Well—is it bad?

BELLBOY   It looks pretty bad, sir.

ED   You mean it's going to burn down?

BELLBOY   We think so—yes, sir.

BOB   (*a low whistle of surprise*)   Well! We'd better leave.

BELLBOY Yes, sir.

BOB Going to burn down, huh?

BELLBOY Yes, sir. If you'll step to the window you'll see. (BOB *goes to* R. *window.*)

BOB Yes, that is pretty bad. H'm. (*To* ED). I say, you really ought to see this——

ED (*crosses up to* R. *window—peering out*) It's reached the floor right underneath.

BELLBOY Yes, sir. The lower part of the hotel is about gone, sir.

BOB (*still looking out—looks up*) Still all right up above, though. (*Turns to boy*). Have they notified the Fire Department?

BELLBOY I wouldn't know, sir. I'm only the bellboy.

BOB Well, that's the thing to do, obviously—(*Nods head to each one as if the previous line was a bright idea*)—notify the Fire Department. Just call them up, give them the name of the hotel——

ED Wait a minute. I can do better than that for you. (*To the boy*). Ring through to the Chief, and tell him that Ed Jamison told you to telephone him (*To* BOB). We went to school together, you know.

BOB That's fine. (*To the boy*). Now, get that right. Tell the Chief that Mr. Jamison said to ring him.

ED Ed Jamison.

BOB Yes, Ed Jamison.

BELLBOY Yes, sir. (*Turns to go.*)

BOB Oh! Boy! (*Pulls out handful of change; picks out a coin*). Here you are.

BELLBOY Thank you, sir. (*Exit* BELLBOY. ED *sits* R. *of table, lights cigarette and throws match downstage, then steps on it. There is a moment's pause.*)

BOB Well! (*Crosses and looks out* L. *window*). Say, we'll have to get out of here pretty soon.

ED (*going to window*) How is it—no better?

BOB Worse, if anything. It'll be up here in a few moments.

ED What floor *is* this?

BOB Eleventh.

ED Eleven. We couldn't jump, then.

BOB Oh, no. You never could jump. (*Comes away from window to dresser*). Well, I've got to get my things together. (*Pulls out suitcase.*)

ED (*smoothing out the plans*) Who made these for you?

BOB A fellow here—Rawlins. (*Turns a shirt in his hand*). I ought to call one of the other hotels for a room.

ED Oh, you can get in.

BOB They're pretty crowded. (*Feels something on the sole of his foot; inspects it*). Say, the floor's getting hot.

ED I know it. It's getting stuffy in the room, too. Phew! (*He looks around, then goes to the 'phone*). Hello.—Ice water in eleven-eighteen. (*Crosses to* R. *of table.*)

BOB (*at bed*) That's the stuff. (*Packs*). You know, if I move to another hotel I'll never get my mail. Everybody thinks I'm stopping here.

ED (*studying the plans*) Say, this isn't bad.

BOB (*eagerly*) Do you like it? (*Remembers his plight*). Suppose I go to another hotel and there's a fire there, too!

ED You've got to take *some* chance.

BOB I know, but here I'm sure. (*'Phone rings*). Oh, answer that, will you, Ed? (*To dresser and back.*)

ED (*crosses to 'phone*) Sure. (*At 'phone*). Hello—— Oh, that's good. Fine. What?—Oh! Well, wait a minute. (*To* BOB). The firemen are downstairs and some of them want to come up to this room.

BOB Tell them, of course.

ED (*at 'phone*) All right. Come right up. (*Hangs up, crosses and sits* R. *of table*). Now we'll get some action.

BOB (*looks out of window* L.) Say, there's an awful crowd of people on the street.

ED (*absently, as he pores over the plans*) Maybe there's been some kind of accident.

BOB (*peering out, suitcase in hand*) No. More likely they heard about the fire. (*A knock at the door* R.). Come in.

BELLBOY (*enters*) I beg pardon, Mr. Barclay, the firemen have arrived.

BOB Show them in. (*Crosses to* R. *The door opens. In the doorway appear two* FIREMEN *in full regalia. The* FIRST FIREMAN *carries a hose and rubber coat; the* SECOND *has a violin case,* R.C.)

FIRST FIREMAN (*enters* R. *Very apologetically*) Mr. Barclay.

BOB I'm Mr. Barclay.

FIRST FIREMEN We're the firemen, Mr. Barclay. (*They remove their hats.*)

BOB How de do?

ED How de do?

BOB A great pleasure, I assure you. Really must apologize for the condition of this room, but——

FIRST FIREMAN Oh, that's all right. I know how it is at home.

BOB May I present a friend of mine, Mr. Ed Jamison——

FIRST FIREMAN How are you?

ED How are you, boys? (SECOND FIREMAN *nods*). I know your Chief.

FIRST FIREMAN Oh, is that so? He knows the Chief—dear old Chiefie. (SECOND FIREMAN *giggles.*)

BOB (*embarrassed*) Well, I guess you boys want to get to work, don't you?

FIRST FIREMAN Well, if you don't mind. We would like to spray around a little bit.

BOB May I help you?

FIRST FIREMAN Yes, if you please. (BOB *helps him into his rubber coat. At the same time the* SECOND FIREMAN, *without a word, lays the violin case on the bed, opens it, takes out the violin, and begins tuning it.*)

BOB (*watching him*) I don't think I understand.

FIRST FIREMAN Well, you see, Sid doesn't get much chance to practice at home. Sometimes, at a fire, while we're waiting for a wall to fall or something, why, a fireman doesn't really have anything to do, and personally I like to see him improve himself symphonically. I hope you don't resent it. You're not anti-symphonic?

BOB Of course not—— (BOB *and* ED *nod understandingly; the* SECOND FIREMAN *is now waxing the bow.*)

FIRST FIREMAN Well, if you'll excuse me—— (*To window* R. *Turns with decision toward the window. You feel that he is about to get down to business.*)

BOB (*crosses* L.) Charming personalities.

ED (*follows over to the window* R.) How *is* the fire?

FIRST FIREMAN (*feels the wall*) It's pretty bad right now. This wall will go pretty soon now, but it'll fall out that way, so it's all right. (*Peers out*). That next room is the place to fight it from. (*Crosses to door* L. BOB *shows ties as* ED *crosses.*)

ED (*sees ties*) Oh! Aren't those gorgeous!

FIRST FIREMAN (*to* BOB) Have you the key for this room?

BOB Why, no. I've nothing to do with that room. I've just got this one. (*Folding a shirt as he talks.*)

ED   Oh, it's very comfortable.

FIRST FIREMAN   That's too bad, I had something up my sleeve. If I could have gotten in there. Oh, well, may I use your 'phone?

BOB   Please do. (*To* ED). Do you think you might hold this? (*Indicates the hose.*)

ED   How?

FIRST FIREMAN   Just crawl under it. (*As he does that*). Thanks. (*At 'phone*). Hello. Let me have the clerk, please. (*To* SECOND FIREMAN). Give us that little thing you played the night the Equitable Building burned down. (*Back to 'phone*). Are you there? This is one of the firemen. Oh, *you* know. I'm in a room—ah—— (*Looks at* BOB.)

BOB   Eleven-eighteen.

FIRST FIREMAN   Eleven-eighteen, and I want to get into the next room—— Oh, goody. Will you send someone up with the key? There's no one in there? Oh, super-goody! Right away. (*Hangs up.*)

BOB   That's fine. (*To* FIREMAN). Won't you sit down?

FIRST FIREMAN   Thanks.

ED   Have a cigar?

FIRST FIREMAN (*takes it*)   Much obliged.

BOB   A light?

FIRST FIREMAN   If you please.

ED (*failing to find a match*)   Bob, have you a match?

BOB (*crosses to* L.C.)   I thought there were some here. (*Hands in pockets.*)

FIRST FIREMAN   Oh, never mind. (*He goes to* R. *window, leans out, and emerges with cigar lighted.* BOB *crosses* L. *to dresser; slams drawer. The* SECOND FIREMAN *taps violin with bow.*)

FIRST FIREMAN   Mr. Barclay, I think he's ready now.

BOB (*takes chair from* R. *table and sits* C.)   Pardon me.

(*They all sit. The* SECOND FIREMAN *takes center of stage, with all the manner of a concert violinist. He goes into "Keep the Home Fires Burning." * BOB, ED *and* FIRST FIREMAN *wipe brow as curtain falls slowly.*)

DISCUSSION

1. Explain the author's motive in writing the play, and give reasons why you feel that he does, or does not, accomplish his purpose. Is there any connection between the title of the play and its *theme*?

2. Why does Kaufman suggest that unless "the entire play . . . be acted calmly and politely . . . the play has no point at all"? Why does he set the scene in a sparsely furnished, upper-floor hotel room rather than in a private apartment or home?
3. What do you learn about the backgrounds of Bob and Ed? Why is so little revealed? Are their personalities distinguishable?
4. How do the actions and gestures of the characters contribute to the humor of the play? How does the dialogue? Give examples.
5. What is your attitude toward the ending? Had the play been longer, would it have been as entertaining?
6. Is this play a satire? A fantasy? A *farce*? Or some other type? Justify your explanation.

TOPICS FOR WRITING

When Warnings Go Unheeded
Reacting to a Crisis

TRIFLES

Susan Glaspell

CHARACTERS

County Attorney
Mrs. Peters
Sheriff
Mr. Hale
Mrs. Hale

Susan Glaspell (1882-1948)

During her lifetime Susan Glaspell established a reputation as a short story writer, a playwright, and a novelist. Her interest in writing began while she was still in grade school, but it was not until she met and married George Cram Cook, organizer and director of the Province-town Players, that she devoted herself seriously to the writing of plays.

Trifles, first performed in 1916, was one of several plays that Miss Glaspell wrote for the Provincetown group. It is an unusual play, about a highly unusual crime. By the time you are acquainted with the facts, you may agree with two well-meaning country women that trifles should should seldom be ignored.

TRIFLES

SCENE *The kitchen in the now abandoned farmhouse of* JOHN WRIGHT, *a gloomy kitchen, and left without having been put in order—the walls covered with a faded wall paper.* D. R. *is a door leading to the parlor. On the* R. *wall above this door is a built-in kitchen cupboard with shelves in the upper portion and drawers below. In the rear wall at* R., *up two steps is a door opening onto stairs leading to the second floor. In the rear wall at* L. *is a door to the shed and from there to*

*the outside. Between these two doors is an old-fashioned
black iron stove. Running along the* L. *wall from the shed
door is an old iron sink and sink shelf, in which is set a hand
pump. Downstage of the sink is an uncurtained window. Near
the window is an old wooden rocker. Center stage is an un-
painted wooden kitchen table with straight chairs on either
side. There is a small chair* D. R. *Unwashed pans under the
sink, a loaf of bread outside the breadbox, a dish towel on the
table—other signs of incompleted work. At the rear the shed
door opens and the* SHERIFF *comes in followed by the* COUNTY
ATTORNEY *and* HALE. *The* SHERIFF *and* HALE *are men in middle
life, the* COUNTY ATTORNEY *is a young man; all are much
bundled up and go at once to the stove. They are followed
by the two women—the* SHERIFF's *wife,* MRS. PETERS, *first;
she is a slight wiry woman, a thin nervous face.* MRS. HALE *is
larger and would ordinarily be called more comfortable looking, but she is disturbed now and looks fearfully about as she
enters. The women have come in slowly, and stand close together near the door.*

COUNTY ATTORNEY (*at stove rubbing his hands*)   This feels good.
Come up to the fire, ladies.

MRS. PETERS (*after taking a step forward*)   I'm not—cold.

SHERIFF (*unbuttoning his overcoat and stepping away from the
stove to right of table as if to mark the beginning of official business*)
Now, Mr. Hale, before we move things about, you explain to Mr.
Henderson just what you saw when you came here yesterday morning.

COUNTY ATTORNEY (*crossing down to left of the table*)   By the
way, has anything been moved? Are things just as you left them yesterday?

SHERIFF (*looking about*)   It's just the same. When it dropped
below zero last night I thought I'd better send Frank out this morning
to make a fire for us—(*sits right of center table*) no use getting pneumonia with a big case on, but I told him not to touch anything except
the stove—and you know Frank.

COUNTY ATTORNEY   Somebody should have been left here yesterday.

SHERIFF   Oh—yesterday. When I had to send Frank to Morris
Center for that man who went crazy—I want you to know I had my

hands full yesterday. I knew you could get back from Omaha by today and as long as I went over everything here myself——

COUNTY ATTORNEY   Well, Mr. Hale, tell just what happened when you came here yesterday morning.

HALE (*crossing down to above table*)   Harry and I had started to town with a load of potatoes. We came along the road from my place and as I got here I said, "I'm going to see if I can't get John Wright to go in with me on a party telephone." I spoke to Wright about it once before and he put me off, saying folks talked too much anyway, and all he asked was peace and quiet—I guess you know about how much he talked himself; but I thought maybe if I went to the house and talked about it before his wife, though I said to Harry that I didn't know as what his wife wanted made much difference to John——

COUNTY ATTORNEY   Let's talk about that later, Mr. Hale. I do want to talk about that, but tell now just what happened when you got to the house.

HALE   I didn't hear or see anything; I knocked at the door, and still it was all quiet inside. I knew they must be up, it was past eight o'clock. So I knocked again, and I thought I heard somebody say, "Come in." I wasn't sure, I'm not sure yet, but I opened the door— this door (*indicating the door by which the two women are still standing*) and there in that rocker—(*pointing to it*) sat Mrs. Wright. (*They all look at the rocker* D. L.)

COUNTY ATTORNEY   What—was she doing?

HALE   She was rockin' back and forth. She had her apron in her hand and was kind of—pleating it.

COUNTY ATTORNEY   And how did she——look?

HALE   Well, she looked queer.

COUNTY ATTORNEY   How do you mean—queer?

HALE   Well, as if she didn't know what she was going to do next. And kind of done up.

COUNTY ATTORNEY (*takes out notebook and pencil and sits left of center table*)   How did she seem to feel about your coming?

HALE   Why, I don't think she minded—one way or other. She didn't pay much attention. I said, "How do, Mrs. Wright, it's cold, ain't it?" And she said, "Is it?"—and went on kind of pleating at her apron. Well, I was surprised; she didn't ask me to come up to the stove, or to set down, but just sat there, not even looking at me, so I said, "I want to see John." And then she—laughed. I guess you would call it a laugh. I though of Harry and the team outside, so I said a little sharp: "Can't I see John?" "No," she says, kind o' dull like. "Ain't he home?" says I. "Yes," says she, "he's home." "Then why can't I see him?" I asked her, out of patience. " 'Cause he's dead," says she. "*Dead?*" says I. She just nodded her head, not getting a bit excited, but rockin' back and forth. "Why—where is he?" says I, not knowing what to say. She just pointed upstairs—like that. (*Himself pointing to the room above*). I started for the stairs, with the idea of going up there. I walked from there to here—then I says, "Why, what did he die of?" "He died of a rope round his neck," says she, and just went on pleatin' at her apron. Well, I went out and called Harry. I thought I might—need help. We went upstairs and there he was lyin'——

COUNTY ATTORNEY   I think I'd rather have you go into that upstairs, where you can point it all out. Just go on now with the rest of the story.

HALE   Well, my first thought was to get that rope off. It looked . . . (*stops, his face twitches*) . . . but Harry, he went up to him, and he said, "No, he's dead all right, and we'd better not touch anything." So we went back downstairs. She was still sitting that same way. "Has anybody been notified?" I asked. "No," says she, unconcerned. "Who did this, Mrs. Wright?" said Harry. He said it business-like—and she stopped pleatin' of her apron. "I don't know," she says. "You don't *know?*" says Harry. "No," says she. "Weren't you sleepin' in the bed with him?" says Harry. "Yes," says she, "but I was on the inside." 'Somebody slipped a rope round his neck and strangled him and you didn't wake up?" says Harry. "I didn't wake up," she said after him. We must 'a' looked as if we didn't see how that could be, for after a minute she said, "I sleep sound." Harry was going to ask her more questions but I said maybe we ought to let her tell her story to the coroner, or the sheriff, so Harry went fast as he could to Rivers' place, where there's a telephone.

COUNTY ATTORNEY   And what did Mrs. Wright do when she knew that you had gone for the coroner?

HALE   She moved from the rocker to that chair over there (*pointing to a small chair in the* D. R. *corner*) and just sat there with her hands held together and looking down. I got a feeling that I ought to make some conversation, so I said I had come in to see if John wanted to put in a telephone, and at that she started to laugh, and then she stopped and looked at me—scared. (*The* COUNTY ATTORNEY, *who has had his notebook out, makes a note*). I dunno, maybe it wasn't scared. I wouldn't like to say it was. Soon Harry got back, and then Dr. Lloyd came, and you, Mr. Peters, and so I guess that's all I know that you don't.

COUNTY ATTORNEY (*rising and looking around*)   I guess we'll go upstairs first—and then out to the barn and around there. (*To the* SHERIFF). You're convinced that there was nothing important here— nothing that would point to any motive?

SHERIFF   Nothing here but kitchen things.

(*The* COUNTY ATTORNEY, *after again looking around the kitchen, opens the door of a cupboard closet in* R. *wall. He brings a small chair from* R.—*gets up on it and looks on a shelf. Pulls his hand away, sticky.*)

COUNTY ATTORNEY   Here's a nice mess. (*The women draw nearer* U. C.)

MRS. PETERS (*to the other woman*)   Oh, her fruit; it did freeze. (*To the* LAWYER). She worried about that when it turned so cold. She said the fire'd go out and her jars would break.

SHERIFF (*rises*)   Well, can you beat the women! Held for murder and worrying about her preserves.

COUNTY ATTORNEY (*getting down from chair*)   I guess before we're through she may have something more serious than preserves to worry about. (*Crosses down* R. C.)

HALE   Well, women are used to worrying over trifles. (*The two women move a little closer together.*)

COUNTY ATTORNEY (*with the gallantry of a young politician*)   And yet, for all their worries, what would we do without the ladies? (*The women do not unbend. He goes below the center table to the sink, takes a dipperful of water from the pail and pouring it into a basin, washes his hands. While he is doing this the* SHERIFF *and* HALE *cross to cupboard, which they inspect. The* COUNT ATTORNEY *starts to wipe his hands on the roller towel, turns it for a cleaner place*). Dirty towels! (*Kicks his foot against the pans under the sink*). Not much of a housekeeper, would you say, ladies?

MRS. HALE (*stiffly*)   There's a great deal of work to be done on a farm.

COUNTY ATTORNEY   To be sure. And yet (*with a little bow to her*)

I know there are some Dickson County farmhouses which do not have such roller towels. (*He gives it a pull to expose its full length again.*)

MRS. HALE   Those towels get dirty awful quick. Men's hands aren't always as clean as they might be.

COUNTY ATTORNEY   Ah, loyal to your sex, I see. But you and Mrs. Wright were neighbors. I suppose you were friends, too.

MRS. HALE (*shaking her head*)   I've not seen much of her of late years. I've not been in this house—it's more than a year.

COUNTY ATTORNEY (*crossing to women U. C.*)   And why was that? You didn't like her?

MRS. HALE   I liked her all well enough. Farmers' wives have their hands full, Mr. Henderson. And then——

COUNTY ATTORNEY   Yes——?

MRS. HALE (*looking about*)   It never seemed a very cheerful place.

COUNTY ATTORNEY   No—it's not cheerful. I shouldn't say she had the homemaking instinct.

MRS. HALE   Well, I don't know as Wright had, either.

COUNTY ATTORNEY   You mean that they didn't get on very well?

MRS. HALE   No, I don't mean anything. But I don't think a place'd be any cheerfuller for John Wright's being in it.

COUNTY ATTORNEY   I'd like to talk more of that a little later. I want to get the lay of things upstairs now. (*He goes past the women to U. R. where steps lead to a stair door.*)

SHERIFF   I suppose anything Mrs. Peters does'll be all right. She was to take in some clothes for her, you know, and a few little things. We left in such a hurry yesterday.

COUNTY ATTORNEY   Yes, but I would like to see what you take, Mrs. Peters, and keep an eye out for anything that might be of use to us.

MRS. PETERS   Yes, Mr. Henderson. (*The men leave by U. R. door to stairs. The women listen to the men's steps on the stairs, then look about the kitchen.*)

MRS. HALE (*crossing L. to sink*)   I'd hate to have men coming into my kitchen, snooping around and criticizing. (*She arranges the pans under sink which the* LAWYER *had shoved out of place.*)

MRS. PETERS   Of course it's no more than their duty. (*Crosses to cupboard U. R.*)

MRS. HALE   Duty's all right, but I guess that deputy sheriff that came out to make the fire might have got a little of this on. (*Gives the roller towel a pull*). Wish I'd thought of that sooner. Seems mean to talk about her for not having things slicked up when she had to come away in such a hurry. (*Crosses* R. *to* MRS. PETERS *at cupboard.*)

MRS. PETERS (*who has been looking through cupboard, lifts one end of a towel that covers a pan*) She had bread set. (*Stands still.*)

MRS. HALE (*eyes fixed on a loaf of bread beside the breadbox, which is on a low shelf of the cupboard*) She was going to put this in there. (*Picks up loaf, then abruptly drops it. In a manner of returning to familiar things*). It's a shame about her fruit. I wonder if it's all gone. (*Gets up on the chair and looks*). I think there's some here that's all right, Mrs. Peters. Yes—here; (*holding it toward the window*) this is cherries, too. (*Looking again*). I declare I believe that's the only one. (*Gets down, jar in her hand. Goes to the sink and wipes it off on the outside*). She'll feel awful bad after all her hard work in the hot weather. I remember the afternoon I put up my cherries last summer.

(*She puts the jar on the big kitchen table, center of the room. With a sigh, is about to sit down in the rocking chair. Before she is seated realizes what chair it is; with a slow look at it, steps back. The chair which she has touched rocks back and forth.* MRS. PETERS *moves to center table and they both watch the chair rock for a moment or two.*)

MRS. PETERS (*shaking off the mood which the empty rocking chair has evoked. Now in a businesslike manner she speaks*) Well, I must get those things from the front room closet. (*She goes to the door at the* R., *but, after looking into the other room, steps back*). You coming with me, Mrs. Hale? You could help me carry them. (*They go in the other room; reappear,* MRS. PETERS *carrying a dress, petticoat and skirt,* MRS. HALE *following with a pair of shoes*). My, it's cold in there. (*She puts the clothes on the big table, and hurries to the stove.*)

MRS. HALE (*right of center table examining the skirt*) Wright was close. I think maybe that's why she kept so much to herself. She didn't even belong to the Ladies' Aid. I suppose she felt she couldn't do her part, and then you don't enjoy things when you feel shabby. I heard she used to wear pretty clothes and be lively, when she was Minnie Foster, one of the town girls singing in the choir. But that—oh, that was thirty years ago. This all you was to take in?

MRS. PETERS She said she wanted an apron. Funny thing to want, for there isn't much to get you dirty in jail, goodness knows. But I suppose just to make her feel more natural. (*Crosses to cupboard*). She said they was in the top drawer in this cupboard. Yes, here. And then her little shawl that always hung behind the door. (*Opens stair door and looks*). Yes, here it is. (*Quickly shuts door leading upstairs.*)

MRS. HALE (*abruptly moving toward her*) Mrs. Peters?

MRS. PETERS Yes, Mrs. Hale? (*At u. r. door.*)

MRS. HALE Do you think she did it?

MRS. PETERS (*in a frightened voice*) Oh, I don't know.

MRS. HALE Well, I don't think she did. Asking for an apron and her little shawl. Worrying about her fruit.

MRS. PETERS (*starts to speak, glances up, where footsteps are heard in the room above. In a low voice*) Mr. Peters says it looks bad for her. Mr. Henderson is awful sarcastic in a speech and he'll make fun of her sayin' she didn't wake up.

MRS. HALE Well, I guess John Wright didn't wake when they was slipping that rope under his neck.

MRS. PETERS (*crossing slowly to table and placing shawl and apron on table with other clothing*) No, it's strange. It must have been done awful crafty and still. They say it was such a—funny way to kill a man, rigging it all up like that.

MRS. HALE (*crossing to left of MRS. PETERS at table*) That's just what Mr. Hale said. There was a gun in the house. He says that's what he can't understand.

MRS. PETERS Mr. Henderson said coming out that what was needed for the case was a motive; something to show anger, or—sudden feeling.

MRS. HALE (*who is standing by the table*) Well, I don't see any signs of anger around here. (*She puts her hand on the dish towel which lies on the table, stands looking down at table, one-half of which is clean, the other half messy*). It's wiped to here. (*Makes a move as if to finish work, then turns and looks at loaf of bread outside the bread-box. Drops towel. In that voice of coming back to familiar things*). Wonder how they are finding things upstairs. (*Crossing below table to d. r.*). I hope she had it a little more red-up up there. You know, it seems kind of *sneaking*. Locking her up in town and then coming out here and trying to get her own house to turn against her!

MRS. PETERS But, Mrs. Hale, the law is the law.

MRS. HALE I s'pose 'tis. (*Unbuttoning her coat*). Better loosen up your things, Mrs. Peters. You won't feel them when you go out. (MRS. PETERS *takes off her fur tippet, goes to hang it on chair back left of table, stands looking at the work basket on floor near* D. L. *window.*)

MRS. PETERS   She was piecing a quilt. (*She brings the large sewing basket to the center table and they look at the bright pieces,* MRS. HALE *above the table and* MRS. PETERS *left of it.*)

MRS. HALE   It's a log cabin pattern. Pretty, isn't it? I wonder if she was goin' to quilt it or just knot it? (*Footsteps have been heard coming down the stairs. The* SHERIFF *enters followed by* HALE *and the* COUNTY ATTORNEY.)

SHERIFF   They wonder if she was going to quilt it or just knot it! (*The men laugh, the women look abashed.*)

COUNTY ATTORNEY (*rubbing his hands over the stove*)   Frank's fire didn't do much up there, did it? Well, let's go out to the barn and get that cleared up. (*The men go outside by* U. L. *door.*)

MRS. HALE (*resentfully*)   I don't know as there's anything so strange, our takin' up our time with little things while we're waiting for them to get the evidence. (*She sits in chair right of table smoothing out a block with decision*). I don't see as it's anything to laugh about.

MRS. PETERS (*apologetically*)   Of course they've got awful important things on their minds. (*Pulls up a chair and joins* MRS. HALE *at the left of the table.*)

MRS. HALE (*examining another block*)   Mrs. Peters, look at this one. Here, this is the one she was working on, and look at the sewing! All the rest of it has been so nice and even. And look at this! It's all over the place! Why, it looks as if she didn't know what she was about! (*After she has said this they look at each other, then start to glance back at the door. After an instant* MRS. HALE *has pulled at a knot and ripped the sewing.*)

MRS. PETERS   Oh, what are you doing, Mrs. Hale?

MRS. HALE (*mildly*)   Just pulling out a stitch or two that's not sewed very good. (*Threading a needle*). Bad sewing always made me fidgety.

MRS. PETERS (*with a glance at door, nervously*)   I don't think we ought to touch things.

MRS. HALE   I'll just finish up this end. (*Suddenly stopping and leaning forward*). Mrs. Peters?

MRS. PETERS   Yes, Mrs. Hale?

MRS. HALE   What do you suppose she was so nervous about?

MRS. PETERS   Oh—I don't know. I don't know as she was nervous.
I sometimes sew awful queer when I'm just tired. (MRS. HALE *starts
to say something, looks at* MRS. PETERS, *then goes on sewing*). Well,
I must get these things wrapped up. They may be through sooner than
we think. (*Putting apron and other things together*). I wonder where
I can find a piece of paper, and string. (*Rises.*)

MRS. HALE   In that cupboard, maybe.

MRS. PETERS (*crosses* R. *looking in cupboard*)   Why, here's a bird-
cage. (*Holds it up*). Did she have a bird, Mrs. Hale?

MRS. HALE   Why, I don't know whether she did or not—I've not
been here for so long. There was a man around last year selling
canaries cheap, but I don't know as she took one; maybe she did. She
used to sing real pretty herself.

MRS. PETERS (*glancing around*)   Seems funny to think of a bird
here. But she must have had one, or why would she have a cage? I
wonder what happened to it?

MRS. HALE   I s'pose maybe the cat got it.

MRS. PETERS   No, she didn't have a cat. She's got that feeling
some people have about cats—being afraid of them. My cat got in
her room and she was real upset and asked me to take it out.

MRS. HALE   My sister Bessie was like that. Queer, ain't it?

MRS. PETERS (*examining the cage*)   Why, look at this door. It's
broke. One hinge is pulled apart. (*Takes a step down to* MRS. HALE's
right.)

MRS. HALE (*looking too*)   Looks as if someone must have been
rough with it.

MRS. PETERS   Why, yes. (*She brings the cage forward and puts it
on the table.*)

MRS. HALE (*glancing toward* U. L. *door*)   I wish if they're going
to find any evidence they'd be about it. I don't like this place.

MRS. PETERS   But I'm awful glad you came with me, Mrs. Hale.
It would be lonesome for me sitting here alone.

MRS. HALE   It would, wouldn't it? (*Dropping her sewing*). But
I tell you what I do wish, Mrs. Peters. I wish I had come over sometimes when *she* was here. I—(*looking around the room*)—wish I had.

MRS. PETERS   But of course you were awful busy, Mrs. Hale—your
house and your children.

MRS. HALE (*rises and crosses* L.)   I could've come. I stayed away

because it weren't cheerful—and that's why I ought to have come. I—
(*looking out* L. *window*)—I've never liked this place. Maybe because
it's down in a hollow and you don't see the road. I dunno what it is,
but it's a lonesome place and always was. I wish I had come over to
see Minnie Foster sometimes. I can see now——— (*Shakes her head.*)

MRS. PETERS (*left of table and above it*) Well, you mustn't re-
proach yourself, Mrs. Hale. Somehow we just don't see how it is with
other folks until—something turns up.

MRS. HALE Not having children makes less work—but it makes
a quiet house, and Wright out to work all day, and no company when
he did come in. (*Turning from window*). Did you know John Wright,
Mrs. Peters?

MRS. PETERS Not to know him; I've seen him in town. They say
he was a good man.

MRS. HALE Yes—good; he didn't drink, and kept his word as well
as most, I guess, and paid his debts. But he was a hard man, Mrs.
Peters. Just to pass the time of day with him——— (*Shivers*). Like a
raw wind that gets to the bone. (*Pauses, her eye falling on the cage*).
I should think she would 'a' wanted a bird. But what do you suppose
went with it?

MRS. PETERS I don't know, unless it got sick and died. (*She
reaches over and swings the broken door, swings it again, both women
watch it.*)

MRS. HALE You weren't raised round here, were you? (MRS.
PETERS *shakes her head*). You didn't know—her?

MRS. PETERS Not till they brought her yesterday.

MRS. HALE She—come to think of it, she was kind of like a bird
herself—real sweet and pretty, but kind of timid and—fluttery. How
—she—did—change. (*Silence; then as if struck by a happy thought
and relieved to get back to everyday things. Crosses* R. *above* MRS.
PETERS *to cupboard, replaces small chair used to stand on to its original
place* D. R.). Tell you what, Mrs. Peters, why don't you take the quilt
in with you? It might take up her mind.

MRS. PETERS Why, I think that's a real nice idea, Mrs. Hale.
There couldn't possibly be any objection to it, could there? Now, just
what would I take? I wonder if her patches are in here—and her
things. (*They look in the sewing basket.*)

MRS. HALE (*crosses to right of table*) Here's some red. I expect
this has got sewing things in it. (*Brings out a fancy box*). What a

pretty box. Looks like something somebody would give you. Maybe
her scissors are in here. (*Opens box. Suddenly puts her hand to her
nose*). Why—— (MRS. PETERS *bends nearer, then turns her face away*).
There's something wrapped up in this piece of silk.

MRS. PETERS Why, this isn't her scissors.

MRS. HALE (*lifting the silk*) Oh, Mrs. Peters—it's—— (MRS.
PETERS *bends closer.*)

MRS. PETERS It's the bird.

MRS. HALE But, Mrs. Peters—look at it! Its neck! Look at its
neck! It's all—other side *to.*

MRS. PETERS Somebody—wrung—its—neck. (*Their eyes meet.
A look of growing comprehension, of horror. Steps are heard outside.*
MRS. HALE *slips box under quilt pieces, and sinks into her chair. Enter*
SHERIFF *and* COUNTY ATTORNEY. MRS. PETERS *steps* D. L. *and stands look-
ing out of window.*)

COUNTY ATTORNEY (*as one turning from serious things to little
pleasantries*) Well, ladies, have you decided whether she was going
to quilt it or knot it? (*Crosses to* C. *above table.*)

MRS. PETERS We think she was going to—knot it. (SHERIFF *crosses
to right of stove, lifts stove lid and glances at fire, then stands warming
hands at stove.*)

COUNTY ATTORNEY Well, that's interesting, I'm sure. (*Seeing the
bird-cage*). Has the bird flown?

MRS. HALE (*putting more quilt pieces over the box*) We think
the—cat got it.

COUNTY ATTORNEY (*preoccupied*). Is there a cat? (MRS. HALE
glances in a quick covert way at MRS. PETERS.)

MRS. PETERS (*turning from window takes a step in*) Well, not
now. They're superstitious, you know. They leave.

COUNTY ATTORNEY (*to* SHERIFF PETERS, *continuing an interrupted
conversation*) No sign at all of anyone having come from the outside.
Their own rope. Now let's go up again and go over it piece by piece.
(*They start upstairs*). It would have to have been someone who knew
just the—— (MRS. PETERS *sits down left of table. The two women sit
there not looking at one another, but as if peering into something and
at the same time holding back. When they talk now it is in the manner
of feeling their way over strange ground, as if afraid of what they are
saying, but as if they cannot help saying it.*)

MRS. HALE (*hesitatively and in hushed voice*) She liked the bird.
She was going to bury it in that pretty box.

MRS. PETERS (*in a whisper*)   When I was a girl—my kitten—there was a boy took a hatchet, and before my eyes—and before I could get there—— (*Covers her face an instant*). If they hadn't held me back I would have— (*catches herself, looks upstairs where steps are heard, falters weakly*)—hurt him.

MRS. HALE (*with a slow look around her*)   I wonder how it would seem never to have had any children around. (*Pause*). No, Wright wouldn't like the bird—a thing that sang. She used to sing. He killed that, too.

MRS. PETERS (*moving uneasily*)   We don't know who killed the bird.

MRS. HALE   I knew John Wright.

MRS. PETERS   It was an awful thing was done in this house that night, Mrs. Hale. Killing a man while he slept, slipping a rope around his neck that choked the life out of him.

MRS. HALE   His neck. Choked the life out of him. (*Her hand goes out and rests on the bird-cage.*)

MRS. PETERS (*with rising voice*)   We don't know who killed him. We don't *know*.

MRS. HALE (*her own feeling not interrupted*)   If there'd been years and years of nothing, then a bird to sing to you, it would be awful—still, after the bird was still.

MRS. PETERS (*something within her speaking*)   I know what stillness is. When we homesteaded in Dakota, and my first baby died— after he was two years old, and me with no other then——

MRS. HALE (*moving*)   How soon do you suppose they'll be through looking for the evidence?

MRS. PETERS   I know what stillness is. (*Pulling herself back*). The law has got to punish crime, Mrs. Hale.

MRS. HALE (*not as if answering that*)   I wish you'd seen Minnie Foster when she wore a white dress with blue ribbons and stood up there in the choir and sang. (*A look around the room*). Oh, I *wish* I'd come over here once in a while! That was a crime! That was a crime! Who's going to punish that?

MRS. PETERS (*looking upstairs*)   We mustn't—take on.

MRS. HALE   I might have known she needed help! I know how things can be—for women. I tell you, it's queer, Mrs. Peters. We live close together and we live far apart. We all go through the same things —it's all just a different kind of the same thing. (*Brushes her eyes, noticing the jar of fruit, reaches out for it*). If I was you I wouldn't tell her her fruit was gone. Tell her it *ain't*. Tell her it's all right. Take this in to prove it to her. She—she may never know whether it was broke or not.

MRS. PETERS (*takes the jar, looks about for something to wrap it in; takes petticoat from the clothes brought from the other room, very nervously begins winding this around the jar. In a false voice*) My, it's a good thing the men couldn't hear us. Wouldn't they just laugh! Getting all stirred up over a little thing like a—dead canary. As if that could have anything to do with—with—wouldn't they *laugh!* (*The men are heard coming downstairs.*)

MRS. HALE (*under her breath*) Maybe they would—maybe they wouldn't.

COUNTY ATTORNEY No, Peters, it's all perfectly clear except a reason for doing it. But you know juries when it comes to women. If there was some definite thing. (*Crosses slowly to above table.* SHERIFF *crosses* D. R. MRS. HALE *and* MRS. PETERS *remain seated at either side of table*). Something to show—something to make a story about—a thing that would connect up with this strange way of doing it—— (*The women's eyes meet for an instant. Enter* HALE *from outer door.*)

HALE (*remaining* U. L. *by door*) Well, I've got the team around. Pretty cold out there.

COUNTY ATTORNEY I'm going to stay awhile by myself. (*To the* SHERIFF). You can send Frank out for me, can't you? I want to go over everything. I'm not satisfied that we can't do better.

SHERIFF Do you want to see what Mrs. Peters is going to take in? (*The* LAWYER *picks up the apron, laughs.*)

COUNTY ATTORNEY Oh, I guess they're not very dangerous things the ladies have picked out. (*Moves a few things about, disturbing the quilt pieces which cover the box. Steps back*). No, Mrs. Peters doesn't need supervising. For that matter a sheriff's wife is married to the law. Ever think of it that way, Mrs. Peters?

MRS. PETERS Not—just that way.

SHERIFF (*chuckling*) Married to the law. (*Moves to* D. R. *door to the other room*). I just want you to come in here a minute, George. We ought to take a look at these windows.

COUNTY ATTORNEY (*scoffingly*) Oh, windows!

SHERIFF We'll be right out, Mr. Hale. (HALE *goes outside. The* SHERIFF *follows the* COUNTY ATTORNEY *into the other room. Then* MRS. HALE *rises, hands tight together, looking intensely at* MRS. PETERS, *whose eyes make a slow turn, finally meeting* MRS. HALE'S. *A moment* MRS. HALE *holds her, then her own eyes point the way to where the box is concealed. Suddenly* MRS. PETERS *throws back quilt pieces and tries to put the box in the bag she is carrying. It is too big. She opens box, starts to take bird out, cannot touch it, goes to pieces, stands there helpless. Sound of a knob turning in the other room.* MRS. HALE *snatches the box and puts it in the pocket of her big coat. Enter* COUNTY ATTORNEY *and* SHERIFF, *who remains* D. R.)

COUNTY ATTORNEY (*crosses to* U. L. *door facetiously*)   Well, Henry, at least we found out that she was not going to quilt it. She was going to—what is it you call it, ladies?

MRS. HALE (*standing* C. *below table facing front, her hand against her pocket*)   We call it—knot it, Mr. Henderson.

CURTAIN

DISCUSSION

1. How do the introductory stage notes arouse your curiosity and at the same time establish the atmosphere of the play? Which of the details mentioned here prove important later?
2. How much do you learn about the characters assembled at the farmhouse before any one of them speaks?
3. What is the purpose of Mr. Hale's explanation of the events of the preceding morning?
4. Account for Mrs. Hale's attitude toward the County Attorney. Why does the playwright make such a point of it?
5. Why is it important that Mrs. Hale and Mrs. Peters remain together in the kitchen while the men begin their investigation of the upstairs bedroom?
6. What is puzzling about Mrs. Wright's request for an apron and a shawl? To what conclusion does Mrs. Hale come? Why?
7. Explain how each of the following comments is ironic in its implications:
   (a) Mrs. Hale: "I don't know as there's anything so strange, our takin' up time with little things while we're waiting for them to get the evidence."
   (b) County Attorney: "No, Mrs. Peters doesn't need supervising. For that matter, a sheriff's wife is married to the law."
   Find and explain other instances of irony in the play.

8. Why does Mrs. Hale wish that she had "come to see Minnie Foster sometimes"? How is it helpful to the playwright's purpose that she had never done so? What lies behind Mrs. Hale's suggestion that her failure to visit Minnie "was a crime"?

9. Interpret Mrs. Peters' and Mrs. Hale's hesitation in the statements: (a) "We think she was going to—knot it" and (b) "We think the —cat got it." How does the behavior of the two women change at this point in the play?

10. To what mutual understanding do Mrs. Hale and Mrs. Peters come? Trace the steps by which they arrive at this understanding. Is the decision a more difficult one for Mrs. Hale or for Mrs. Peters? Why?

11. How has the playwright managed to acquaint you with the main characters of the play, even though neither of them ever appears on stage? How do they differ in temperament? How would you describe their homelife before the tragedy?

12. Discuss the *symbolic* function in the play of (a) the quilt, (b) the bird cage, and (c) the extreme cold.

TOPICS FOR WRITING

Contrast the personality and outlook of Mrs. Hale and Mrs. Peters (or) of John Wright and Minnie Wright

Discuss the attitudes of men toward women or of women toward men, in *Trifles*.

Reconstruct the crime

THE MILLION-POUND
BANK NOTE

Mark Twain
Adapted by Walter Hackett

CHARACTERS

Henry	Manager
Hastings	Cockney 2
Cockney	Man 1
Gordon	Man 2
Abel	Woman 1
Hawkins	Man 3
Servant	Butler
Tod	Portia
Smedley	Sir Alfred

Mark Twain (1835-1910)

If you are acquainted with the writings of Mark Twain, you know that he is most famous for his stories of boyhood and growing up in the Mississippi River towns of late nineteenth century America. You also know that beneath the humor of his stories some fundamental truth about human nature can usually be found. Look for such a truth as you are reading this play adaptation by Walter Hackett of The Million-Pound Bank Note.

Mark Twain, whose real name was Samuel Clemens, was born in Florida, Missouri, in 1835. During the early years of his life he gained experience at a variety of jobs, and traveled widely. At one time he was a printer's apprentice; at another time he piloted steamboats on the Mississippi River. Twain loved people and treasured the simple pleasures of daily living. These attitudes, reflected in almost everything he wrote, are the basis for his enduring reputation as a writer.

THE MILLION-POUND
BANK NOTE

HENRY When I was twenty-seven years old, I was a mining broker's clerk in San Francisco. I was alone in the world, and had nothing to depend upon but my wits and a clean reputation. These were setting my feet in the road to eventual fortune, and I was content with the prospect. During my spare time, I did outside work. One of my part-time employers was Lloyd Hastings, a mining broker. During this period I was helping Hastings to verify the Gould and Curry Extension papers, covering what seemed to be a highly valuable gold mine. One morning at two, after six hard hours of work on these papers, Lloyd Hastings and I went to the What Cheer restaurant in Frisco. As we lingered over our coffee, he offered me a proposition.

HASTINGS   Henry, how would you like to go to London?

HENRY   Thank you, no.

HASTINGS   Listen to me. I'm thinking of taking a month's option on the Gould and Curry Extension for the locators.

HENRY   And—?

HASTINGS   They want one million dollars for it.

HENRY   Not too much—if the claim works out the way it appears it may.

HASTINGS   I'm going to try to sell it to London interests, which means a trip there, and I want you to go with me, because you know more about these papers than I.

HENRY   No, thanks.

HASTINGS   I'll make it well worth your while. I'll pay all your expenses, and give you something over if I make the sale.

HENRY   I have a job.

HASTINGS   I'll arrange for you to get a leave of absence. What do you say?

HENRY   No.

HASTINGS   Why?

HENRY   If I go to London, I'll get out of touch with my work and with mining conditions here, and that means months getting the hang of things again.

HASTINGS   That's a pretty slim excuse, Henry.

HENRY   More important, perhaps, I think you're doomed to failure.

HASTINGS   But you just said the claim is valuable.

HENRY   It may well turn out that way, but right now its real value can't be proved. And even so, a month's option may leave you too little time to sell it; unless you sell it within the option time, you'll go stone broke.

HASTINGS   I'm willing to gamble.

HENRY   Well, I'm not.

HASTINGS   Think—a free trip to London.

HENRY   I've no desire to go to London. I'll remain right here in Frisco.

HASTINGS   (*Fading*)   Very well, but I know you're making a mistake, Henry.

HENRY   One of my few diversions was sailing in the bay. One day I ventured too far, and was carried out to sea. Late that night, I was picked up by a freighter which was bound for London. It was a long voyage, and the captain made me work my passage without pay, as a common sailor. When I stepped ashore at London my clothes were ragged and shabby, and I had only a dollar in my pocket. This money fed and sheltered me for twenty-four hours. During the next twenty-four I went without food and shelter. I tried to get a job, doing manual labor. But the reply was always the same.

COCKNEY   I'm not sure you'd do. You ain't the sort. (*Suspiciously*) Look, 'ere, you're a Yank, ain't you?

HENRY   The next morning, seedy and hungry, I was dragging myself along Portland Place, when my desiring eye fell on a tempting treasure lying in the gutter. It was a luscious big pear—minus one bite. My mouth watered for it. But every time I made a move to get it, some passing eye detected my purpose. I was just getting desperate enough to brave all the shame, when a window behind me was raised.

GORDON   (*Away*)   I say, you there, will you step in here, please?

HENRY   It was a very sumptuous house and an equally sumptuous room into which I was ushered by a servant. A couple of elderly gentlemen were sitting by the window. At that moment if I had known what they had in mind, undoubtedly I would have bolted for the door. They looked me over very thoroughly.

GORDON   He looks poor enough, don't you think, brother?

ABEL   Very. Er, young man, you are poor?

HENRY   Extremely!

ABEL   Good! And honest, too?

HENRY   Honesty is about all I have left; that, and character.

ABEL   Splendid!

GORDON   If my brother and I are judges of people, we'd say you are just the man for whom we have been searching. By the way, you are also intelligent, I would say.

HENRY   Yes, sir, I am. But what do you mean by saying that I appear to be just the man for whom you have been searching?

GORDON   And we don't know you. You're a perfect stranger. And better still, an American.

HENRY   It's very kind of you gentlemen to call me into your home, but I'm a bit puzzled. Could you tell me what you have in mind?

ABEL   Might we inquire into your background?

HENRY   Pretty soon they had my full story. Their questions were complete and searching, and I gave them straight-forward answers. Finally one said:

GORDON   Oh, yes, we're certain you will do, eh, brother?

ABEL   Definitely! He is elected.

HENRY   To what am I elected, please?

GORDON   This envelope will explain everything. Here, take it. (*Hastily*) No, don't open it now. Take it to your lodgings and look it over carefully.

ABEL   Being sure not to be rash or hasty.

HENRY   I'd like to discuss the matter.

GORDON   There is nothing to discuss at the moment.

HENRY   Is this a joke?

ABEL   Not at all, And now good day.

GORDON   And good luck.

ABEL   Cheerio!

HENRY   As soon as I was out of sight of the house I opened my envelope and saw it contained money. I lost not a moment, but shoved note and money into my pocket, and broke for the nearest cheap eating house. How I did eat! Finished, I took out my money and unfolded it. I took one glimpse and nearly fainted. It was a single million-pound bank note. Five millions of dollars! It made my head swim. The next thing I noticed was the owner of the eating house. His eyes were on the note, and he was petrified. He couldn't stir hand or foot. I tossed the note toward him in careless fashion.

HAWKINS   I-is it real, sir? A million-pound note?

HENRY   (*Casually*)   Certainly. Let me have my change, please.

HAWKINS   Oh, I'm very sorry, sir, but I can't break the bill.

HENRY   Look here—

HAWKINS   Hawkins is the name, Albert Hawkins, proprietor. It's only a matter of two shillings you owe, a trifling sum. Please owe it to me.

HENRY   I may not be in this neighborhood again for a good time.

HAWKINS   It's of no consequence, sir. And you can have anything you want, any time you choose, and let the account run as long as you please. I'm not afraid to trust as rich a gentleman as you, just because you choose to play larks by dressing as a tramp.

HENRY   Well, thank you. I shall take advantage of your kindness.

HAWKINS   Not at all, sir, (*Fading*) and please, sir, enter my humble restaurant place any time you wish. I shall be honored to receive you.

SERVANT   I was frightened, afraid that the police might pick me up. I was afraid of the two brothers' reaction when they discovered they had given me a million-pound note instead of what they must have intended giving—a one-pound note. I hurried to their house and rang the bell. The same servant appeared. I asked for the brothers.

HENRY   I was frightened, afraid that the police might pick me up. I was afraid of the two brothers' reaction when they discovered they had given me a million-pound note instead of what they must have intended giving—a one-pound note. I hurried to their house and rang the bell. The same servant appeared. I asked for the brothers.

SERVANT   They are gone.

HENRY   Gone! Where?

SERVANT   On a journey.

HENRY   But whereabouts?

SERVANT   To the Continent, I think.

HENRY   The Continent?

SERVANT   Yes, sir.

HENRY   Which way—by what route?

SERVANT   I can't say, sir.

HENRY   When will they be back?

SERVANT   In a month, they said.

HENRY   A month! This is awful! Tell me how to get word to them. It's of great importance.

SERVANT   I can't, indeed. I've no idea where they've gone, sir.

HENRY   Then I must see some member of the family.

SERVANT   Family's been away too; been abroad months—in Egypt and India, I think.

HENRY   There's been an immense mistake made. They'll be back before night. Tell them I've been here, and that I'll keep coming till it's all made right, and they needn't worry.

SERVANT   I'll tell them, if they come back, but I'm not expecting them. They said you'd be here in an hour to make inquiries, but I must tell you it's all right, they'll be here on time to meet you. (*Fading*) And that's all they said.

HENRY   (*Slowly*)   I had to give it up and go away. What a riddle it all was; They would be here "on time." What could that mean? Then I thought of the letter. I got it out and read it. It said: "You are an intelligent and honest man, as one can see by your face. We conceive you to be poor and a stranger. Enclosed you will find a sum of money. It is lent to you for thirty days, without interest. Report to this house at the end of that time. I have a bet on you. If I win it you shall have any situation that is in my gift, any, that is, that you shall be able to prove yourself familiar with and competent to fill." That was all. No signature, no address, no date. I hadn't the least idea what the game was, nor whether harm was meant me or kindness. The letter said there was a bet on me. What kind of a bet? Was the bet that I would abscond with the million-pound bank note? Which brother was betting on my honesty? I reasoned this way: if I ask the Bank of England to deposit it to the credit of the man it belongs to, they'll ask me how I came by it, and if I tell the truth, they'll put me in the asylum; on the other hand, if I lie, they'll put me in jail. The same result would follow if I try to bank it anywhere or borrow money on it. Therefore, I have to carry this burden around until those men come back. A month's suffering without wages or profit—unless I help win that bet, whatever it may be. If I do, I will get the situation I am promised. My hopes began to rise high. Then I looked at my rags. Could I afford a new suit? No, for I had nothing in the world but a million pounds. Finally I gave in and entered a fashionable tailor shop. The clerk looked at me very arrogantly.

TOD (*Icily*)   No chores to be done here. Get out!

HENRY   Perhaps you have a misfit suit.

TOD   We don't give away suits, even misfits.

HENRY   I can pay for it.

TOD   Follow me.

HENRY   He took me into a back room, and overhauled a pile of rejected suits. He tossed the rattiest looking one at me. I put it on. It didn't fit. It wasn't in any way attractive.

TOD   You may have that for four pounds, cash.

HENRY   It would be an accommodation to me if you could wait some days for the money. I haven't any small change about me.

TOD (*Sarcastically*)   Oh, you haven't? Well, of course, I didn't expect it. I'd only expect gentlemen like you to carry large change.

HENRY (*Nettled*)   My friend, you shouldn't judge a stranger always by the clothes he wears. I am quite able to pay for this suit.

TOD   Hah!

HENRY   I simply don't wish to put you to the trouble of changing a large note.

TOD   As long as rebukes are going around, I might say that it wasn't quite your affair to infer that we couldn't change any note that you might happen to be carrying around. On the contrary, we *can*.

HENRY   Oh, very well. I apologize. Here you are.

TOD Thank you. (*A complete change. He stutters and fumbles.*)
Ah—it's—ah—that is—we—ah—you see— It's— (*Quickly*) take it
back, please. (*Raising voice*) Mr. Smedley! Mr. Smedley! Help! Oh,
Mr. Smedley.

SMEDLEY (*Coming in. A fussy man*) What is it, Tod, what is it?
Stop shouting!

TOD Oh, but Mr. Smedley, I can't control myself.

SMEDLEY What's up? What's the trouble? What's wanting? Who's
this?

HENRY I am a customer and I am waiting for my change.

SMEDLEY Change, change! Tod, give him his change. Get it for
him.

TOD Get him his change! It's easy for you to say that, Mr. Smedley, but look at the bill yourself.

SMEDLEY Bill, bill! Let me see it! (*Pause*) Tod, you ass, selling
an eccentric millionaire such an unspeakable suit as that. Tod, you're
a fool—a born fool! Drives every millionaire away from this place, because he can't tell a millionaire from a tramp. Here, sir, are some suits
more in keeping with your position.

HENRY Thank you, but this one will do.

SMEDLEY Of course it won't do! I shall burn it. Tod, burn this
suit at once.

TOD Yes, Mr. Smedley.

SMEDLEY We shall be honored to outfit you completely, sir . . .
morning clothes, evening dress, sack suits, tweeds, shetlands—everything you need. Come, Tod, book and pen. Now—length of leg, 32
inches; sleeve—

HENRY But look here, I can't give you an order for suits, unless
you can wait indefinitely, or change this bill.

SMEDLEY Indefinitely, sir. It's a weak word, a weak word. *Eter-
nally, that's* the word, sir. Tod, rush these things through. Let the minor
customers wait. Set down the gentleman's address and—

HENRY I'm changing my quarters. I'll drop in and leave the new
address.

SMEDLEY Quite right, sir, quite right. One moment—allow me
to show you out, sir. And don't worry about paying us. (*Fading*) Your
credit is the highest. Good day, sir, good day. You honor us greatly, sir.

HENRY (*As though sighing*) Well, don't you see what was bound
to happen? I drifted naturally into whatever I wanted. Take my hotel,

for example. I merely showed the resident manager my million-pound note, and he said:

MANAGER   We are honored to have you as a guest, sir. Now, I have just the suite for you. It consists of a bedroom, sitting room, a dressing room, a dining room, two baths and—

HENRY   I'll pay you a month in advance with this.

MANAGER   (*Laughing*)   You honor our simple hotel, sir. Pray, don't worry about the bill.

HENRY   But it may be several months before I can pay you.

MANAGER   We're not worried, Mr.—er—

HENRY   Henry Adams.

MANAGER   Mr. Adams, you are a most distinguished guest. (*Fading*) Anything you desire, please name it and we shall procure it for you immediately. Thank you, sir.

HENRY   And there I was, sumptuously housed in an expensive hotel in Hanover Square. I took my dinners there, but for breakfast I stuck by Hawkins' humble feeding-house, where I had got my first meal on my million-pound bank note. I was the making of Hawkins.

SOUND   *Rattle of dishes and silver, customers' voices ad libbing in background.*

HAWKINS   Business is brisk, sir, very brisk, indeed, and has been ever since you and your million-pound bank note became patrons of my humble establishment. I've had to hire extra help, put in additional tables. Look for yourself, sir. There's a long queue waiting to get in. Why, I'm famous and fair on my way to becoming wealthy.

COCKNEY 2   Pardon me, Guv'ner, but aren't you the gentleman what owns the million-pound bank note?

HAWKINS   Look here, you, go away and stop bothering Mr.—Mr.—

HENRY   Adams.

HAWKINS   Mr. Adams.

COCKNEY 2   I was just anxious to get a look at him.

HAWKINS   Who? Mr. Adams?

COCKNEY 2   No. The bank note.

HENRY   Glad to oblige. There you are.

COCKNEY 2   By George, it *is* real. (*Fading*) Now I can go home and tell me old lady I've seen it with me own eyes. I hopes she believes me, but she won't.

HAWKINS Mr. Adams, I wonder if I couldn't force upon you a small loan—even a large one.

HENRY Oh, no.

HAWKINS Please allow me, sir.

HENRY (*Relenting*) Well, as a matter of fact, I haven't gotten around to changing this note.

HAWKINS Fifty pounds might help tide you over. You know, a little spending money?

HENRY It would help, a bit.

HAWKINS I consider it a great honor. (*Fading*) Indeed, a very great honor. Here you are, Mr. Adams, fifty pounds it is. (*Fading*) And don't worry about repaying me.

HENRY I was in, now, and must sink or swim. I walked on air. And it was natural, for I had become one of the notorieties of London. It turned my head, not just a little, but a great deal. The newspapers referred to me as the "Vest-Pocket Millionaire." Then came the climaxing stroke: "Punch" caricatured me! Wherever I went, people cried:

MAN 1 There he goes!

MAN 2 That's him!

WOMAN 1 Morning, Guv'ner.

MAN 3 He's a bit of all right, he is.

HENRY Why, I just swam in glory all day long. About the tenth day of my fame I fulfilled my duty to my country by calling upon the American Ambassador. He received me with enthusiasm, and insisted that I attend a dinner party he was giving the following night. Two important things happened at that dinner. I met two people who were to play important roles in the little drama I was living. Among the guests was a lovely English girl, named Portia Langham, whom I fell in love with in two minutes, and she with me; I could see it without glasses. And just before dinner, the butler announced:

BIZ *Guests ad libbing in background, very politely*

BUTLER (*Calling out*) Mr. Lloyd Hastings.

HENRY I stared at Hastings and he at me, his mouth open in surprise.

HASTINGS I, er—pardon me, but are you? No, of course you can't be.

HENRY (*Chuckling*) But I am, Lloyd.

HASTINGS Henry, I'm speechless. (*Suddenly*) Don't tell me that you're also the Vest-Pocket Millionaire?

HENRY   Correct!

HASTINGS   I've seen your own name coupled with the nickname, but it never occurred to me you were *the* Henry Adams. Why, it isn't six months since you were clerking in Frisco, and sitting up nights helping me verify the Gould and Curry Extension papers. The idea of your being in London, and a vast millionaire, and a colossal celebrity! It's out of the Arabian Nights!

HENRY   I can't realize it myself.

HASTINGS   It was just three months ago that we were eating together, and I tried to persuade you to come to London with me. You turned me down and now here you are. How did you happen to come, and what gave you this incredible start?

HENRY   I'll tell you all about it, but not now.

HASTINGS   When?

HENRY   The end of this month.

HASTINGS   Make it a week.

HENRY   I can't. How's your business venture coming along?

HASTINGS   (*Sighing*) You were a true prophet, Henry. I wish I hadn't come.

HENRY   Stop with me, when we leave here, and tell me all about it. I want to hear the whole story.

HASTINGS   You'll hear it, every last dismal word. (*Fading a bit*) I'm so grateful to find a willing and sympathetic ear.

> BIZ   *Background ad libbing out. A pause, then:*
> PIANO   *Playing semi-classical tune in background.*

HENRY   After dinner there was coffee and an informal piano recital and dear Miss Langham—lovely Portia Langham, the English girl. I eased her away from the music and the guests, to the library, where we talked.

> PIANO   *Out.*

PORTIA   I'm really quite excited, Mr. Adams, meeting you like this. A millionaire!

HENRY   But I'm not one.

PORTIA   B-but of course you are.

HENRY   You're wrong.

PORTIA   I don't understand.

HENRY You will! You will, that is, if you allow me to see you tomorrow.

PORTIA (*As though smiling*) Well, Mr. Adams—

HENRY Henry.

PORTIA Henry, then. I will give the invitation serious thought.

HENRY Tomorrow is going to be a sunny day, just right for a picnic in the country. Yes?

PORTIA Yes.

HENRY I'll tell you the whole story then.

PORTIA Do you think you should?

HENRY Certainly! After all, we're going to be married.

PORTIA (*Amazed*) We—we're—going to—marry!

HENRY Absolutely! I'll call for you at noon. Where?

PORTIA Meet me here.

HENRY You're a guest here?

PORTIA N—no, but it will be more convenient.

HENRY Do you like me?

PORTIA Yes, Henry (*Fading*) You're a very unusual young man, even if you are a millionaire, and even if you claim you aren't.

HENRY All the way home I was in the clouds, Hastings talking, and I not hearing a word. When we reached my suite, he said to me:

HASTINGS This luxury makes me realize how poor, how defeated I am. Even the drippings of your daily income would seem like a tremendous fortune to me.

HENRY Unreel your story, Lloyd.

HASTINGS I told you the whole story on the way over here.

HENRY You did?

HASTINGS Yes.

HENRY I'll be hanged if I heard a word of it.

HASTINGS Are you well?

HENRY Yes. I'm in love.

HASTINGS That English girl you were speaking to?

HENRY Yes. I'm going to marry her.

HASTINGS Small wonder you didn't hear a word I said.

HENRY Now I'm all attention.

HASTINGS I came here with what I thought was a grand opportunity. I have an option to sell the Gould and Curry Mine and keep all I can get over a million dollars.

HENRY Sounds like a good proposition.

HASTINGS Yes, it's a fine claim.

HENRY Well?

HASTINGS The parties here whom I tried to interest have backed down. And so here I am trying to peddle a gold mine, but with nary a buyer in sight. In addition, I am almost penniless.

HENRY Surely you'll find a buyer.

HASTINGS My option on the mine expires in a matter of days; in fact, at the end of this month.

HENRY You *are* in a fix.

HASTINGS Henry, you can save me. Will you do it?

HENRY I? How?

HASTINGS Give me a million dollars and my passage home for my option.

HENRY I can't.

HASTINGS But you're wealthy.

HENRY I—I—not really.

HASTINGS You have a million pounds—five millions of dollars. Buy the mine and you'll double, maybe triple your investment.

HENRY I'd like to help, but I can't.

HASTINGS You know the value of this mine, as well as I do.

HENRY (*Tired*) Oh, Lloyd, I wish I could explain, but I can't. What you ask is impossible.

HASTINGS That's quite all right. I'm sorry to have bothered you, Henry. (*Fading*) You must have a good reason in turning me down, I'm sure.

HENRY It hurt me to have to refuse Lloyd, but it made me comprehend my delicate and precarious position. Here I was, deep in debt, not a cent in the world, in love with a lovely girl, and nothing in front of me but a promise of a position, if, *if* I won the bet for the nameless brother. Nothing could save me. The next day, Portia and I went on our picnic in the country. I told her the story, down to the last detail. Her reaction wasn't exactly what I thought it would be.

SOUND *Bird singing in background. Weave in and out of this scene.*

PORTIA (*Laughs*) Oh, Henry, that's priceless.

HENRY (*A bit stiffly*) I fail to see the humor.

PORTIA But I do, more than you can imagine.

HENRY   Here I am mixed up in a bet between two eccentric old men, and for all they care I might well be in jail.

PORTIA   (*Still laughing*)   Wonderful, the funniest thing I've ever heard.

HENRY   Pardon me if I don't laugh.

PORTIA   (*Stops laughing*)   Sorry, but it is both funny and pathetic. But you say that one of the men is going to offer you a position?

HENRY   If I win the bet.

PORTIA   Which one is he?

HENRY   I don't know. But I have one solution. If I win, I get the position. Now, I've kept a very careful track of every cent I either owe or have borrowed, and I'm going to pay it back from my salary. If the position pays me six hundreds pounds a year, I'll—I'll—

PORTIA   You'll what?

HENRY   I'll— (*He whistles.*)   To date I owe exactly six hundred pounds, my whole year's salary.

PORTIA   And the month isn't ended.

HENRY   If I'm careful, my second year's salary may carry me through. Oh, dear, that *is* going to make it difficult for us to get married immediately, isn't it?

PORTIA   (*Dreamily*)   Yes, it is. (*Suddenly*)   Henry, what are you talking about? Marriage! You don't know me.

HENRY   I know your name, your nationality, your age, and most important, I know that I love you. I also know that you love me.

PORTIA   Please be sensible.

HENRY   I can't. I'm in love.

PORTIA   All this sounds like a play.

HENRY   It is—a wonderful one. I'll admit my owing my first two years' pay is going to pose a problem insofar as our getting married is concerned. (*Suddenly*)   I have it! The day I confront those two old gentlemen, I'll take you with me.

PORTIA   Oh, no. It wouldn't be proper.

HENRY   But so much depends upon that meeting. With you there, I can get the old boys to raise my salary—say, to a thousand pounds a year. Perhaps fifteen hundred. Say you'll go with me.

PORTIA   I'll go.

HENRY   In that case, I'll demand two thousand a year, so we can get married immediately.

PORTIA   Henry?

HENRY Yes?

PORTIA Keep your expenses down for the balance of the month. Don't dip into your third year's salary.

HENRY And that is how matters stood at that point. Thoughts raced through my mind. What if I lost the bet for my nameless benefactor? What if he failed to give me a position? Then the answer came to me, like a flash of lightning. I roused Lloyd Hastings from bed. He was a bit bewildered.

HASTINGS I don't understand you. What are you getting at?

HENRY Lloyd, I'm going to save you. Save you—understand!

HASTINGS No.

HENRY I'll save you, but not in the way you ask, for that wouldn't be fair, after your hard work and the risks you've run. Now, I don't need to buy a mine. I can keep my capital moving without that; it's what I'm doing all the time. I know all about your mine; I know its immense value and can swear to it if anybody wishes it. You shall sell it inside of the fortnight for three million cash.

HASTINGS Three million!

HENRY Right!

HASTINGS But how?

HENRY By using my name freely—and right now my name is on the tip of everybody's tongue. We'll divide the profits, share and share alike.

HASTINGS (*Overjoyed*) I may use your name! Your name—think of it! Man, they'll flock in droves, these rich English. They'll fight for that stock. I'm a made man, a made man forever. (*Fading*) I'll never forget you as long as I live . . . never, never . . .

HENRY In less than twenty-four hours London was abuzz! I hadn't anything to do, day after day, but sit home, and wait for calls.

SIR ALFRED Then I may assume, Mr. Adams, that you consider this mining property a sound investment?

HENRY A very sound investment, Sir Alfred.

SIR ALFRED And what of this American chap, Hastings?

HENRY I know him very well, and he is as sound as the mine.

SIR ALFRED Then I think I shall invest in this property. Your recommendation does it.

SOUND *Telephone bell.*

HENRY Excuse me, Sir Alfred.

SOUND *Receiver lifted from hook.*

HENRY (*Into phone*) Yes, this is Henry Adams. Who? Sir John Hardcastle. Yes, Sir John. The Gould and Curry Extension? Yes, I know a great deal about it. I certainly would recommend it as a shrewd investment. The mine is worth far more than the asking price. Yes, Mr. Hastings is very well known in the States. Honest as the day is long, as they say. Yes, I suggest you contact Mr. Hastings. Thank you. Not at all. Good day, Sir John.

SOUND *Receiver replaced onto hook.*

SIR ALFRED That clinches it. If Sir John is in, so am I. Do you suppose that your Mr. Hastings would mind if I brought in a few discreet friends on this venture?

HENRY Er, no, in fact I'm sure he wouldn't. Mr. Hastings is a very democratic chap.

SIR ALFRED Directly I shall go and call upon Mr. Hastings. By the way, exactly where is this mine?

HENRY California.

SIR ALFRED Is that near Washington, D. C.?

HENRY Not exactly.

SIR ALFRED A pity, for I had thought of asking the British Ambassador to look at it. (*Fading*) Well, I'm off. Thank you for your advice. Good day, Mr. Adams.

HENRY And that's the way it went—a steady stream of wealthy Londoners asking my advice, which, of course, I gave freely. Meanwhile I said not a word to Portia about the possible sale of the mine. I wanted to save it as a surprise; and then there always was the possibility the sale might fall through. The day the month was up, she and I, dressed in our best, went to the house on Portland Place. As we waited for the two old gentlemen to enter, we talked excitedly.

PORTIA You're certain you have the bank note with you?

HENRY Right here. Portia, dearest, the way you look it's a crime to ask for a salary a single penny under three thousand a year.

PORTIA You'll ruin us.

HENRY Just trust in me. It'll come out all right.

PORTIA (*Worried*) Please remember if we ask for too much we may get no salary at all; and then what will become of us, with no way in the world to earn our living? (*Fading*) Please handle this delicately, Henry.

HENRY   When the two old gentlemen entered, of course they were surprised to see Portia with me. I asked them to introduce themselves, which they did.

GORDON   I am Gordon Featherstone.

ABEL   And I am Abel Featherstone.

HENRY   Gentlemen, I am ready to report, but first may I ask which of you bet on me?

GORDON   It was I. Have you the million-pound note?

HENRY   Here it is, sir.

GORDON   Ah! I've won. *Now* what do you say, Abel?

ABEL   I say he did survive, and I've lost twenty thousand pounds. I never would have believed it.

HENRY   Perhaps you might enlighten me as to the terms of the bet.

GORDON   Gladly! The Bank of England once issued two notes of a million pounds each. Only one of these had been used and cancelled; the other lay in the vaults. Well, Abel and I got to wondering what would happen to a perfectly honest and intelligent stranger turned adrift in London without a friend and with no money in the world but the million-pound bank note. Abel said he would starve to death, and I claimed he wouldn't. My brother said he would be arrested if he offered the note at a bank. Well, we went on arguing until I bet him twenty thousand pounds that the man would live thirty days, *anyway*, on that million, and keep out of jail, too.

ABEL   And I took him up.

HENRY   How did you know I was the right choice?

ABEL   After talking with you, we decided you had all the qualifications.

GORDON   And that pear incident, if you had picked it up very boldly, it would have proved to us you were nothing but a tramp.

HENRY   You don't know how tempted I was to do just that.

GORDON   And so you shall receive your reward—a choice of any position you can fill.

HENRY   First I ask that you look at this scrap of paper, all of you. You, too, Portia.

GORDON   A certificate of deposit in the London and County Bank—

ABEL   In the sum of—

GORDON   Two hundred thousand pounds.

PORTIA   Henry, is it yours?

HENRY   It is. It represents my share of the sale of a mining property in California, sold by my friend Lloyd Hastings; a sort of commission, as it were. It all came about by thirty days' judicious use of that little loan you gentlemen let me have. And the only use I made of it was to buy trifles and offer the bill in change.

ABEL   Come, this is astonishing.

GORDON   It's incredible.

HENRY   (*Laughing*)   I can prove it.

PORTIA   Henry, is that really your money? Have you been fibbing to me?

HENRY   I have, indeed. But you'll forgive me, I know.

PORTIA   (*Half-smiling*)   Don't you be so sure.

HENRY   Oh, you'll get over it. Come, let's be going.

GORDON   Wait! I promised to give you a situation, you know.

HENRY   Thank you, but I really don't want one.

PORTIA   Henry, I'm ashamed of you. You don't even thank the good gentleman. May I do it for you?

HENRY   If you can improve upon it.

PORTIA   I shall. Uncle Abel, first, thank you for making this possible. And, dear Father—

HENRY   Hold on. You're her uncle?

ABEL   I am.

HENRY   And you—

GORDON   Yes, I'm her step-father.

PORTIA   And the dearest one that ever was. You understand now, don't you, Henry, why I was able to laugh when you told me the story of the bet with the two nameless gentlemen. Of course I couldn't miss knowing that it was this house and that the two men were Father and Uncle Abel.

HENRY   Sir, you *have* got a situation open that I want.

GORDON   Name it.

HENRY   Son-in-law.

GORDON   Well, well, well! But if you haven't ever served in that capacity, you of course can't furnish satisfactory recommendations to satisfy the conditions of the contract.

HENRY   Only just try me for thirty or forty years.

GORDON   What do you think, Abel?

ABEL   Well, he does look to be a satisfactory sort.

GORDON   And you, Portia?

PORTIA   I agree—heartily.

GORDON   Very well. Take her along. If you hurry, you can reach the license bureau before it closes. (*Fading*) Hop to it now.

HENRY   Happy, we two? Indeed, yes! And when London got the whole history of my adventure for a month, how it did talk. My Portia's father took the million-pound bank note to the Bank of England, cashed it, had it cancelled, and he gave it to us at our wedding. Framed, it now hangs in our home. It gave me my Portia, but for it I could not have remained in London, would not have appeared at the American Ambassador's, never should have met her. And so I always say: Yes, it's a million-pounder; but it made but one purchase in its life, and then got the article for only about a tenth part of its value.

THE END

DISCUSSION

1. What do you conclude about Henry Adams from his observations as narrator? Do you find that there is much consistency between the things Henry says about himself and the things he does?

2. Henry is both recalling his experiences and reliving them. Why is it important that you be aware of this distinction as you are reading the play?

3. Henry claims that he is unwilling to take a gamble, and so rejects Hastings' initial offer. How do you reconcile this decision with Henry's behavior later in the play?

4. What is the dramatic purpose of the line, "At that moment if I had known what they had in mind, undoubtedly I would have bolted for the door."?

5. How do the Featherstones decide that Henry is "just the man for whom (they) have been searching"?

6. How does possession of the million-pound bank note affect Henry? How does it affect the people with whom he comes in contact? What point do you think the author is trying to make?

7. Is it in keeping with his character that Henry continues to breakfast at Hawkins', even after he has established residence in Hanover Square? Why?

8. Why is it essential to the story that Hastings and Henry meet again? How has their relationship changed since their last meeting? In what respect has it remained the same?

9. Hastings compares Henry's good fortune to something "out of the Arabian nights." After Henry explains his position to Portia, she replies, "All this sounds like a play." Do these comments strengthen or weaken the credibility of the plot? How?

10. What bearing does it have on your attitude toward the outcome of the story that Henry manages to earn two hundred thousand pounds through his own initiative?

11. Explain the meaning of Henry's final speaking line.

TOPICS FOR WRITING

The Million-Pound Note as a *comedy*
The author's use of coincidence
Judging character from first impressions

THE CLOD

Lewis Beach

CHARACTERS

Thaddeus Trask
Mary Trask
A Northern Private
A Southern Sergeant
A Southern Private

Lewis Beach (1891-1947)

In every war there are the valiant and the weak, the daredevils and the deserters, those whose courage inspires men, and those whose cowardice humiliates or destroys them. There are even some who do not know the reason why there is fighting, and who are indifferent to what the outcome will be. Such a person is Mary Trask of The Clod.

Lewis Beach was born in 1891 and perfected his writing skills at George Pierce Baker's renowned Harvard Workshop. The Clod *was first performed in 1916 by the Washington Square Players, the theatrical group that was instrumental in bringing Beach's talent to the attention of the American public.*

THE CLOD

SCENE   *The kitchen of a farmhouse on the borderline between the Northern and Southern states. It is ten o'clock in the evening, September, 1863.*

The back wall is broken at stage left by the projection at right angles of a partially enclosed staircase; the four steps leading to the landing cut into the room. Underneath the enclosed part of the stairway, a cubby-hole; in front of it a small table which partially hides the door. To the left of the

*table a kitchen chair. A door, leading to the yard, is the center
of the unbroken wall, back. To the right of the door, a cupboard; to the left, a small cooking-stove. Two windows in the
right wall. Between them a bench on which a pail and a tin
dipper stand. Above the bench a towel hanging on a nail,
and above the towel a double-barrelled shotgun suspended
on two pegs. Well downstage left, a closed door leading to a
second room. In the center of the kitchen a large table;
straight-backed chairs to the right and left of it. A lighted
candle on this table. ("Right" and "left" are the actors' "right"
and "left.")*

*The moon shines into the room through the windows, but
at no time is the kitchen brightly lighted. The characters appear as silhouettes except when they stand near the candle
or the lantern, and then the lights throw huge shadows on the
roughly plastered walls. When the door, back, is opened one
sees a bit of the farmyard, desolate even in the moonlight.*

As the curtain rises, THADDEUS TRASK, *a man of sixty-odd
years, short and thick-set, slow in speech and action, yet in
perfect health, sits at the left of the center table. He is pressing tobacco into his corncob pipe. He lights it with the candle.
After a moment,* MARY TRASK, *a tired, emaciated woman,
whose years equal her husband's, enters from the yard carrying a heavy pail of water and a lighted lantern. She puts the
pail on the bench and hangs the lantern above it; then crosses
to the stove.*

MARY   Ain't got wood 'nough fer breakfast, Thad.

THADDEUS   I'm too tired t' go out now. Wait 'til mornin'. (*Pause.*
MARY *lays the fire in the stove*) Did I tell yuh that old man Reed saw
three Southern troopers pass his house this mornin'?

MARY (*takes coffee-pot from stove, crosses to bench, fills pot with
water*)   I wish them soldiers would git out o' the neighborhood. Whenever I see 'em passin', I have t' steady myself 'gainst somethin' or I'd
fall. I couldn't hardly breathe yesterday when them Southerners came
after fodder. I'd died if they'd spoke t' me.

THADDEUS   Yuh needn't be afraid o' Northern soldiers.

MARY (*carries coffee-pot to stove*)   I hate 'em all—Union or Southern. I can't make head or tail t' what all this fightin's 'bout. An' I don't

care who wins, so long as they git through, an' them soldiers stop stealin' our corn an' potatoes.

THADDEUS   Yuh can't hardly blame 'em if they're hungry, ken yuh?

MARY   It ain't right that they should steal from us poor folk. (*Lifts a huge gunny sack of potatoes from the table, and begins setting the table for breakfast, getting knives, forks, spoons, plates, cups and saucers—two of each—from the cupboard*) We have hard 'nough times t' make things meet now. I ain't set down once today 'cept fer meals. An' when I think o' the work I got t' do t'morrow, I ought t' been in bed hours ago.

THADDEUS   I'd help if I could, but it ain't my fault if the Lord seed fit t' lay me up so I'm always ailin'. (*Rises lazily*) Yuh better try an' take things easy t'morrow.

MARY   It's well enough t' say, but them apples is got t' be picked an' the rest o' the potatoes sorted. If I could sleep at night it'd be all right, but with them soldiers 'bout, I can't.

THADDEUS   (*crosses right; fondly handles his gun*)   Golly, wish I'd see a flock o' birds.

MARY   (*nervously*)   I'd rather go without than hear yuh fire. I wish yuh didn't keep it loaded.

THADDEUS   Yuh know I ain't got time t' stop an' load when I see the birds. They don't wait fer yuh. (*Hangs gun on wall, drops into his chair; dejectedly*) Them pigs has got t' be butchered.

MARY   Wait 'til I git a chance t' go t' sister's. I can't stand it t' hear 'em squeal.

THADDEUS   (*pulling off his boots—grunting meanwhile*)   Best go soon then, 'cause they's fat as they'll ever be, an' there ain't no use in wastin' feed on 'em. (*Pause; rises*) Ain't yuh 'most ready fer bed?

MARY   Go on up. (THADDEUS *takes the candle in one hand, his boots in the other, and climbs the stairs.* MARY *speaks when he reaches the landing*) An' Thad, try not t' snore t'night.

THADDEUS   Poke me if I do. (*Disappears.*)

> (MARY *fills the kettle with water and puts it on the stove; closes the door, back; takes the lantern from the wall and tries twice before she succeeds in blowing it out. Puts the lantern on the table before the cubby-hole. Slowly drags herself up the stairs, pausing a moment on the top step for breath before she disappears. There is a silence. Then the door, back, is*

opened a trifle and a man's hand is seen. Cautiously the door is opened wide and a young Northern private stands silhouetted on the threshold. He wears a dirty uniform, and a bloody bandage is tied about his head. He is wounded, sick, and exhausted. He stands at the door a moment, listening intently; then hastily moves to the center table looking for food. He bumps against a chair and mutters an oath. Finding nothing on the table, he hurries to the cupboard. Suddenly the galloping of horses is heard in the distance. The NORTHERNER *starts, then rushes to the window nearer the audience. For a moment the sound ceases, then it begins again, growing gradually louder and louder. The* NORTHERNER *hurries into the room at the left. Horses and voices are heard in the yard, and almost immediately heavy, thundering knocks sound on the door, back. The men at the door grow impatient and push the door open. A large, powerfully built* SOUTHERN SERGEANT, *and a smaller, younger trooper of the same army enter.* THADDEUS *appears on the stairs, carrying a candle.*)

SERGEANT (*to* THADDEUS; *not unkindly*)   Sorry, my friend, but you were so darn slow 'bout openin' the door that we had to walk in. Has there been a Northern soldier round here today?

THADDEUS (*timidly*)   I ain't seed one. (*Comes down the stairs.*)

SERGEANT   Have you been here all day?

THADDEUS   I ain't stirred from the place.

SERGEANT   Call the rest of your family down.

THADDEUS   My wife's all there is. (*Goes to foot of stairs, and calls loudly and excitedly*) Mary! Mary! Come down. Right off!

SERGEANT   You better not lie to me or it'll go tough with you.

THADDEUS   I swear I ain't seed no one. (MARY *comes downstairs slowly. She is all atremble*) Say, Mary, you was here——

SERGEANT   Keep still, man. I'll do the talkin' (*To* MARY) You were here at the house all day? (MARY *is very frightened and embarrassed, but after a moment manages to nod her head slowly*) You didn't take a trip down to the store? (MARY *shakes her head slowly*) Haven't you got a tongue?

MARY (*with difficulty*)   Y-e-s.

SERGEANT   Then use it. The Northern soldier who came here a while ago was pretty badly wounded, wasn't he?

MARY   I—I—no one's been here.

SERGEANT   Come, come, woman, don't lie. (MARY *shows a slight sign of anger*) He had a bad cut in his forehead, and you felt sorry for him, and gave him a bite to eat.

MARY   (*haltingly*)   No one's been near the house t'day.

SERGEANT   (*trying a different tone*)   We're not going to hurt him, woman. He's a friend of ours. We want to find him, and put him in a hospital, don't we, Dick? (*Turning to his companion.*)

DICK   He's sick and needs to go to bed for a while.

MARY   He ain't here.

SERGEANT   What do you want to lie for?

MARY   (*quickly*)   I ain't lyin'. I ain't seed no soldier. (*She stands rooted to the spot where she stopped when she came downstairs. Her eyes are still fixed on the* SERGEANT.)

SERGEANT   I reckon you know what'll happen if you are hidin' the spy.

THADDEUS   There ain't no one here. We both been here all day, an' there couldn't no one come without our knowin' it. What would they want round here anyway?

SERGEANT   We'll search the place, Dick.

MARY   (*quickly*)   Yuh ain't got no—

SERGEANT   (*sharply*)   What's that, woman?

MARY   There ain't no one here, an' yer keepin' us from our sleep.

SERGEANT   Your sleep? This is an affair of life and death. Get us a lantern. (THADDEUS *moves to the small table and lights the lantern with the candle which he holds in his hand. He gives the lantern to the* SERGEANT. *The* SERGEANT *notices the door to the cubby-hole*) Ha! Tryin' to hide the door, are you, by puttin' a table in front of it? You can't fool me. (*To* THADDEUS) Pull the table away and let's see what's behind the door.

THADDEUS   It's a cubby-hole an' ain't been opened in years.

SERGEANT   (*sternly and emphatically*)   I said to open the door. (THADDEUS *sets the candle on the larger table, moves the smaller table to the right, and opens the door to the cubby-hole.* MARY *is angry. The* SERGEANT *takes a long-barreled revolver from his belt and peers into the cubbyhole. Returning his revolver to his belt*) We're goin' to tear this place to pieces 'til we find him. You might just as well hand him over now.

MARY   There ain't no one here.

SERGEANT   All right. Now we'll see. Dick, you stand guard at the door. (DICK *goes to the door, back, and stands gazing out into the night,—his back to the audience. To* THADDEUS) Come along, man. I'll have to look at the upstairs. (*To* MARY) You sit down in that chair. (*Points to chair at right of center table, and feels for a sufficiently strong threat*) Don't you stir or I'll—I'll set fire to your house. (*To* THADDEUS) Go on ahead.

> (THADDEUS *and the* SERGEANT *go upstairs.* MARY *sinks lifelessly into the chair. She is the picture of fear. She sits facing left. Suddenly she leans forward. She opens her eyes wide, and draws her breath sharply. She opens her mouth as though she would scream, but makes no sound. The* NORTHERNER *has opened the door. He enters slowly and cautiously, his gun pointed at* MARY. DICK *cannot see him because of the jog in the wall.* MARY *only stares in bewilderment at the* NORTHERNER, *as he, with eyes fixed appealingly on her, opens the door to the cubby-hole and crawls inside.*)

DICK   Woman!

MARY   (*almost with a cry, thinking that* DICK *has seen the* NORTHERNER) Yes.

DICK   Have you got an apple handy? I'm starved.

> (MARY *rises and moves to the cupboard. The* SERGEANT *and* THADDEUS *come downstairs. The* SERGEANT, *seeing that* MARY *is not where he left her, looks about rapidly and discovers her at the cupboard.*)

SERGEANT   Here, what did I tell you I'd do if you moved from that chair?

MARY   (*terrified*) Oh, I didn't—I only—he wanted——

DICK   It's all right, Sergeant. I asked her to get me an apple.

SERGEANT   Take this lantern and search the barn. (DICK *takes the lantern from the* SERGEANT *and goes out, back. To* THADDEUS) Come in here with me. (*The* SERGEANT *picks up the candle. He and* THADDEUS *move toward the door, left. As though in a stupor,* MARY *starts to follow*) Sit down! (MARY *drops into the chair at the right of the table. The* SERGEANT *and* THADDEUS *go into the room, left. They can be heard moving furniture about.* MARY *sees a pin on the floor. She stoops, picks it up and fastens it in her belt. The* SERGEANT *and* THADDEUS *return*) If I find him now after all the trouble you've given me, you know what'll happen. There's likely to be two dead men and a woman, instead of only the Yankee.

DICK (*bounding into the room*) Sergeant!

SERGEANT What is it? (DICK *hurries to the* SERGEANT *and says something to him in a low voice. The* SERGEANT *smiles*) Now, my good people, how did that horse get here?

THADDEUS What horse?

DICK There's a horse in the barn with a saddle on his back. I swear he's been ridden lately.

THADDEUS (*amazed*) There is?

SERGEANT You know it. (*To* MARY) Come, woman, who drove that horse here?

MARY (*silent for a moment, her eyes on the floor*) I don't know. I didn't hear nothin'.

THADDEUS (*moving toward the door*) Let me go an' see.

SERGEANT (*pushing* THADDEUS *back*) No, you don't. You two have done enough to justify the harshest measures. Show us the man's hiding place.

THADDEUS If there's anybody here, he's come in the night without our knowin' it. I tell yuh I didn't see anybody, an' she didn't, an'——

SERGEANT (*has been watching* MARY) Where is he?

(*His tone makes* THADDEUS *jump. There is a pause, during which* MARY *seems trying to compose herself. Then slowly she lifts her eyes and looks at the* SERGEANT.)

MARY There ain't nobody in the house 'cept us two.

SERGEANT (*to* DICK) Did you search all the out-buildings?

DICK Yes. There's not a trace of him except the horse.

SERGEANT (*wiping the perspiration from his face; speaks with apparent deliberation at first, but becomes very emphatic*) He didn't have much of a start of us, and I think he was wounded. A farmer down the road said he heard hoof-beats. The man the other side of you heard nothin', *and the horse is in your barn.* (*Slowly draws his revolver and points it at* THADDEUS) There are ways of making people confess.

THADDEUS (*covering his face with his hands*) For God's sake, don't. I know that horse looks bad, but, as I live, I ain't heard a sound, or seen anybody. I'd give the man up in a minute if he was here.

SERGEANT (*lowering his gun*) Yes, I guess you would. You wouldn't want me to hand you and your wife over to our army to be shot down like dogs. (MARY *shivers.* SERGEANT *swings round sharply and points the gun at* MARY) Your wife knows where he's hid.

MARY (*breaking out in irritating, rasping voice*) I'm sure I wish I did. I'd tell yuh quick an' git yuh out o' here. 'Tain't no fun fer me t' have yuh prowlin' all over my house, trackin' it up with yer dirty boots. Yuh ain't got no right t' torment me like this. Lord knows how I'll git my day's work done, if I can't have my sleep out.

SERGEANT (*has been gazing at her in astonishment; lowers his gun*) Good God! Nothing but her own petty existence. (*In different voice to* MARY) I'll have to ask you to get us some breakfast. We're famished. (*With relief but showing some anger,* MARY *turns to the stove. She lights the fire and puts more coffee in the pot*) Come, Dick, we better give our horses some water. They're all tired out. (*In lower voice*) The man isn't here. If he were he couldn't get away while we're in the yard. (*To* THADDEUS) Get us a pail to give the horses some water in. (*Sees the pails on the bench. Picks one of them up and moves toward the door.*)

MARY   That ain't the horses' pail.

SERGEANT (*to* THADDEUS) Come along. You can help.

MARY (*louder*) That's the drinkin' water pail.

SERGEANT   That's all right.

> (*The* SERGEANT, THADDEUS, *and* DICK—*carrying the lantern—go out back.* MARY *needs more wood for the fire, so she follows in a moment. When she has disappeared, the* NORTH-ERNER *drags himself from the cubby-hole.* MARY *returns with an armful of wood.*)

MARY (*sees the* NORTHERNER. *Shows no sympathy for him in this speech nor during the entire scene*) Yuh git back! Them soldiers'll see yuh.

NORTHERNER   Some water. Quick. (*Falls into chair at left of table*) It was so hot in there.

MARY (*gives him water in the dipper*) Don't yuh faint here! If them soldiers git yuh, they'll kill me an' Thad. Hustle an' git back in that cubby-hole. (*Turns quickly to the stove.*)

(*The* NORTHERNER *drinks the water, puts the dipper on the table. Then, summoning all his strength, rises and crosses to* MARY. *He touches her on the sleeve.* MARY *is so startled that she jumps and utters a faint cry.*)

NORTHERNER Be still or they'll hear you. How are you going to get me out of here?

MARY Yuh git out! Why did yuh come here, a-bringin' me all this extra work, an' maybe death?

NORTHERNER I couldn't go any farther. My horse and I were ready to drop. Won't you help me?

MARY No, I won't. I don't know who yuh are or nothin' 'bout yuh, 'cept that them men want t' ketch yuh. (*In a changed tone of curiosity*) Did yuh steal somethin' from 'em?

NORTHERNER Don't you understand? Those men belong to the Confederacy, and I'm a Northerner. They've been chasing me all day. (*Pulling a bit of crumpled paper from his breast*) They want this paper. If they get it before tomorrow morning it will mean the greatest disaster that's ever come to the Union army.

MARY (*with frank curiosity*) Was it yuh rode by yesterday?

NORTHERNER Don't you see what you can do? Get me out of here and away from those men, and you'll have done more than any soldier could do for the country—for *your* country.

MARY I ain't got no country. Me an' Thad's only got this farm. Thad's ailin', an' I do most the work, an'—

NORTHERNER The lives of thirty thousand men hang by a thread. I must save them. And you must help me!

MARY I don't know nothin' 'bout yuh, an' I don't know what yer talkin' 'bout.

NORTHERNER Only help me get away.

MARY (*angrily*) No one ever helped me or Thad. I lift no finger in this business. Why yuh come here in the first place is beyond me— sneakin' in our house, spoilin' our well-earned sleep. If them soldiers ketch yuh, they'll kill me an' Thad. Maybe you didn't know that.

NORTHERNER What's your life and your husband's compared to thirty thousand? I haven't any money or I'd give it to you.

MARY I don't want yer money.

NORTHERNER What do you want?

MARY I want yuh t' git out. I don't care what happens t' yuh. Only git out o' here.

NORTHERNER I can't with the Southerners in the yard. They'd shoot me like a dog. Besides, I've got to have my horse.

MARY (*with naïve curiosity*) What kind o' lookin' horse is it?

NORTHERNER (*dropping into the chair at left of center table in disgust and despair*) Oh, God! If I'd only turned in at the other farm. I might have found people with red blood. (*Pulls out his gun and hopelessly opens the empty chamber.*)

MARY (*alarmed*) What yuh goin' t' do with that gun?

NORTHERNER Don't be afraid——

MARY I'd call 'em if I wasn't—

NORTHERNER (*leaping to the wall, left, and bracing himself against it*) Go call them in. Save your poor skin and your husband's if you can. Call them in. You can't save yourself. (*Laughs hysterically*) You can't save your miserable skin. 'Cause if they get me, and don't shoot you, *I will.*

MARY (*leaning against the left side of the table for support; in agony*) Oh!

NORTHERNER You see? You've got to help me whether you want to or not.

MARY (*feeling absolutely caught*) I ain't done nothin'. I don't see why yuh an' them others come here a-threatenin' t' shoot me. I don't want nothin'. I don't want t' do nothin'. I jest want yuh all t' git out o' here an' leave me an' Thad t' go t' sleep. Oh, I don't know what t' do. Yuh got me in a corner where I can't move. (*Passes her hand back along the table. Touches the dipper accidentally, and it falls to the floor. Screams at the sound.*)

NORTHERNER (*leaping toward her*) Now you've done it. They'll be here in a minute. You can't give me up. They'll shoot me if you do. *They'll shoot.* (*Hurries up the stairs and disappears.*)

(MARY *stands beside the table, trembling terribly. The* SERGEANT, DICK, *and* THADDEUS *come running in.*)

SERGEANT What did you yell for? (MARY *does not answer. He seizes her by the arm*) Answer!

MARY I knocked the dipper off the table. It scared me.

SERGEANT (*dropping wearily into chair at left of center table*) Well, don't drop our breakfast. Put it on the table. We're ready.

MARY (*stands looking at the* SERGEANT) It ain't finished.

SERGEANT (*worn out by his day's work and* MARY'S *stupidity, from now on absolutely brutish*) You've had time to cook a dozen meals. What did you do all the time we were in the yard?

MARY I didn't do nothin'.

SERGEANT You good-for-nothin'—— Get a move on and give us something fit to eat. Don't try to get rid of any left-overs on us. If you do, you'll suffer for it. (MARY *stands looking at him*) Don't you know anything, you brainless farmdrudge? *Hurry*, I said.

(MARY *picks up the dipper and turns to the stove.* THADDEUS *sits in the chair at left of smaller table.*)

DICK What a night! My stomach's as hollow as these people's heads. (*Takes towel which hangs above the bench, and wipes the barrel of his gun with it.*)

MARY That's one of my best towels.

DICK Can't help it.

SERGEANT 'Tend to the breakfast. That's enough for you to do at one time. (DICK *puts his gun on the smaller table, and sits at the right of the larger. Then the* SERGEANT *speaks, quietly*) I don't see how he gave us the slip.

DICK He knew we were after him, drove his horse in here, and went on afoot. Clever scheme, I must admit.

THADDEUS (*endeavoring to get them into conversation*) Have yuh rid far t'night, Misters?

DICK (*shortly*) Far enough.

THADDEUS Twenty miles or so?

DICK Perhaps.

THADDEUS How long yuh been chasin' the critter?

SERGEANT Oh, shut up! Don't you see we don't want to talk to you? Take hold and hurry, woman. My patience's at an end.

(MARY *puts a loaf of bread, some fried eggs, and a coffee-pot on the table.*)

MARY   There! I hope yer satisfied.

(DICK *and the* SERGEANT *pull up their chairs and begin to eat.*)

SERGEANT   Is this all we get? Come, it won't do you any good to be stingy.

MARY   It's all I got.

SERGEANT   It isn't a mouthful for a chickadee! Give us some butter.

MARY   There ain't none.

SERGEANT   No butter on a farm? God, the way you lie.

MARY   I——

SERGEANT   Shut up!

DICK   Have you got any cider?

SERGEANT   Don't ask. She and the man probably drank themselves stupid on it. (*Throws fork on floor*) I never struck such a place in my life. Get me another fork. How do you expect me to eat with that bent thing? (MARY *stoops with difficulty and picks up the fork. Gets another from the cupboard and gives it to the* SERGEANT) Now give me some salt. Don't you know that folks eat it on eggs? (MARY *crosses to the cupboard; mistakes the pepper for the salt and puts it on the table.* SERGEANT *sprinkles pepper on his food*) I said salt, woman. (*Spelling*) S-a-l-t. Salt! Salt! (MARY *gets the salt and gives it to the* SERGEANT. *Almost ready to drop, she drags herself to the window nearer the back and leans against it, watching the* SOUTHERNERS *like a hunted animal.* THADDEUS *is nodding in the corner. The* SERGEANT *and* DICK *go on devouring the food. The former pours the coffee, puts his cup to his lips, takes one swallow; then, jumping to his feet and upsetting his chair as he does so, he hurls his cup to the floor. Bellowing and pointing to the fluid trickling on the floor*) Have you tried to poison us, you God damn hag?

(MARY *screams and the faces of the men turn white. It is the cry of an animal goaded beyond endurance.*)

MARY (*screeching*)   Break my cup? Call my coffee poison? Call me a hag, will yuh? I'll learn yuh! I'm a woman, but yer drivin' me crazy. (*She has snatched the gun from the wall and pointed it at the* SERGEANT. *Fires.*)

(*The* SERGEANT *falls to the floor.* MARY *keeps on screeching.* DICK *rushes for his gun.*)

THADDEUS   Mary! Mary!

MARY (*aiming at* DICK *and firing*)   I ain't a hag. I'm a woman, but yer killin' me.

(DICK *falls just as he reaches his gun.* THADDEUS *is in the corner with his hands over his ears. The* NORTHERNER *stands on the stairs.* MARY *continues to pull the trigger of the empty gun. The* NORTHERNER *is motionless for a moment; then he goes to* THADDEUS *and shakes him.*)

NORTHERNER   Go get my horse. Quick! (THADDEUS *hurries out. The* NORTHERNER *turns to* MARY *and speaks with great fervor. She gazes at him but does not understand a word he says*) I'm ashamed of what I said. The whole country will hear of this, and you. (*He takes her hand and presses it to his lips; then turns and hurries out of the house.*)

(MARY *still holds the gun in her hand. She pushes a strand of gray hair back from her face, and begins to pick up the fragments of the broken cup.*)

MARY (*in dead, flat tone*)   I'll have t' drink out the tin cup now.

(*The hoof-beats of the* NORTHERNER's *horse are heard.*)

CURTAIN

DISCUSSION

1. The word "clod" refers to anything earthy or base. It can also refer to a stupid, thickheaded person. Are both definitions applicable to Mary Trask?
2. What are the Trasks discussing as the play begins? How does their discussion reveal the kind of people they are? Does it serve any other useful function?
3. Why is it ironic that Mary reacts as she does to Thaddeus' talk about shooting birds and butchering pigs? Why, later in the play, does Beach liken Mary's desperation to that of a "hunted animal"?
4. Which characters are at the point of exhaustion when they first appear on stage? How have they expended their energies?

5. Why does Beach persist in describing the sluggish movements and mannerisms of his central character?
6. Although Mary and Thaddeus are alike in many respects, why does the playwright arrange for it to be Mary, not Thaddeus, who discovers the Northerner?
7. What line of dialogue represents the *climax* of the play?
8. Does it surprise you that Thaddeus remains "in the corner with his hands over his ears" instead of rushing to his wife's side while she is firing the gun? Why?
9. How accurately does the Northerner interpret Mary's motive for killing the sergeant and the trooper? Explain the irony.
10. Does Mary undergo any basic change of outlook during her experience, or as a result of it? How does her preoccupation with pins, pails, and towels suggest the answer? How does the ending of the play provide final confirmation?
11. The impact of the play depends largely upon the author's use of dramatic irony. Prove this point, by citing examples. Does the manner in which the author times the entrances and exits of his characters have any bearing on the issue?
12. How is the playwright's use of stage lighting and of setting symbolic?

TOPICS FOR WRITING

Contrast Mary Trask to the Northern private
Discuss why apathetic people are a burden to society

SHE WALKS IN BEAUTY

Ken Kolb

CHARACTERS

Dr. Styner
Grace Fallgren
Henry Fallgren
Jenny
Dr. Baird
Dick
Dr. Keller

SHE WALKS IN BEAUTY was first presented on the "Medic" program on NBC, under the direction of John Brahm.

Ken Kolb (1926-   )

Ken Kolb was born in Portland, Oregon, in 1926. After graduating from high school, he served two years in the U.S. Navy. In 1951, after completing his studies at the University of California (Berkeley), he began writing short stories for popular magazines. Before becoming a successful writer of television scripts, Kolb supplemented his income by working as a shipfitter, a forest fire lookout, a cannery laborer, and an advertising man. At the present time, he is living with his wife and family in California where he continues to write for television. He now has over seventy shows to his credit.

She Walks In Beauty, first presented by the National Broadcasting Company on its Medic program in 1956, develops the theme that the human problems associated with sickness and disease can often be more painful than the illness itself.

SHE WALKS IN BEAUTY

FADE IN: DR. KONRAD STYNER—MEDIUM SHOT
(*The background is unrecognizable.*)
STYNER   Konrad Styner—Doctor of Medicine. Our story has the title: *She Walks in Beauty.*

FADE OUT

CLOSE UP—CENTER OF SHIELD

(*It contains a gnarled staff with a single serpent twined around it. The figure of the staff and serpent is in relief, finely wrought in metal. It is executed in scrupulous detail.*)

VOICE (*Off stage*)   And the qualities of the worthy physician are three . . .

(*Camera pulls back slowly, revealing the entire shield. It is a detailed piece of metalwork hanging against a backdrop of rich drapery. The shield is marked off in thirds, all sections equal. The upper right portion contains the head of a lion. The upper left, the head of an eagle. The lower third contains the hand of a woman. All the figures are in relief, finely detailed. Lighting is low-key. Camera holds on shield.*)

VOICE (*Off stage*)   . . . the heart of a lion . . . the eye of an eagle . . . the hand of a woman.

(*The single word "MEDIC" is superimposed. The letters fill the entire screen.*)

FADE OUT

FADE IN: DR. KONRAD STYNER—MEDIUM CLOSE SHOT

STYNER   Our presentation tonight, the field of orthopedics. The object in point . . . (*Displaying*) a book of poems. The case in point: Jenny Fallgren. She's twelve years old, in good general health, and happy as only a child on summer vacation can be. She has no idea that this will be the most important year of her life . . .

DISSOLVE TO

INTERIOR FALLGREN LIVING ROOM—DAY—MEDIUM SHOT—GRACE FALLGREN

(*The living room is that of a low-middle income family in a small town. It is comfortably but inexpensively furnished. A stairway rises on one side of the room; the stairs are uncarpeted. A couple of windows are open, perhaps even the front*)

door, which is covered by a screen door. MRS. GRACE FALLGREN
*is arranging flowers by a front window. She is a woman in her
mid-thirties, growing a trifle plump; dark hair, pleasant face.
She wears a summer cotton dress. After only a few seconds
of this, she hears footsteps on the front porch.* GRACE *looks
out, reacts in surprise, then goes out on the porch.*)

EXTERIOR FRONT PORCH—DAY

GRACE   You're early!
HENRY   The peeler broke down . . . Too late to fix it till tomorrow.

(HENRY FALLGREN *moves in on this line. He is a year-round
worker and summer foreman at the local canning plant. He
is medium height, wide-shouldered and well-muscled, a man
who has worked all his life at some sort of physical labor. He
wears a pair of work pants and a work shirt open at the neck,
sleeves rolled up. He carries two large, plump pears in his
hands.*)

GRACE   Better now than later in the season . . . Is the fruit any
good yet?
HENRY   (*Extending a pear to her*)   Fine! Some of the peaches are
a little green still, but I've eaten a dozen of these things today . . .
Thought you and Jenny'd like a taste.
GRACE   (*Taking pear*)   They look good. I just put dinner in the
oven. It'll be an hour yet. (*She sits on the porch swing, dabbing at her
face and neck. The kitchen has made her over-warm.*)
HENRY   I'm not too hungry yet. Anyway, it's cooler out here . . .
(*He sits on the rail*)   Where's Jenny?
GRACE   Up in her room, reading—as usual.
HENRY   (*Smiling*)   More poetry?
GRACE   (*Nodding*)   What else?

(*Suddenly we hear the sound of* JENNY'S *footsteps inside.
Her steps form an irregular rhythm, halting—a quick step
then a slow one.* HENRY *turns toward the sound, moves toward the screen door, half opens it.*)

HENRY (*Calling in*) Hi, punkin'!

JENNY (*Appearing on the line*) Hi, Dad! (HENRY *catches her in his arms, lifts her delightedly.*)

JENNY What'cha doin' home early?

HENRY Peeler broke down. Where's my kiss? (*She kisses him, and he makes elaborate groans at her tight hug. He puts her down.* JENNY *moves to the rail. She limps as she walks, but not badly, not enough to slow her down. She is a very pretty girl, rather thin, with delicate features and large, expressive eyes. She is twelve, a great reader, very sharp for her age, with quite a mature outlook. She wears a shirt and a pair of jeans.*)

HENRY (*After embrace*) My little bookworm . . . You weren't reading lying down, were you?

JENNY Huh-uh. At my desk.

HENRY That's right. Bad for your eyes to read lying down. You hold the book too close.

JENNY (*Affectionately*) I know. You told me a dozen times.

HENRY Brought ya something . . . (*He produces the pear, which he has kept hidden from her.* JENNY *shows pleased surprise, bounces off the rail.*)

JENNY Oh boy! . . . Thanks. (*They both sit on the rail;* GRACE *watches them tenderly.* JENNY *brings the pear to her mouth and opens her jaws around it for a delicious bite.*)

GRACE Ah, ah, ah, young lady. Not till after dinner. (JENNY *is just starting to bite as her mother's warning catches her. Her mouth remains opened longingly, but she is obviously going to obey.*)

GRACE We're going to eat in an hour. You'll spoil your dinner. (JENNY *reluctantly lowers the pear from her mouth. She shines it on the leg of her jeans, then regards it briefly before handing it over to* GRACE, *who has moved in for it.*)

GRACE (*Going in*) I'll set the table.

JENNY (*Following* GRACE *into the house*) Can I go over to Dick's and play till dinner?

INTERIOR THE LIVING ROOM—DAY

(GRACE *deposits the pear in a bowl;* HENRY *has followed* JENNY *in.*)

GRACE All right . . . but don't get any farther away. (JENNY *starts, gets almost to the door, then remembers something. She turns back to* HENRY.)

JENNY   Dick and I decided to get married. (*Her delivery is very matter-of-fact. A simple question settled.* HENRY'S *eyebrows rise, but he quickly conceals his surprise and amusement.*)

HENRY   (*Gravely*)   Right away?

JENNY   Of course not! When we grow up.

HENRY   Do you think Dick can support you all right?

JENNY   Sure, he's gonna be a pilot and I'm gonna be a stewardess.

HENRY   Then I approve. Can I be best man?

JENNY   No, silly! You have to give me away. Haven't you ever seen a wedding?

HENRY   Only my own . . . and I was very nervous then.

JENNY   Oh! You're always fooling. (*Her tone is one of slight impatience mixed with tolerant amusement for this father who cannot comprehend a serious subject. She moves to the door, her hand upon it.*)

HENRY   What does your mother think of your engagement?

JENNY   I told her already. She said it's fine, if I can stand my mother-in-law.

GRACE   (*Reprovingly*)   Jenny! (*But* JENNY *is out the door and away.* GRACE *stares after her for a moment, then meets* HENRY'S *eye. He is grinning broadly. In a second,* GRACE *gives a half-embarrassed smile.*)

INTERIOR LIVING ROOM—ANOTHER ANGLE— GRACE, HENRY

(*As* HENRY *moves to a small table, picks up the afternoon paper and settles himself in the armchair opposite the couch.*)

HENRY   Have to be careful what you say. She doesn't forget a thing. (*He unfolds the paper in front of him and starts to read.* GRACE *is looking at the front door, vaguely troubled. There is silence for a few seconds.*)

GRACE   (*Bit troubled*)   She's growing up so fast lately.

HENRY   (*After pause, preoccupied*)   Uh-huh.

GRACE   I found her trying out my lipstick the other day . . .

HENRY   (*Still reading*)   Oh? . . . What'd you do?

GRACE   Nothing, of course . . . There's no harm in it. But it gave me a shock when I looked at her.

HENRY   Must've looked like a clown.

CLOSE SHOT—GRACE

(*As she continues to work at her darning. Her face is deeply and genuinely troubled.*)

GRACE   No . . . she didn't. She looked like a young lady. (*Pause*) Now she's talking about getting married.

MEDIUM CLOSE SHOT—HENRY

(*As he reluctantly lowers his paper and looks at* GRACE. *He obviously does not want to be drawn into this discussion, but the seriousness of* GRACE'S *tone compels him. He forces an amused laugh, then:*)

HENRY   When I was twelve I was gonna marry Flora Beesgartner and go be a fireman in Des Moines . . .

INTERIOR LIVING ROOM—MEDIUM SHOT—GRACE, HENRY

GRACE   I know it's only kid stuff . . . but . . . one day you watch them play at being grown-ups. You turn away—it seems for a moment only—and when you look again they've grown—suddenly.

HENRY   Don't worry. She's got years to think about marrying Dick —or anybody.

GRACE   (*Quietly*)   If she'll *ever* marry.

HENRY   (*Startled*)   What? (GRACE *puts down her darning. She hates what she knows she has to say.* HENRY *senses what is coming. They look at each other tensely for a moment.*)

GRACE   Who would there be? Who'll marry a girl with a club foot? (*The blow has fallen.* HENRY *folds his paper and thrusts it away with finality. His face is grave.*)

HENRY   Look, Grace, we've been all through this . . .

GRACE   We *haven't* been through it. We talked about it a hundred times. But it was always something off in the dim future . . . a problem we'd have to face *someday* . . . (*With despair*) Now it's here. She's not just a kid with a limp any more. She's a young lady with an ugly deformity. (*These words cost* GRACE *a terrible effort. But she has been worrying about the problem all day—since* JENNY's *announcement—and she is determined to state it in the bluntest possible way. The words strike* HENRY *like blows. He breathes deeply, abruptly rises, walks to the open screen door and looks out till he can regain control of himself. There are tears in* GRACE's *eyes*) We can't go on putting it off, Henry . . . (*He goes on fighting for control, becoming more and more subdued*) You can't pretend you haven't been worried about it— I've seen it . . . (*Pause.* HENRY *returns. There is no conviction in his protests.*)

HENRY   She still seems like such a baby to me.

GRACE   Only because you want her to be. So do I. But we can't fool ourselves much longer. We've got to do something.

HENRY   What?

GRACE   Something we should've done long before this. (*She looks over at the phone, and he follows her eyes, looking too.*)

INTERIOR LIVING ROOM—ANOTHER ANGLE— GRACE, HENRY

(*Camera shooting from point near telephone table as* HENRY *crosses to it. He moves slowly, reluctantly. He picks up the telephone receiver, dials one number, then breaks the connection with his finger. Still holding the receiver, he turns to* GRACE.)

HENRY   She's so happy now . . . Can't we wait? . . . Just a little longer?

GRACE   (*Looking up*) Until she really wants to get married? There'll be dates—*real* dates, sooner than you think . . . and then the *real* humiliation begins . . . one hurt after another . . . How long will she take *that* before she starts to hate us?

MEDIUM CLOSE SHOT—HENRY, PHONE

(*As his face reflects his decision. Abruptly, he begins to dial the phone, his fingers moving swiftly.*)

DISSOLVE TO

INTERIOR FALGREN LIVING ROOM—MEDIUM
SHOT—GRACE, HENRY, DR. BAIRD

(*They are seated in conversation as scene opens.* GRACE *and*
HENRY *have changed clothes. They are better dressed than
we saw them yesterday, but still informal.* DR. BAIRD *is about
fifty, a bit stout, balding. He has a pleasant voice and manner. He wears a tie and suit, the coat of which rests across
his knees.*)

HENRY   We asked you to come out here because we don't want
to get her all upset unless there's a real reason . . . unless you can
really help her.

BAIRD   I wish we could have done this four years ago . . . Remember, when you first moved to town, I said . . .

HENRY (*Sharply*)   I know. We're not asking you to remind us of
anything. We did what we thought was best for her . . . The question
is, what can you do now?

BAIRD (*Not taking offense*)   I'll tell you what I want you to do.
Take her to a specialist—a Dr. Keller, in the city. I've worked with
him before.

HENRY   What will he do?

BAIRD   That's for Dr. Keller to say after he makes a thorough
examination. He may want her to wear braces. It may mean an operation.

GRACE   But you think he can help her?

BAIRD   Yes, I think . . .

(*Suddenly we hear children's laughter and sounds of running. A boy about twelve runs through from the kitchen
across the living room and out the screen door. This is* DICK,
the neighbor boy. Close after him comes JENNY, *limping, but
running at a good clip.* HENRY *reaches out and stops her.*)

HENRY   All right, just hold on a minute, young lady. Jenny, do you
remember Dr. Baird?

JENNY   Uh-huh. When I got an infection, he lanced my ear. That
hurt!

BAIRD   I'm sorry to leave a bad impression on you, Jenny. You're a good patient.

HENRY   (*Putting arm around her*)   Jenny, we've been talking about you . . . Would you like to take a trip to the city? To see about your foot?

JENNY   What for?

GRACE   To . . . to change it. To make it like your other one.

(JENNY *is not sure how to take all this. She senses that the adults are all very serious. Too serious. She looks around and settles on* DR. BAIRD *as the instigator. She addresses him.*)

JENNY   What would they do to it?

BAIRD   Perhaps give you a brace. Maybe a little operation.

JENNY   (*Shaking head*)   Huh-uh. It'd hurt.

BAIRD   Not so much.

JENNY   I don't wanna go t' the hospital. Or wear an old brace . . . This is summer vacation!

HENRY   Wouldn't you like your foot to be . . . (*Painfully*) . . . like everybody else's?

CLOSE SHOT—JENNY

JENNY   (*Emphatically*)   No . . . I don't mind it. Lord Byron had a club foot and he swam the Hellespont.

BAIRD   Do you like Byron, Jenny?

JENNY   He's my favorite. Especially the one that goes:

> "Maid of Athens, ere we part,
> Give, oh give me back my heart."

(*Her delivery is slightly sing-song, but she has a genuine feeling for the poem, and has not learned it merely by rote.*)

INTERIOR LIVING ROOM—MEDIUM CLOSE SHOT—JENNY, DR. BAIRD

BAIRD   That's very pretty. Do you know this one?

> "She walks in beauty, like the night
> Of cloudless climes and starry skies.
> And all that's best of dark and bright
> Meet in her aspect, and her eyes."

(*He speaks the lines with a surprising sensitivity.* JENNY *listens with rapt admiration.* DR. BAIRD *has just risen about a thousand percent in her estimation.*)

JENNY   That's beautiful . . . (*Defensively*) And he had a club foot.

BAIRD (*Gently*)   If Lord Byron were to live now . . . instead of long ago . . . do you think he'd keep his club foot, by choice? (JENNY *regards the doctor solemnly. This is a whole new question. Camera moves in on her as she considers.*)

DISSOLVE TO

EXTERIOR FALLGREN FRONT PORCH—EVENING— MEDIUM SHOT—JENNY, DICK

(*They are sitting in a large, old-fashioned wooden porch swing, hung from the porch ceiling by chains, one of which squeaks gently as they rock slowly back and forth. They sit toward opposite ends of the swing. Lighting is very low key.*)

JENNY   She walks in beauty, like the night of cloudless climes and starry skies . . . Isn't that beautiful?

DICK   It's okay . . .

JENNY   I've decided where we're going to live after we get married.

DICK   Oh?

(*They speak without looking at each other, not out of embarrassment, of which they feel none at all, but because their friendship establishes a deep communication which does not require the ogling tactics of adults.*)

JENNY   Right here in Oakville . . . What's wrong with that?

DICK   I can't be a pilot *here*. We'll have to go some place they've got a big airport, where the mainliners land.

JENNY   Did you tell your folks that we decided to get married?
DICK   Ummm.
JENNY   I told mine. They said that was fine. (*Remembering his evasive mumble*) Did you tell yours?
DICK   Yeah. Who was that guy that was here today?
JENNY   Dr. Baird . . . What did your parents say?
DICK   Nothin'. Grown-ups are crazy anyway. Who's Dr. Baird?
JENNY   Just a doctor. He wants me to go to the city about my foot. (DICK *looks at her, suddenly interested.*)
DICK   You gonna do it?
JENNY   I don't think so. It's okay . . . Besides, it'd hurt.
DICK   Maybe you oughta . . .
JENNY   Why?

CLOSE SHOT—DICK

(*He is uncomfortable. He carefully examines a skinned place on the back of one knuckle while he speaks.*)

DICK   Aw . . . when I told my folks we were gonna get married, they laughed.
JENNY   Did you tell 'em we didn't mean *now*?
DICK   Sure . . . I told 'em I was gonna be a pilot and you were gonna be a stewardess.

TIGHT TWO SHOT—JENNY, DICK

JENNY   (*After pause*)   Well?
DICK   They said they never saw a stewardess with a club foot. (*They look at each other for a moment, very serious about this one cloud in their otherwise beautiful future.*)

DISSOLVE TO

CLOSE SHOT—DAY—JENNY'S LEGS AND FEET

(*Her left foot is turned inward, with the toes curled inward. Her left calf is considerably thinner than her right one—an effect achieved by the use of a cosmetic stocking on the right leg.*)

INTERIOR DOCTOR'S TREATMENT ROOM—MEDIUM
SHOT—JENNY, GRACE, DR. KELLER

(JENNY *sits on the edge of the treatment table, her legs extended before her, while* DR. KELLER *examines them.* GRACE *is seated in a chair to one side.* DR. KELLER *is around forty, tall, slender.* JENNY *holds a thin book in her hands, the object in point from story opening.*)

JENNY (*Holding up book*) Dr. Baird gave me this. It's a book of poems . . . by everybody.

KELLER (*Continuing his examination*) Dr. Baird's a pretty nice guy.

JENNY Do you have a favorite poem?

KELLER (*Looking up*) I'm afraid I've always been too busy reading textbooks . . . All right, Jenny, you can go out in the office with Miss Nelson for a while. (JENNY *slides off the table, standing.*)

JENNY It's all right. You can talk in front of me.

KELLER (*Laughing*) I'm sure we can. But I'm sure you'd find your poetry book much more interesting.

GRACE Run along, Jenny. We won't be long.

JENNY Okay. (*She exits, closing the door behind her.* DR. KELLER *turns and crosses over to a position nearer to* GRACE.)

INTERIOR TREATMENT ROOM—ANOTHER ANGLE
—GRACE, DR. KELLER

KELLER First of all, I'll say that we *can* help her . . . but it would have been so much easier if we had seen her years ago . . . Why didn't you take her to someone when she was a baby?

GRACE Well, until she was six, we lived in the Midwest, on a little farm way out in the country. We hardly ever saw a doctor.

KELLER When did you first notice her foot?

GRACE Not until she started to walk, really . . . I mean, it was always turned in, but all babies' feet are turned in. She limped as soon as she started to walk, but her grandmother—my mother, that is—said that it was nothing, that she'd grow out of it.

CLOSE SHOT—DR. KELLER

(*As he very forcefully—but without anger—makes this point.*)

KELLER Mrs. Fallgren . . . that one phrase has caused a lot of pain, a lot of suffering . . . "They'll grow out of it." (*Shaking his head*) I don't know how many times doctors hear that . . . You can *never* grow out of a deformity. It will only become harder and harder to correct.

CLOSE SHOT—GRACE

GRACE I suppose we did wrong . . . but by the time we could see that it wasn't getting any better, we had all just accepted the situation. Jenny never seemed hampered . . . She got around as quickly as anyone, and she was happy. People in the country are used to things like that. Everyone just said that she had a club foot, and let it go at that . . . We didn't even know that something could be done.

MEDIUM CLOSE SHOT—DR. KELLER

(*As he moves to a wall chart showing the bony structure of the leg and foot. He uses appropriate gestures as he explains to* GRACE.)

KELLER Mrs. Fallgren, I wish we could make everyone in the country understand what I'm about to tell you . . . Because what you call "club foot" is a very common condition. It's just a lay term for any kind of foot deformity. Some turn out, some turn in. With some the bone structure is shortened, and so on. Many of these cases are very mild, hardly noticable . . . (*With emphasis*) But all of them can be corrected. Almost always it can be done without surgery . . . if the baby is taken in time. Before the child is a year old.
GRACE (*Surprised*) Before one year?
KELLER That's right. The earlier, the better. You see all these bones in the foot, here. While these are still soft and pliable, they can

be wedged into a normal shape quite easily with braces and special shoes. The older the child gets, the more solidly the bones set . . . and the more difficult, and expensive, it becomes to make any improvement.

INTERIOR TREATMENT ROOM—MEDIUM SHOT—
DR. KELLER, GRACE

(GRACE *looks very disturbed at the mention of surgery.*)

GRACE   But you said you could help Jenny . . . She's not too old for the braces, is she?

KELLER   She's twelve, isn't she?

GRACE   That's right . . . be thirteen this December.

KELLER   (*Shaking head slightly*)   I doubt that braces would do the job . . . We can try, if you like. But at this age, it would be a long, difficult process, with no assurance of success.

GRACE   How long?

KELLER   Years . . . In her case I'd say that an operation would be better—both quicker and more certain. Is she greatly afraid of the idea of surgery?

GRACE   (*Attempting a smile, little success*)   Not nearly so much as I am. What kind of operation do you do for club foot?

KELLER   There again it depends on the foot . . . on the individual case. Sometimes it's just the matter of cutting a tendon that's too short.

GRACE   But in Jenny's case?

KELLER   In Jenny's case, the operation is called an arthrodesis. It's a fusion of the bones into a normal position.

GRACE   Is it very expensive?

KELLER   Not terribly . . . considering the amount of good it accomplishes. I'll tell you this, however—it will cost many times more than it would have to correct the condition when she was a baby.

(GRACE *is resigned to the idea of the operation, but she cannot keep herself from continuing to raise small objections.*)

GRACE   I'll have to call my husband. He couldn't get away from work to come with us.

KELLER   By all means, call him and discuss it with him.

GRACE   What are the chances of success? In the operation, I mean.
KELLER   (*Smiling*)   Excellent.
GRACE   Will it hurt her? Will there be a lot of pain?

CLOSE SHOT—DR. KELLER

KELLER   During the operation, she'll feel nothing. There will be a certain amount of soreness afterward, till the healing is well started.
GRACE   We've always hated to have her hurt in any way.
KELLER   (*Gently*)   I'd say that the operation will be much less painful than spending even one evening on the sidelines at a high-school dance.

INTERIOR TREATMENT ROOM—MEDIUM SHOT— DR. KELLER, GRACE

(*As* JENNY *opens the door and thrusts her head through.*)

JENNY   Hey, you said you wouldn't be long.
GRACE   Come in, honey. We're all through. (JENNY *enters and crosses to her mother's chair. It is near the window. We are apparently in a tall building, for the view is unobstructed; perhaps a rooftop or two in sight*) Dr. Keller says your foot can be fixed . . . good as new. But you'll have to have an operation.
JENNY   Now . . . in summer vacation?
GRACE   I'm afraid so.

> (JENNY *is very disappointed and alarmed at the interruption of her vacation, and by all the fears that the operation calls up. She and* GRACE *and* DR. KELLER *regard each other silently for a moment. Gradually, we become aware of the sound of a plane flying overhead. It grows louder, obviously a multiengined passenger plane on its run. It passes overhead as* JENNY *moves to the window, craning her neck upward to get a glimpse of it. Gradually, the sound fades.* JENNY *looks back into the room, first at her mother, then at* DR. KELLER.)

JENNY   (*Simple acceptance*)   Okay.

DISSOLVE TO

MONTAGE—JENNY'S PRE-OPERATION EXAM

    A. MEDIUM CLOSE SHOT—JENNY UNDER X-RAY
        MACHINE

    B. CLOSE SHOT—JENNY'S ARM AND BLOOD-
        PRESSURE GAUGE

        (*As the tubing around her arm is inflated and the
        needle of the gauge jumps up to indicate her blood
        pressure.*)

    C. MEDIUM CLOSE SHOT—DR. KELLER
        (*As he studies the x-ray plates of* JENNY's *foot.*)

DISSOLVE TO

INTERIOR HOSPITAL ROOM—DAY—MEDIUM SHOT
—JENNY, GRACE, HENRY

(JENNY *lies on a gurney, ready to be wheeled to surgery.*
GRACE *and* HENRY *are doing their best to be bright and cheer-*
ful, but their faces and manners reveal their anxiety. JENNY
seems much the calmest of the three.)

    HENRY Dick says to tell you you're not missin' anything. The
filtering plant broke down and they closed the swimming pool for a
while.

    GRACE And Marlene says not to worry about your goldfish. She
feeds them every day . . . (*Weak effort at humor*) In fact, I think she
feeds them three times a day. They're getting fat as little whales.
(*This effort amuses no one, and the conversation lapses into silence.*
HENRY *massages one ear vigorously.* GRACE *examines the floor with*
great interest. JENNY *regards them fondly.*)

    JENNY Don't worry.

    GRACE (*Looking up quickly*) Why, we're not worried, honey . . .
There's nothing to worry about.

    JENNY Dr. Keller's funny. I taught him my poem, you know, by
Lord Byron . . . So he learned one and taught it to me. You wanta hear
it?

HENRY Sure, punkin'. (*As* JENNY *starts to recite, a* NURSE *enters and starts to wheel the gurney out into the hall.*)

JENNY
"Timothy Fry could fly without wings,
But he went around knocking down chimneys and things."

(JENNY *is wheeled through the door,* HENRY *and* GRACE *following. Camera pans with* JENNY *to the door, then holds on the empty doorway as* JENNY's *voice fades down the hall.*)

JENNY (*Voice fading*)
"He lived in a belfry, with a number of bats;
'Cause they hung upside down they could never wear hats."

DISSOLVE TO

INTERIOR SURGERY—MEDIUM SHOT—
ARTHRODESIS OPERATION

DISSOLVE TO

CLOSE SHOT—JENNY

(*As she struggles to wake from the anesthetic. She is in a hospital bed. Her eyes are closed.*)

JENNY (*Faintly disconnected*) Timothy fire-fly . . . without any rings . . . (*Abruptly her eyes pop open. She struggles for an instant to focus them. As she succeeds, a smile breaks through.*)

CLOSE SHOT—GRACE, HENRY

(*Their faces are close together. Camera shooting from* JENNY's *point of view. The image shimmers for a moment, then comes clear. They are both smiling happily.*)

GRACE Jenny . . . Jenny, it worked fine. The operation was fine.
HENRY Dr. Keller says your foot will be just like normal.
JENNY (*Faintly*) Thank you . . . Timothy.

(GRACE *and* HENRY *exchange smiles. They are weeping with happiness.*)

DISSOLVE TO

EXTERIOR FALLGREN FRONT PORCH—CLOSE
SHOT—PORCH RAIL

(*As a boy's baseball bat collides with it, then is withdrawn,
collides, and is withdrawn again. With the rhythmic thump
of the bat is alternated the squeak of the chain supporting
the porch swing. Together the sounds make a sleepy summer
music.*)

EXTERIOR FALLGREN PORCH—MEDIUM SHOT—
JENNY, DICK

(*As they rock back and forth in the swing,* DICK *using the
baseball bat against the porch railing to keep them in motion.*)

DICK   I'll bet it didn't hurt as much as when I fell off the horse and
broke my arm.
JENNY   (*Shrugging*)   Maybe not . . . I didn't feel anything when
they did it. They told me to start counting, and I never even got to
four . . . I just felt all dreamy.

(DICK *regards her with interest. He is just a little jealous of
her dramatic experience. He would like to cap her experience
with one of his own, but at the moment* JENNY *holds all the
advantages. The evidence—her foot still encased in a cast—
rests on the swing between them.* DICK *cannot help looking
at it with respect. With the baseball bat he very gently and
tentatively taps on it.*)

DICK   That hurt?
JENNY   Huh-uh. It wouldn't hurt if you did it ten times that hard.
DICK   How long you gonna wear it?
JENNY   Three months.
DICK   Gee, you get to go back to school in it. (JENNY *nods. Her
manner indicates she finds this prospect a happy one. The cast will be
a great attention-getter at school.*)

JENNY Maybe it'll be four months. I go to see Dr. Keller in three months, and he'll take x-rays to see whether to take it off then.

DICK And your foot's gonna be just like anybody's?

JENNY Uh-huh . . . My leg won't, though. Not for quite a while, anyway. 'Cause the muscles haven't developed . . . but it's just got to be ready by Halloween . . .

DICK Why?

JENNY 'Cause you're going to take me to the party at school.

DICK Oh . . . sure . . .

JENNY You thought up your costume yet?

DICK Why? It's still four months away.

JENNY (*Seriously*) We have to plan for the future, Dick.

DICK Oh, well, I guess I'll go as a pilot.

JENNY That isn't Halloweeny at all!

DICK Doesn't matter. And you can be a stewardess.

JENNY (*Thoughtfully*) I don't know if I want to be a stewardess any more.

DICK (*Worried*) You mean—not ever?

JENNY Unh-unh . . . I think maybe I'm going to be a dancing teacher.

DICK (*Surprised*) But what about me?

JENNY What *about* you? Why don't you be a dancing teacher too?

MEDIUM CLOSE SHOT—JENNY, DICK

(*We see only their faces and upper bodies as they confront this moment of crisis.* DICK's *nose wrinkles as he considers this heretical suggestion as to his future.*)

DICK Dancing teacher! (*Then*) Naw . . . you can do what you want. But I'm gonna be a pilot.

JENNY Well . . . I guess you can do what *you* want to . . . (*A silence begins to grow . . . Finally, he rises.*)

DICK Well . . . good-bye, Jenny.

JENNY (*Surprised*) You going?

DICK Yeah . . .

JENNY But I thought you were going to stay for the afternoon . . .

DICK Oh . . . well . . . I got these things to do and think about . . . and . . . (*Pause*) I brought you a present. (*He gives it.*)

JENNY Me? What is it, Dick?

DICK Oh, just something—well, so long . . .

JENNY So long. (*He goes. She opens her present.*)

INSERT: STEWARDESS' "WINGS"

DISSOLVE TO

INTERIOR FALLGREN LIVING ROOM—NIGHT—
MEDIUM SHOT—HENRY, GRACE, DICK

(GRACE *and* HENRY *are seated, reading the evening paper.*
DICK *squats on the floor. He is dressed in partial masquerade
for a Halloween party. He holds a Halloween noisemaker in
his hand, examining it. Finally, he gives it a trial whirl, shat-
tering the silence.* GRACE *and* HENRY *look up.*)

HENRY (*Slight irony*) That's a good one.

DICK (*Glancing upward*) Why doesn't she hurry up?

GRACE Girls are always late, Dick. You'd better get used to it.

HENRY You've got plenty of time yet. I can drive you over there
in five minutes. What time's the party over?

DICK Ten o'clock.

HENRY You phone up if it's going to be any later than that. I
don't want to drive over there and sit in the car for half an hour.

GRACE What've you been doing with yourself the last few weeks,
Dick? You haven't been around after school very much . . .

DICK (*Softly, after a difficult pause*) I've been—taking dancing
lessons. (GRACE *and* HENRY *exchange an amused look.*)

HENRY You like it?

DICK (*Not so sure*) Yeah—it's all right.

(*Suddenly we hear the offstage sound of* JENNY *descending
the stairs, which are off stage. She is wearing heels, and they
click steadily, rhythmically, perfectly spaced, as she descends.
All eyes in the room are turned to follow her.*)

CLOSE SHOT—BOTTOM OF STAIRWAY

(*As* JENNY's *legs and feet walk into shot and turn toward the
living room. The high heels she wears are those of her mother,*

slightly too big for her, but they reveal a pair of perfectly normal feet.)

INTERIOR LIVING ROOM—MEDIUM SHOT—
ANOTHER ANGLE

(*Showing the stairs, with* JENNY *standing at the bottom of them, the other three looking at her. She wears a party dress, the stewardess wings are conspicuous instead of a brooch.*)

DICK (*Brief laugh*) Boy, do you look funny in those shoes.

JENNY (*Unperturbed*) I know it. I just wore them down here to show off. (*She steps out of the high heels and pads over to the end of the couch, where her own shoes are resting. They are a pair of ballet slippers which she quickly slips on.* DICK *clambers to his feet first, then* GRACE *and* HENRY *rise.* JENNY *picks up her coat.*)

DICK C'mon, let's get goin'. (JENNY *kisses her mother good-bye, then walks across the front door with* DICK, *moving without the trace of a limp.* DICK *opens the front door.*)

HENRY The car's out front. Run and get in it . . . I'll get my coat.

(JENNY *and* DICK *exit, closing the door behind them.* HENRY *gets his coat from the closet, and* GRACE *helps him to put it on. As they turn toward the door,* GRACE *bends and picks up the high-heeled shoes.*)

MEDIUM CLOSE SHOT—GRACE, HENRY

(*As they regard the shoes.*)

HENRY It won't be long before she doesn't look silly in them. (*Happy smile*) What's that Lord Byron poem she's always spouting?

GRACE (*Returning smile*) She walks in beauty . . .

FADE OUT

DISCUSSION

1. What indications do you find that the Fallgrens are an affectionate, closely-knit family? Why is it important that you be aware of this from the beginning of the play?

2. How does the playwright establish the fact of Jenny's deformity without referring to it directly? Do you feel that a more direct reference would have served as well?

3. Why had the Fallgrens postponed treatment for Jenny's deformity in the past? What prompts them to consider it now? Explain why Mrs. Fallgren's words "strike Henry like blows."

4. Describe Jenny's attitude toward her deformity. Is it in any way unusual? In what respect does Jenny's attitude change during the play? Why?

5. Why does Mrs. Fallgren continue to "raise small objections" to the operation, even after she has resigned herself to it? What causes Jenny to overcome her last-minute hesitancy and agree to the operation with a simple "okay"?

6. How is it a comment on their relationship that it should be Jenny who is reassuring her parents, just before the operation, instead of the other way around?

7. What is the dramatic purpose of the poem that Jenny recites as she is being wheeled to the operating room?

8. Why doesn't the play end with the report that the operation has been a success? What remains to be shown?

9. How does the author use the occasion of the masquerade party to clarify the changing relationship between Jenny and Dick?

10. What is symbolized in Dick's gift to Jenny? In Mr. Fallgren's final reference to Lord Byron's poem?

11. In what sense has Jenny always "walk(ed) in beauty?"

12. Discuss the nature of the conflict in this play. Does it develop within a character? As the result of some outside force? Or what?

TOPICS FOR WRITING

According to a centuries-old definition, the function of literature is both to entertain and instruct the reader. Explain how *She Walks in Beauty* accomplishes these two purposes.

Use one of the following titles as the point of departure for a theme: (a) Judging by Appearances, (b) The Power of Persuasion, (c) The High Cost of Ignorance. You may relate your comments to the play directly, or to your own feelings and experiences.

Read Lord Byron's brief poem, *She Walks in Beauty* and explain its relationship to the theme of this play.

I L E

Eugene O'Neill

Ben, the cabin boy
The Steward
Captain Keeney
Slocum, second mate
Mrs. Keeney
Joe, a harpooner
Members of the crew of the steam whaler Atlantic Queen

Eugene O'Neill (1888-1953)

Eugene O'Neill was born in New York City in 1888, the son of a well-known actor. During his childhood he traveled with his parents on their road tours, gaining an intimate acquaintance with the traditions of the theater. After a brief period of study at Princeton University, O'Neill tried his hand at a number of jobs, including acting, gold-prospecting, seafaring, and newspaper reporting. In 1914 he enrolled in a writing course at Harvard, and his career as a professional writer began soon after. The first of O'Neill's plays to be acted in a theater was Bound East for Cardiff, performed in Provincetown in 1916. By the time of his death in 1953, he had written approximately forty plays and had received a number of literary awards, among them the coveted Pulitzer Prize for drama.

Ile is one of O'Neill's earliest plays. In this brief tragedy you will see how a skillful playwright can suggest the inner workings of a man's mind without ever revealing his thoughts directly.

ILE

SCENE CAPTAIN KEENEY's *cabin on board the steam whaling ship* Atlantic Queen—*a small, square compartment about eight feet high with a skylight in the center looking out on the poop deck. On the left [the stern of the ship] a long bench with rough cushions is built in against the wall. In front of the bench, a table. Over the bench, several curtained portholes.*

In the rear, left, a door leading to the captain's sleeping quarters. To the right of the door a small organ, looking as if it were brand new, is placed against the wall.

On the right, to the rear, a marble-topped sideboard. On the sideboard, a woman's sewing basket. Farther forward, a doorway leading to the companion way, and past the officer's quarters to the main deck.

In the center of the room, a stove. From the middle of the ceiling a hanging lamp is suspended. The walls of the cabin are painted white.

There is no rolling of the ship, and the light which comes through the skylight is sickly and faint, indicating one of those gray days of calm when ocean and sky are alike dead. The silence is unbroken except for the measured tread of some one walking up and down on the poop deck overhead.

It is nearing two bells—one o'clock—in the afternoon of a day in the year 1895.

At the rise of the curtain there is a moment of intense silence. Then the STEWARD *enters and commences to clear the table of the few dishes which still remain on it after the* CAPTAIN's *dinner. He is an old, grizzled man dressed in dungaree pants, a sweater, and a woolen cap with ear flaps. His manner is sullen and angry. He stops stacking up the plates and casts a quick glance upward at the skylight; then tiptoes over to the closed door in rear and listens with his ear pressed to the crack. What he hears makes his face darken and he mutters a furious curse. There is a noise from the doorway on the right and he darts back to the table.*

BEN enters. He is an over-grown, gawky boy with a long, pinched face. He is dressed in sweater, fur cap, etc. His teeth are chattering with the cold and he hurries to the stove, where he stands for a moment shivering, blowing on his hands, slapping them against his sides, on the verge of crying.

THE STEWARD [*In relieved tones—seeing who it is.*]   Oh, 'tis you, is it? What're ye shiverin' 'bout? Stay by the stove where ye belong and ye'll find no need of chatterin'.

BEN   It's c-c-cold. [*Trying to control his chattering teeth—derisively.*] Who d'ye think it were—the Old Man?

THE STEWARD—[*Makes a threatening move—*BEN *shrinks away.*]

None o' your lip, young un, or I'll learn ye. [*More kindly.*] Where was it ye've been all o' the time—the fo'c's'tle?

BEN   Yes.

THE STEWARD   Let the Old Man see ye up for'ard monkeyshinin' with the hands and ye'll get a hidin' ye'll not forget in a hurry.

BEN   Aw, he don't see nothin'. [*A trace of awe in his tones—he glances upward.*] He just walks up and down like he didn't notice nobody—and stares at the ice to the no'the'ard.

THE STEWARD   [*The same tone of awe creeping into his voice.*] He's always starin' at the ice. [*In a sudden rage, shaking his fist at the skylight.*] Ice, ice, ice! Damn him and damn the ice! Holdin' us in for nigh on a year—nothin' to see but ice—stuck in it like a fly in molasses!

BEN   [*Apprehensively.*]   Ssshh! He'll hear ye.

THE STEWARD   [*Raging.*]   Aye, damn him, and damn the Arctic seas, and damn this stinkin' whalin' ship of his, and damn me for a fool to ever ship on it! [*Subsiding as if realizing the uselessness of this outburst—shaking his head—slowly, with deep conviction.*] He's a hard man—as hard a man as ever sailed the seas.

BEN   [*Solemnly.*]   Aye.

THE STEWARD   The two years we all signed up for are done this day. Blessed Christ! Two years o' this dog's life, and no luck in the fishin', and the hands half starved with the food runnin' low, rotten as it is; and not a sign of him turnin' back for home! [*Bitterly.*] Home! I begin to doubt if ever I'll set foot on land again. [*Excitedly.*] What is it he thinks he' goin' to do? Keep us all up here after our time is worked out till the last man of us is starved to death or frozen? We've grub enough hardly to last out the voyage back if we started now. What are the men goin' to do 'bout it? Did ye hear any talk in the fo'c's'tle?

BEN   [*Going over to him—in a half whisper.*]   They said if he don't put back south for home today they're goin' to mutiny.

THE STEWARD   [*With grim satisfaction.*]   Mutiny? Aye, 'tis the only thing they can do; and serve him right after the manner he's treated them—'s if they wern't no better nor dogs.

BEN   The ice is all broke up to s'uth'ard. They's clear water 's far 's you can see. He ain't got no excuse for not turnin' back for home, the men says.

THE STEWARD   [*Bitterly.*]   He won't look nowheres but no'the'ard where they's only the ice to see. He don't want to see no clear water. All he thinks on is gittin' the ile—'s if it was our fault he ain't had good luck with the whales. [*Shaking his head.*] I think the man's mighty nigh losin' his senses.

BEN [*Awed.*] D'you really think he's crazy?

THE STEWARD Aye, it's the punishment o' God on him. Did ye ever hear of a man who wasn't crazy do the things he does? [*Pointing to the door in rear.*] Who but a man that's mad would take his woman —and as sweet a woman as ever was—on a stinkin' whalin' ship to the Arctic seas to be locked in· by the rotten ice for nigh on a year, and maybe lose her senses forever—for it's sure she'll never be the same again.

BEN [*Sadly.*] She useter be awful nice to me before—— [*His eyes grow wide and frightened.*] she got—like she is.

THE STEWARD Aye, she was good to all of us. 'Twould have been hell on board without her, for he's a hard man—a hard, hard man— a driver if there ever was one. [*With a grim laugh.*] I hope he's satisfied now—drivin' her on till she's near lost her mind. And who could blame her? 'Tis a God's wonder we're not a ship full of crazed people —with the damned ice all the time, and the quiet so thick you're afraid to hear your own voice.

BEN [*With a frightened glance toward the door on right.*] She don't never speak to me no more—jest looks at me 's if she didn't know me.

THE STEWARD She don't know no one—but him. She talks to him —when she does talk—right enough.

BEN She does nothin' all day long now but sit and sew—and then she cries to herself without makin' no noise. I've seen her.

THE STEWARD Aye, I could hear her through the door a while back.

BEN [*Tiptoes over to the door and listens.*] She's cryin' now.

THE STEWARD [*Furiously—shaking his fist.*] God send his soul to hell for the devil he is!

[*There is the noise of someone coming slowly down the companionway stairs.* THE STEWARD *hurries to his stacked up dishes. He is so nervous from fright that he knocks off the top one, which falls and breaks on the floor. He stands aghast, trembling with dread.* BEN *is violently rubbing off the organ*

with a piece of cloth which he has snatched from his pocket.
CAPTAIN KEENEY *appears in the doorway on right and comes
into the cabin, removing his fur cap as he does so. He is a
man of about forty, around five-ten in height but looking
much shorter on account of the enormous proportions of his
shoulders and chest. His face is massive and deeply lined,
with gray-blue eyes of a bleak hardness, and a tightly
clenched, thin-lipped mouth. His thick hair is long and gray.
He is dressed in a heavy blue jacket and blue pants stuffed
into his seaboots.*

[*He is followed into the cabin by the* SECOND MATE, *a
rangy six-footer with a lean weather-beaten face. The* MATE
*is dressed about the same as the captain. He is a man of
thirty or so.*]

KEENEY [*Comes toward the* STEWARD—*with a stern look on his
face. The* STEWARD *is visibly frightened and the stack of dishes rattles
in his trembling hands.* KEENEY *draws back his fist and the* STEWARD
shrinks away. The fist is gradually lowered and KEENEY *speaks slowly.*]
'Twould be like hitting a worm. It is nigh on two bells, Mr. Steward,
and this truck not cleared yet.

THE STEWARD [*Stammering.*] Y-y-yes, sir.

KEENEY Instead of doin' your rightful work ye've been below
here gossipin' old woman's talk with that boy. [*To* BEN, *fiercely.*] Get
out o' this, you! Clean up the chart room. [BEN *darts past the* MATE *to
the open doorway.*] Pick up that dish, Mr. Steward!

THE STEWARD [*Doing so with difficulty.*] Yes, sir.

KEENEY The next dish you break, Mr. Steward, you take a bath
in the Bering Sea at the end of a rope.

THE STEWARD [*Trembling.*] Yes, sir. [*He hurries out. The* SECOND
MATE *walks slowly over to the* CAPTAIN.]

MATE I warn't 'specially anxious the man at the wheel should
catch what I wanted to say to you, sir. That's why I asked you to come
below.

KEENEY [*Impatiently.*] Speak your say, Mr. Slocum.

MATE [*Unconsciously lowering his voice.*] I'm afeard there'll be
trouble with the hands by the look o' things. They'll likely turn ugly,
every blessed one o' them, if you don't put back. The two years they
signed up for is up to-day.

KEENEY And d'you think you're tellin' me somethin' new, Mr. Slocum? I've felt it in the air this long time past. D'you think I've not seen their ugly looks and the grudgin' way they worked?

[*The door in rear is opened and* MRS. KEENEY *stands in the doorway. She is a slight, sweet-faced little woman primly dressed in black. Her eyes are red from weeping and her face drawn and pale. She takes in the cabin with a frightened glance and stands as if fixed to the spot by some nameless dread, clasping and unclasping her hands nervously. The two men turn and look at her.*]

KEENEY [*With rough tenderness.*] Well, Annie?

MRS. KEENEY [*As if awakening from a dream.*] David, I—— [*She is silent. The* MATE *starts for the doorway.*]

KEENEY [*Turning to him—sharply.*] Wait!

MATE Yes, sir.

KEENEY D'you want anything, Annie?

MRS. KEENEY [*After a pause, during which she seems to be endeavoring to collect her thoughts.*] I thought maybe—I'd go up on deck, David, to get a breath of fresh air. [*She stands humbly awaiting his permission. He and the* MATE *exchange a significant glance.*]

KEENEY It's too cold, Annie. You'd best stay below to-day. There's nothing to look at on deck—but ice.

MRS. KEENEY [*Monotonously.*] I know—ice, ice, ice! But there's nothing to see down here but these walls. [*She makes a gesture of loathing.*]

KEENEY You can play the organ, Annie.

MRS. KEENEY [*Dully.*] I hate the organ. It puts me in mind of home.

KEENEY [*A touch of resentment in his voice.*] I got it jest for you.

MRS. KENNEY [*Dully.*] I know. [*She turns away from them and walks slowly to the bench on left. She lifts up one of the curtains and looks through the porthole; then utters an exclamation of joy.*] Ah, water! Clear water! As far as I can see! How good it looks after all these months of ice! [*She turns round to them, her face transfigured with joy.*] Ah, now I must go up on deck and look at it, David.

KEENEY [*Frowning.*] Best not to-day, Annie. Best wait for a day when the sun shines.

MRS. KEENEY [*Desperately.*] But the sun never shines in this terrible place.

KEENEY [*A tone of command in his voice.*] Best not to-day, Annie.

MRS. KEENEY [*Crumbling before this command—abjectly.*] Very well, David. [*She stands there staring straight before her as if in a daze. The two men look at her uneasily.*]

KEENEY [*Sharply.*] Annie!

MRS. KEENEY [*Dully.*] Yes, David.

KEENEY Me and Mr. Slocum has business to talk about—ship's business.

MRS. KEENEY Very well, David. [*She goes slowly out, rear, and leaves the door three-quarters shut behind her.*]

KEENEY Best not have her on deck if they's goin' to be any trouble.

MATE Yes, sir.

KEENEY And trouble they's goin' to be. I feel it in my bones. [*Takes a revolver from the pocket of his coat and examines it.*] Got your'n?

MATE Yes, sir.

KEENEY Not that we'll have to use 'em—not if I know their breed of dog—jest to frighten 'em up a bit. [*Grimly.*] I ain't never been forced to use one yit; and trouble I've had by land and by sea 's long as I kin remember, and will have till my dyin' day, I reckon.

MATE [*Hesitatingly.*] Then you ain't goin'—to turn back?

KEENEY Turn back! Mr. Slocum, did you ever hear 'o me pointin' s'uth for home with only a measly four hundred barrel of ile in the hold?

MATE [*Hastily.*] No, sir—but the grub's gittin' low.

KEENEY They's enough to last a long time yit, if they're careful with it; and they's plenty o' water.

MATE They say it's not fit to eat—what's lett: and the two years they signed on fur is up to-day. They might make trouble for you in the courts when we git home.

KEENEY To hell with 'em! Let them make what law trouble they kin. I don't give a damn 'bout the money. I've got to git the ile! [*Glancing sharply at the MATE.*] You ain't turnin' no damned sea lawyer, be you, Mr. Slocum?

MATE [*Flushing.*] Not by a hell of a sight, sir.

KEENEY What do the fools want to go home fur now? Their share o' the four hundred barrel wouldn't keep 'em in chewin' terbacco.

MATE [*Slowly.*]   They wants to git back to their folks an' things,
I s'pose.

KEENEY [*Looking at him searchingly.*]   'N you want to turn back,
too. [*The* MATE *looks down confusedly before his sharp gaze.*] Don't
lie, Mr. Slocum. It's writ down plain in your eyes. [*With grim sarcasm.*]
I hope, Mr. Slocum, you ain't agoin' to jine the men agin me.

MATE [*Indignantly.*]   That ain't fair, sir, to say sich things.

KEENEY [*With satisfaction.*]   I warn't much afeared o' that, Tom.
You been with me nigh on ten year and I've learned ye whalin'. No
man kin say I ain't a good master, if I be a hard one.

MATE   I warn't thinkin' of myself, sir—'bout turnin' home, I mean.
[*Desperately.*] But Mrs. Keeney, sir—seems like she ain't jest satisfied
up here, ailin' like—what with the cold an' bad luck an' the ice an' all.

KEENEY [*His face clouding—rebukingly but not severely.*]   That's
my business, Mr. Slocum. I'll thank you to steer a clear course o' that.
[*A pause.*] The ice'll break up soon to no'th'ard. I could see it startin'
to-day. And when it goes and we git some sun Annie'll perk up. [*Another pause—then he bursts forth:*] It ain't the damned money what's
keepin' me up in the Northern seas, Tom. But I can't go back to Homeport with a measly four hundred barrel of ile. I'd die fust. I ain't never
came back home in all my days without a full ship. Ain't that truth?

MATE   Yes, sir; but this voyage you been icebound, an'——

KEENEY [*Scornfully.*]   And d'you s'pose any of 'em would believe
that—any o' them skippers I've beaten voyage after voyage? Can't
you hear 'em laughin' and sneerin'—Tibbots 'n' Harris 'n' Simms and
the rest—and all o' Homeport makin' fun o' me? "Dave Keeney what
boasts he's the best whalin' skipper out o' Homeport comin' back with
a measly four hundred barrel of ile?" [*The thought of this drives him
into a frenzy, and he smashes his fist down on the marble top of the
sideboard.*] Hell! I got to git the ile, I tell you. How could I figger
on this ice? It's never been so bad before in the thirty year I been
acomin' here. And now it's breakin' up. In a couple o' days it'll be all
gone. And they's whale here, plenty of 'em. I know they is and I ain't
never gone wrong yit. I got to git the ile! I got to git it in spite of all
hell, and by God, I ain't agoin' home till I do git it! [*There is the
sound of subdued sobbing from the door in rear. The two men stand
silent for a moment, listening. Then* KEENEY *goes over to the door and
looks in. He hesitates for a moment as if he were going to enter—then
closes the door softly.* JOE, *the harpooner, an enormous six-footer with*

a battered, ugly face, enters from right and stands waiting for the captain to notice him.]

KEENEY [*Turning and seeing him.*] Don't be standin' there like a gawk, Harpooner. Speak up!

JOE [*Confusedly.*] We want—the men, sir—they wants to send a depitation aft to have a word with you.

KEENEY [*Furiously.*] Tell 'em to go to——[*Checks himself and continues grimly.*] Tell 'em to come. I'll see 'em.

JOE Aye, aye, sir. [*He goes out.*]

KEENEY [*With a grim smile.*] Here it comes, the trouble you spoke of, Mr. Slocum, and we'll make short shift of it. It's better to crush such things at the start than let them make headway.

MATE [*Worriedly.*] Shall I wake up the First and Fourth, sir? We might need their help.

KEENEY No, let them sleep. I'm well able to handle this alone, Mr. Slocum. [*There is the shuffling of footsteps from outside and five of the crew crowd into the cabin, led by JOE. All are dressed alike— sweaters, seaboots, etc. They glance uneasily at the CAPTAIN, twirling their fur caps in their hands.*]

KEENEY [*After a pause.*] Well? Who's to speak fur ye?

JOE [*Stepping forward with an air of bravado.*] I be.

KEENEY [*Eyeing him up and down coldly.*] So you be. Then speak your say and be quick about it.

JOE [*Trying not to wilt before the CAPTAIN's glance and avoiding his eyes.*] The time we signed up for is done to-day.

KEENEY [*Icily.*] You're tellin' me nothin' I don't know.

JOE You ain't pintin' fur home yit, far 's we kin see.

KEENEY No, and I ain't agoin' to till this ship is full of ile.

JOE You can't go no further no'the with the ice afore ye.

KEENEY The ice is breaking up.

JOE [*After a slight pause during which the others mumble angrily to one another.*] The grub we're gittin' now is rotten.

KEENEY It's good enough fur ye. Better men than ye have eaten worse. [*There is a chorus of angry exclamations from the crowd.*]

JOE [*Encouraged by this support.*] We ain't agoin' to work no more less you puts back for home.

KEENEY [*Fiercely.*] You ain't ain't you?

JOE No; and the law courts'll say we was right.

KEENEY To hell with your law courts! We're at sea now and I'm the law on this ship. [*Edging up toward the harpooner.*] And every mother's son of you what don't obey orders goes in irons. [*There are more angry exclamations from the crew.* MRS. KEENEY *appears in the doorway in rear and looks on with startled eyes. None of the men notice her.*]

JOE [*With bravado.*]   Then we're agoin' to mutiny and take the old hooker home ourselves. Ain't we, boys? [*As he turns his head to look at the others,* KEENEY's *fist shoots out to the side of his jaw.* JOE *goes down in a heap and lies there.* MRS. KEENEY *gives a shriek and hides her face in her hands. The men pull out their sheath knives and start a rush, but stop when they find themselves confronted by the revolvers of* KEENEY *and the* MATE.]

KEENEY [*His eyes and voice snapping.*]   Hold still! [*The men stand huddled together in a sullen silence.* KEENEY's *voice is full of mockery.*] You've found out it ain't safe to mutiny on this ship, ain't you? And now git for'ard where ye belong, and—— [*He gives* JOE's *body a contemptuous kick.*] Drag him with you. And remember the first man of ye I see shirkin' I'll shoot dead as sure as there's a sea under us, and you can tell the rest the same. Git for'ard now! Quick! [*The men leave in cowed silence, carrying* JOE *with them.* KEENEY *turns to the* MATE *with a short laugh and puts his revolver back in his pocket.*] Best get up on deck, Mr. Slocum, and see to it they don't try none of their skulkin' tricks. We'll have to keep an eye peeled from now on. I know 'em.

MATE   Yes, sir. [*He goes out, right.* KEENEY *hears his wife's hysterical weeping and turns around in surprise—then walks slowly to her side.*]

KEENEY [*Putting an arm around her shoulder—with gruff tenderness.*]   There, there, Annie. Don't be afeared. It's all past and gone.

MRS. KEENEY [*Shrinking away from him.*]   Oh, I can't bear it! I can't bear it any longer!

KEENEY [*Gently.*]   Can't bear what, Annie?

MRS. KEENEY [*Hysterically.*]   All this horrible brutality, and these brutes of men, and this terrible ship, and this prison cell of a room, and the ice all around, and the silence. [*After this outburst she calms down and wipes her eyes with her handkerchief.*]

KEENEY [*After a pause during which he looks down at her with a puzzled frown.*]   Remember, I warn't hankerin' to have you come on this voyage, Annie.

MRS. KEENEY I wanted to be with you, David, don't you see? I didn't want to wait back there in the house all alone as I've been doing these last six years since we were married—waiting, and watching, and fearing—with nothing to keep my mind occupied—not able to go back teaching school on account of being Dave Keeney's wife. I used to dream of sailing on the great, wide, glorious ocean. I wanted to be by your side in the danger and vigorous life of it all. I wanted to see you the hero they make you out to be in Homeport. And instead—— [*Her voice grows tremulous.*] All I find is ice and cold—and brutality! [*Her voice breaks.*]

KEENEY I warned you what it'd be, Annie. "Whalin' ain't no ladies' tea party," I says to you, and "you better stay to home where you've got all your woman's comforts." [*Shaking his head.*] But you was so set on it.

MRS. KEENEY [*Wearily.*] Oh, I know it isn't your fault, David. You see, I didn't believe you. I guess I was dreaming about the old Vikings in the story books and I thought you were one of them.

KEENEY [*Protestingly.*] I done my best to make it as easy and comfortable as could be. [MRS. KEENEY *looks around her in wild scorn.*] I even sent to the city for that organ for ye, thinkin' it might be soothin' to ye to be playin' it times when they was calms and things was dull like.

MRS. KEENEY [*Wearily.*] Yes, you were very kind, David. I know that. [*She goes to left and lifts the curtains from the porthole and looks out—then suddenly bursts forth:*] I won't stand it—I can't stand it—pent up by these walls like a prisoner. [*She runs over to him and throws her arms around him, weeping. He puts his arm protectingly over her shoulders.*] Take me away from here, David! If I don't get away from here, out of this terrible ship, I'll go mad! Take me home, David! I can't think any more. I feel as if the cold and the silence were crushing down on my brain. I'm afraid. Take me home!

KEENEY [*Holds her at arm's length and looks at her face anxiously.*] Best go to bed, Annie. You ain't yourself. You got fever. Your eyes look so strange like. I ain't never seen you look this way before.

MRS. KEENEY [*Laughing hysterically.*] It's the ice and the cold and the silence—they'd make any one look strange.

KEENEY [*Soothingly.*] In a month or two, with good luck, three at the most, I'll have her filled with ile and then we'll give her everything she'll stand and pint for home.

MRS. KEENEY But we can't wait for that—I can't wait. I want to get home. And the men won't wait. They want to get home. It's cruel, it's brutal for you to keep them. You must sail back. You've got no excuse. There's clear water to the south now. If you've a heart at all you've got to turn back.

KEENEY [*Harshly.*] I can't, Annie.

MRS. KEENEY Why can't you?

KEENEY A woman couldn't rightly understand my reason.

MRS. KEENEY [*Wildly.*] Because it's a stupid, stubborn reason. Oh, I heard you talking with the second mate. You're afraid the other captains will sneer at you because you didn't come back with a full ship. You want to live up to your silly reputation and starve men and drive me mad to do it.

KEENEY [*His jaw set stubbornly.*] It ain't that, Annie. Them skippers would never dare sneer to my face. It ain't so much what any one'd say—but—— [*He hesitates, struggling to express his meaning.*] You see—I've always done it—since my first voyage as skipper. I always come back—with a full ship—and—it don't seem right not to— somehow. I been always first whalin' skipper out o' Homeport, and—— Don't you see my meanin', Annie? [*He glances at her. She is not looking at him but staring dully in front of her, not hearing a word he is saying.*] Annie! [*She comes to herself with a start.*] Best turn in, Annie, there's a good woman. You ain't well.

MRS. KEENEY [*Resisting his attempts to guide her to the door in rear.*] David! Won't you please turn back?

KEENEY [*Gently.*] I can't, Annie—not yet awhile. You don't see my meanin'. I got to git the ile.

MRS. KEENEY It'd be different if you needed the money, but you don't. You've got more than plenty.

KEENEY [*Impatiently.*] It ain't the money I'm thinkin' of. D'you think I'm as mean as that?

MRS. KEENEY [*Dully.*] No—I don't know—I can't understand—— [*Intensely.*] Oh, I want to be home in the old house once more and see my own kitchen again, and hear a woman's voice talking to me and be able to talk to her. Two years! It seems so long ago—as if I'd been dead and could never go back.

KEENEY [*Worried by her strange tone and the far-away look in her eyes.*] Best go to bed, Annie. You ain't well.

MRS. KEENEY [*Not appearing to hear him.*] I used to be lonely when you were away. I used to think Homeport was a stupid, monotonous place. Then I used to go down on the beach, especially when it was windy and the breakers were rolling in, and I'd dream of the fine free life you must be leading. [*She gives a laugh which is half a sob.*] I used to love the sea then. [*She pauses; then continues with slow intensity:*] But now—I don't ever want to see the sea again.

KEENEY [*Thinking to humor her.*] 'Tis no fit place for a woman, that's sure. I was a fool to bring ye.

MRS. KEENEY [*After a pause—passing her hand over her eyes with a gesture of pathetic weariness.*] How long would it take us to reach home—if we started now?

KEENEY [*Frowning.*] 'Bout two months, I reckon, Annie, with fair luck.

MRS. KEENEY [*Counts on her fingers—then murmurs with a rapt smile.*] That would be August, the latter part of August, wouldn't it? It was on the twenty-fifth of August we were married, David, wasn't it?

KEENEY [*Trying to conceal the fact that her memories have moved him—gruffly.*] Don't *you* remember?

MRS. KEENEY [*Vaguely—again passes her hand over her eyes.*] My memory is leaving me—up here in the ice. It was so long ago. [*A pause—then she smiles dreamily.*] It's June now. The lilacs will be all in bloom in the front yard—and the climbing roses on the trellis to the side of the house—they're budding. [*She suddenly covers her face with her hands and commences to sob.*]

KEENEY [*Disturbed.*] Go in and rest, Annie. You're all wore out cryin' over what can't be helped.

MRS. KEENEY [*Suddenly throwing her arms around his neck and clinging to him.*] You love me, don't you, David?

KEENEY [*In amazed embarrassment at this outburst.*] Love you? Why d'you ask me such a question, Annie?

MRS. KEENEY [*Shaking him—fiercely.*] But you do, don't you, David? Tell me!

KEENEY I'm your husband, Annie, and you're my wife. Could there be aught but love between us after all these years?

MRS. KEENEY [*Shaking him again—still more fiercely.*] Then you do love me. Say it!

KEENEY [*Simply.*] I do, Annie.

MRS. KEENEY [*Gives a sigh of relief—her hands drop to her sides. Keeney regards her anxiously. She passes her hand across her eyes and murmurs half to herself:*] I sometimes think if we could only have had a child. [KEENEY *turns away from her, deeply moved. She grabs his arm and turns him around to face her—intensely.*] And I've always been a good wife to you, haven't I, David?

KEENEY [*His voice betraying his emotion.*] No man has ever had a better, Annie.

MRS. KEENEY And I've never asked for much from you, have I, David? Have I?

KEENEY You know you could have all I got the power to give ye, Annie.

MRS. KEENEY [*Wildly.*] Then do this this once for my sake, for God's sake—take me home! It's killing me, this life—the brutality and cold and horror of it. I'm going mad. I can feel the threat in the air. I can hear the silence threatening me—day after gray day and every day the same. I can't bear it. [*Sobbing.*] I'll go mad, I know I will. Take me home, David, if you love me as you say. I'm afraid. For the love of God, take me home! [*She throws her arms around him, weeping against his shoulder. His face betrays the tremendous struggle going on within him. He holds her out at arm's length, his expression softening. For a moment his shoulders sag, he becomes old, his iron spirit weakens as he looks at her tear-stained face.*]

KEENEY [*Dragging out the words with an effort.*] I'll do it, Annie —for your sake—if you say it's needful for ye.

MRS. KEENEY [*With wild joy—kissing him.*] God bless you for that, David! [*He turns away from her silently and walks toward the companionway. Just at that moment there is a clatter of footsteps on the stairs and the* SECOND MATE *enters the cabin.*]

MATE [*Excitedly.*] The ice is breakin' up to no'the'ard, sir. There's a clear passage through the floe, and clear water beyond, the lookout says.

[KEENEY *straightens himself like a man coming out of a trance.* MRS. KEENEY *looks at the* MATE *with terrified eyes.*]

KEENEY [*Dazedly—trying to collect his thoughts.*] A clear passage? To no'the'ard?

MATE Yes, sir.

KEENEY [*His voice suddenly grim with determination.*] Then get her ready and we'll drive her through.

MATE Aye, aye, sir.

MRS. KEENEY [*Appealingly.*] David!

KEENEY [*Not heeding her.*] Will the men turn to willin' or must we drag 'em out?

MATE They'll turn to willin' enough. You put the fear o' God into 'em, sir. They're meek as lambs.

KEENEY Then drive 'em—both watches. [*With grim determination.*] They's whale t'other side o' this floe and we're going to git 'em.

MATE Aye, aye, sir. [*He goes out hurriedly. A moment later there is the sound of scuffling feet from the deck outside and the* MATE's *voice shouting orders.*]

KEENEY [*Speaking aloud to himself—derisively.*] And I was agoin' home like a yaller dog!

MRS. KEENEY [*Imploringly.*] David!

KEENEY [*Sternly.*] Woman, you ain't adoin' right when you meddle in men's business and weaken 'em. You can't know my feelin's. I got to prove a man to be a good husband for ye to take pride in. I got to git the ile, I tell ye.

MRS. KEENEY [*Supplicatingly.*] David! Aren't you going home?

KEENEY [*Ignoring this question—commandingly.*] You ain't well. Go and lay down a mite. [*He starts for the door.*] I got to git on deck. [*He goes out. She cries after him in anguish:*] David! [*A pause. She passes her hand across her eyes—then commences to laugh hysterically and goes to the organ. She sits down and starts to play wildly an old hymn.* KEENEY *reënters from the doorway to the deck and stands looking at her angrily. He comes over and grabs her roughly by the shoulder.*]

KEENEY Woman, what foolish mockin' is this? [*She laughs wildly and he starts back from her in alarm.*] Annie! What is it? [*She doesn't answer him.* KEENEY's *voice trembles.*] Don't you know me, Annie? [*He puts both hands on her shoulders and turns her around so that he can look into her eyes. She stares up at him with a stupid expression, a vague smile on her lips. He stumbles away from her, and she commences softly to play the organ again.*]

KEENEY [*Swallowing hard—in a hoarse whisper, as if he had difficulty in speaking.*] You said —you was a-goin' mad—God! [*A long wail is heard from the deck above.*] Ah bl-o-o-o-ow! [*A moment later the* MATE's *face appears through the skylight. He cannot see* MRS. KEENEY.]

MATE [*In great excitement.*] Whales, sir—a whole school of 'em —off the star'b'd quarter 'bout five miles away—big ones!

KEENEY [*Galvanized into action.*]   Are you lowerin' the boats?

MATE   Yes, sir.

KEENEY [*With grim decision.*]   I'm a-comin' with ye.

MATE   Aye, aye, sir. [*Jubilantly.*] You'll git the ile now right enough, sir. [*His head is withdrawn and he can be heard shouting orders.*]

KEENEY [*Turning to his wife.*]   Annie! Did you hear him? I'll git the ile. [*She doesn't answer or seem to know he is there. He gives a hard laugh, which is almost a groan.*] I know you're foolin' me, Annie. You ain't out of your mind—[*Anxiously.*] be you? I'll git the ile now right enough—jest a little while longer, Annie—then we'll turn hom'ard. I can't turn back now, you see that, don't ye? I've got to git the ile. [*In sudden terror.*] Answer me! You ain't mad, be you? [*She keeps on playing the organ, but makes no reply. The MATE's face appears again through the skylight.*]

MATE   All ready, sir. [KEENEY *turns his back on his wife and strides to the doorway, where he stands for a moment and looks back at her in anguish, fighting to control his feelings.*]

MATE   Comin', sir?

KEENEY [*His face suddenly grown hard with determination.*]   Aye. [*He turns abruptly and goes out.* MRS. KEENEY *does not appear to notice his departure. Her whole attention seems centered in the organ. She sits with half-closed eyes, her body swaying from side to side to the rhythm of the hymn. Her fingers move faster and faster and she is playing wildly and discordantly as*

[CURTAIN]

DISCUSSION

1. What is the basic conflict in *Ile*? Comment on the effectiveness with which you feel O'Neill's stage directions at the beginning of the play anticipate this conflict. Consider carefully each of the following details: (1) the small organ and the woman's sewing basket, (2) the "faint" and "sickly" light within the cabin, (3) the "silence . . . unbroken except for the measured tread of someone walking up and down . . .", (4) the manner of the steward, and of the cabin boy, Ben.

2. How does the opening conversation between Ben and the steward clarify the relationship between Captain Keeney and the crew? What similarities do you see between this relationship and that of the captain and Mrs. Keeney? What differences?

3. How does the steward's appraisal of Captain Keeney prepare for the captain's entrance?

4. Examine the captain's opening conversations with the steward, with the second mate, and with his wife, Annie. Do you notice any differences in Keeney's manner as he addresses these three? In their reactions to him? Explain.

5. How does Captain Keeney explain his motive for pursuing the "ile"? How would you explain it?

6. Comment upon Mrs. Keeney's interpretation of her husband's behavior in the passage that begins, "Because it's a stupid, stubborn reason . . ." Does the captain's reply really refute her point?

7. What were Mrs. Keeney's motives in wishing to accompany the captain on this voyage? Why was she totally unprepared for the realities of life at sea?

8. Why does Keeney at last yield to his wife's entreaties? Considering the violence with which he greeted the previous demands of the crew, does his behavior at this moment seem believable? Consistent?

9. Is Keeney's subsequent reversal equally believable? Find evidence to support your conclusion.

10. Explain why the line, "Then get her ready and we'll drive her through," is a fitting climax to the action of the play. Do you detect a double meaning in the line?

11. How does Keeney's final decision affect Annie? Why is he now only briefly moved by her distress?

12. State the theme of *Ile* and discuss whether or not you feel that it has *universal* application.

TOPICS FOR WRITING

Discuss O'Neill's use of repetition for dramatic effect, in *Ile*.

Write an imaginative ship's log, describing the noteworthy events of the return voyage to Homeport. Be certain to include references, in your account, to the disposition of the captain, Annie, and the crew.

The story of a ship cursed with bad luck at sea is by no means a new one. Read Samuel Taylor Coleridge's *The Rime of the Ancient Mariner*, and compare Coleridge's treatment of the subject with O'Neill's.

NATIVE DANCER

David Shaw

NATIVE DANCER

CHARACTERS

Shirley Kochendorfer
Dr. Max Binder
Mama
Oscar Miller
Frances

NATIVE DANCER was first presented on the "Goodyear Television Playhouse" on March 28, 1954 on NBC, under the direction of Vincent Donehue.

David Shaw (1917-   )

A native New Yorker, David Shaw studied to be an illustrator, but changed his mind and became a writer instead. He has written for the motion picture screen and the Broadway stage, and has been extremely successful as the writer of dramatic scripts for television.

Native Dancer first appeared in 1954 on the Goodyear Playhouse, with actors Gwen Verdon and Jack Warden heading the cast. This play has something unusual to say about failure and success.

NATIVE DANCER

FADE IN: The clock atop the Paramount Building. Day. Pan slowly down building to street level, Broadway, and dolly in towards the drug store on the corner of 44th Street. DISSOLVE THRU TO: Drug store interior. The long fountain at which people are eating. Behind the fountain with her back to us is SHIRLEY, *the short order cook. Her equipment includes a large griddle, an electric toaster which she feeds incessantly, and which pops up incessantly, and a*

sandwich board. She is terribly busy at the moment trying
to fulfill the various orders that FRANCES, *the waitress behind*
the counter, keeps shouting to her.

FRANCES   One toasted American. Two egg salad on rye up. Hold
the butter on one. Where's my bacon and tomato?

SHIRLEY (*cutting the just-finished bacon and tomato sandwich in
half*)   Bacon and tomato. Pick up.

FRANCES (*picking it up*)   One fried egg on whole wheat toast.

SHIRLEY   Gee.

FRANCES   Is my toasted American working?

(*During this camera has panned down to* SHIRLEY's *feet which
are clad in ballet slippers. For while she works* SHIRLEY *also
practises a few positions. After this shot is established, pan
up again*)

SHIRLEY   No harder than I am.

FRANCES   Well, it'd be a lot easier on you if you did your ballet
lessons on your own time.

SHIRLEY   My teacher says every minute counts if you want to be
a great dancer.

FRANCES   Sure, what does he care? He doesn't have to eat here.
Shirley, the customers are beginning to complain about the service.

SHIRLEY   Tell them I'm on my toes.

(*and she is*)

FRANCES   Boy, if determination is all you need to become a ballet
dancer, you're the next Pavlova.

SHIRLEY   I saw her dance once. Mama took me when I was a little
girl. She seemed to just—float, Frances. You know what I mean?

FRANCES   Like a balloon.

SHIRLEY   Like a bird. After that I knew the only thing I ever
wanted was to be like she was.

FRANCES   In the meantime you got a toasted American coming up
and two egg salads on—

SHIRLEY (*seeing a man come up to the fountain*)   Oscar Miller!

FRANCES   Who?

SHIRLEY   That's—Oscar Miller.

FRANCES   Friend of the family's?

SHIRLEY   Oscar Miller is only the biggest ballet producer in the world. Frances, let me wait on him.

FRANCES   Look, Shirley, you're four orders behind now and—oh, go ahead.

SHIRLEY   How do I look?

FRANCES   Fine. Now hurry up.

(SHIRLEY *tries to walk down to where* MILLER *is seated in the grand, classic manner of a ballerina. She more than overdoes it.* MILLER *watches her, puzzled. Being as gracefully theatrical as she can,* SHIRLEY *leans over the counter toward him*)

SHIRLEY   What is your pleasure, Mr. Miller?

MILLER   A glass of water, please.

SHIRLEY   But of course.

(*She spins artistically around to get a glass which she fills from the tap. All her movements are very elaborate. She sets the water before him. He watches her closely as he pops a pill into his mouth and takes a sip of water. She gets a napkin for him as though the whole movement has been badly choreographed*)

SHIRLEY   Headache, Mr. Miller?

MILLER   Toothache.

SHIRLEY   (*striking a pose of dismay*)   Ahhhhhhhh . . .

MILLER   Thanks for the water, Miss.

SHIRLEY   Kochendorfer.

(*He exits quickly leaving* SHIRLEY *in a rather ridiculous pose.* FRANCES *comes up behind her carrying plates of sandwiches in both hands*)

FRANCES   Well, did he sign you up for the Ballet Russe?

SHIRLEY   He must've been in awful pain not to notice me.

(FRANCES *goes about serving the sandwiches to the customers while* SHIRLEY *picks up the napkin* MILLER *used and cherishes it as though it is a beautiful rose.* FRANCES *re-enters frame*)

FRANCES   I need two salami and eggs.

SHIRLEY   Someday—when I'm his premiere danseuse—I'll remind Oscar of this. He won't remember it but I'll remind him by showing him this napkin. . . . What did you order?

FRANCES   Two salami and eggs. . . .

SHIRLEY   (*putting the paper napkin in her bosom*)   We'll both have a good laugh about it—

FRANCES   On rye.

SHIRLEY   (*sighs*)   Someday.

FRANCES   Never mind. I'll get it myself.

(*She leaves frame and* SHIRLEY—*in her dream world. Now* DR. MAX BINDER *climbs up on the stool across the counter from her. He wears an overcoat, no hat, and we can see his white doctor's jacket with its high neck under the unbuttoned coat*)

MAX   Hello, Shirley.

SHIRLEY   (*still entranced*)   Hi— (*Now really sees* MAX *and comes back to earth*)   Hi.

MAX   Think I can have a cup of coffee?

SHIRLEY   (*the short order cook again*)   Sure.

(*She pours a cup.* MAX *watches her idyllically*)

How's the doctor today?

MAX   As long as he can always come down ten floors and have you here to serve him a cup of coffee, he can't complain.

SHIRLEY   I guess I'll be here for some time yet—(*Serves him the coffee*)   You want something else?

MAX   Yes.

SHIRLEY   A piece of Danish, maybe?

MAX   I want you to marry me.

SHIRLEY   (*This is an old story.*)   Ma-a-a-x.

MAX   Listen, is there any law that says you can't be a ballerina if you're married to a dentist?

SHIRLEY   Max, people are looking at us.

MAX   I would like to know what's so incompatible about it. It would be different if you didn't love me. But you do.

SHIRLEY   I know, Max. Only my aim in life is to dance, not to get married.

MAX   Married women don't dance? You marry me and you can dance until doomsday. I'll send you to ten dancing schools.

SHIRLEY   We've been all through this and you promised me yesterday not to bring the subject up again.

MAX   I love you, Shirley.

SHIRLEY   Max.

MAX   All right, I'll change the subject. Will I see you tonight?

SHIRLEY   (*shaking her head*)   Tonight is rhythmics. You know that.

MAX   Tomorrow night?

SHIRLEY   Tomorrow's Thursday?

MAX   Yes.

SHIRLEY   I take Interpretive on Thursdays.

MAX   Friday.

SHIRLEY   I'm sorry but I can't, Max.

MAX   You were always free on Fridays.

SHIRLEY   I start a new course . . . Modern.

MAX   You mean the only times I'll ever see you again is when I come in here for a cup of coffee?

SHIRLEY   And Legal Holidays. There's no school on Legal Holidays.

MAX   (*disgusted*)   That's fine.

SHIRLEY   Don't hate me, Max.

MAX   Just when my practise is starting to grow. I'm a good dentist, Shirley. I'm going to make a very respectable income.

(FRANCES *moves into frame carrying a wire basket of glasses*)

FRANCES   Pardon the intrusion but I need a double chocolate malted.

SHIRLEY   Okay.

(FRANCES *moves out of frame and* SHIRLEY *starts to make the malted*)

MAX   I'm even getting a few celebrities for patients. I had Oscar Miller in my chair just a half hour ago.

SHIRLEY   Oscar Miller!

MAX (*proudly*) Yop.

SHIRLEY Is he a patient of yours?

MAX And will be for a long time. His teeth are in a terrible condition.

(FRANCES *returns*)

FRANCES So where's the malted?

SHIRLEY (*vaguely*) What? . . . Oh.

FRANCES (*taking the metal container out of* SHIRLEY's *hand*) Never mind. (*she exits*)

MAX I'd better be getting back upstairs.

SHIRLEY Max. . . . About tonight. Can a girl change her mind?

MAX (*delighted*) Really?

SHIRLEY I'll meet you out front at six-thirty.

MAX Where'll we go? You just name it.

SHIRLEY Ohhhhh—anywhere.

(*DISSOLVE QUICKLY TO: Sign "Madam Slovenskia's School of Dancing"*)

(*DISSOLVE THROUGH TO: A rehearsal room where there are many hopeful ballerinas individually going about their dancing. Finally camera dollies in and finds* SHIRLEY *in a work outfit working on the bar.* MAX *is seated near her, holding his hat and coat, watching her, admiring her. Throughout this scene* SHIRLEY *continues her exercises—though not very well*)

MAX Shirley.

SHIRLEY (*in the midst of a complicated routine*) Just a minute . . . (*she finishes*)

How did that look to you?

MAX Anything you do looks beautiful.

SHIRLEY (*chiding him*) Oh, Max . . .

MAX Only don't you think we ought to go? It's after nine.

SHIRLEY (*going back to work*) I've got to perfect this.

MAX All the restaurants'll be closed.

SHIRLEY Watch me and tell me if it's better.

MAX I wanted to take you out real fancy tonight. I thought we might even take in a show. Can't you even skip one night of dancing school?

SHIRLEY Not with my big audition coming up. I want to be at my best for Oscar Miller.

MAX (*surprised*) Are you going to audition for Oscar Miller?

SHIRLEY That's up to you, Max.

(*She dances away leaving* MAX *stunned and puzzled as we*)

(*DISSOLVE TO: Living room of a Brooklyn apartment house. 11 P.M. Pictures of ballerinas on the walls, otherwise the room is quite typical.* MRS. KOCHENDORFER, *a woman of fifty, is alone mending a ballet costume with needle and thread. She holds it up to examine it, is satisfied, and starts to put away sewing things. The door in the foyer opens*)

MAMA That you, Shirley?

SHIRLEY (*off*) Yeah, Mama.

MAMA You're late tonight.

SHIRLEY (*off*) I thought you'd be asleep.

MAMA I just finished sewing that so-so for you.

SHIRLEY Tu-tu, mama.

MAMA Tu-tu. You'll take it with you tomorrow.

SHIRLEY (*off*) Max is here, Mama.

MAMA Max? . . . Doctor Max?

(*Crosses to foyer and sees* MAX *and* SHIRLEY. SHIRLEY *has her coat off.* MAX *hasn't.* MAMA *extends her hand to* MAX)

So quiet? I didn't even know somebody was here.

MAX (*glum*) Good evening, Mrs. Kochendorfer.

MAMA Come in. Take your coat off. I'll make coffee.

MAX No, thanks very much but I got to go.

MAMA (*sensing something*) You two had a fight?

(SHIRLEY *and* MAX *avoid her question*)

SHIRLEY Mama, I'm too tired to go all over it again.

MAMA Go splash cold water on your face. You'll feel better, Doctor Max will tell me. Go.

SHIRLEY (*to* MAX) Will you stay?

MAX I'll wait till you come out.

SHIRLEY I won't be long.

(*She exits into hall leading to bedroom*)

MAMA So what's the argument now, Doctor?

MAX What's always the argument?

MAMA Career versus wedding bells, huh?

MAX Worse. Mrs. Kochendorfer, your daughter is going to work herself into a state. I tell you this as a medical man. She can't go on working all day in the drug store and practising ballet all night.

MAMA This is news you're telling me? I worry plenty about my Shirley.

MAX Tonight, for instance. We made a date—

MAMA She made a date on a school night? I'm very surprised.

MAX She had her reasons all right. I was going to take her out to an expensive restaurant. Maybe even to a Broadway show. You know where we went? To her dancing school. You know where we ate? Nedicks. Two hot dogs was her dinner. She's ruining her health.

MAMA Haven't I told her? Haven't I tried to stop her? She's got this ballet bug in her head and it's like moving the mountains to talk to her. But this has been going on for years, Doctor Max. Why, tonight all of a sudden, should you and Shirley have a fight about it?

MAX Because tonight the situation has come to a head. She wants me to use my influence to get her an audition with Oscar Miller.

MAMA You've got influence with Oscar Miller?

MAX He's one of my patients.

MAMA (*very impressed*) My!

MAX But I don't like to ask favors of my patients. It doesn't look nice.

MAMA That's the only reason, Doctor? It doesn't look nice?

MAX (*sheepishly*) No . . .

MAMA Look, Doctor Max. Nothing is going to stop Shirley from trying. Not you. Not me. Not even Oscar Miller. She'll get her chance to show what she's got someday. She'll make her own chance. So why delay the agony?

MAX Agony is right.

(SHIRLEY *enters, visibly refreshed*)

SHIRLEY (*to* MAX) Wouldn't you like to take your coat off?

MAX (*rising*) I was just waiting to say good-night.

MAMA Why don't you stay and have a sandwich? I'm going to make one for Shirley anyway.

SHIRLEY I'm not hungry, Mama.

MAMA Don't tell me what you're not, Miss Two-Hot-Dogs-For-Dinner.

(*to* MAX)

I've got some nice chicken from dinner left over. How about it, Doctor?

MAX Shirley can tell you—I'm a pushover for a chicken sandwich.

SHIRLEY He eats them all the time at the drug store.

MAMA (*to* SHIRLEY) A man like this. The day after I took you to see Pavlova I should've had my head examined.

(*She exits into kitchen. There is an embarrassed pause between* SHIRLEY *and* MAX)

SHIRLEY I'll take your coat.

MAX Oh . . . thanks.

(*She helps him off with it and hangs it in the closet. Comes back and picks up the tu-tu that* MAMA *had draped over a chair.*)

SHIRLEY (*examining it*) Mama did a beautiful job on this. It was all torn.

MAX Your mother is a wonderful woman.

SHIRLEY Did you discuss—our problem?

MAX I mentioned it, yes.

SHIRLEY Bet I can guess what she said. She said: "Don't let anything she does now upset you, Dr. Max. She'll get over this ballet business once and for all and then you can settle down in a nice house in Flatbush. With lots of children."

MAX Is that bad?

SHIRLEY Not if that's what you want.

MAX How do you know it isn't what you want until you try it?

SHIRLEY Marriage isn't like buying a coat, Max. Once you accept it there are no returns in five days like in Klein's. . . . But I guessed right about what Mama said, didn't I? That's all I get from everybody. Discouragement.

MAX   Your mother thinks I ought to try and get you that audition with Oscar Miller.

SHIRLEY   Mama said that!

MAX   Why prolong the agony, she said.

SHIRLEY   Then why won't you do it, Max? Even Mama knows how much it means to me. It could be the beginning of something wonderful for me—everything I've ever wanted. You have no reason to say no.

MAX   No reason? I love you. Is that a reason? And you say you love me. That's another reason. And that house in Flatbush and all the kids. More reasons. I don't know anything about it but to me you're a great dancer, Shirley. Oscar Miller will take one look at you and good-bye my love and the house and the kids and you. You have no right to ask a man to arrange for his own heartaches. Don't you see, Shirley, I'm trying to hold onto you as long as I can.

SHIRLEY   (*in tears she throws her arms around him and buries her head on his shoulder*)   All right, Max. That's enough. . . . I—I'll never mention Oscar Miller's name to you again.

MAX   (*moved*)   Shirley—darling—

SHIRLEY   I'll just have to get an audition with him some other way.

(MAX *goes limp. He walks over and gets his coat*)

Where are you going, Max?

MAX   He's coming in to have an inlay fitting tomorrow. I'll speak to him then.

SHIRLEY   But what about your chicken sandwich?

(MAX *leaves.* SHIRLEY *stands there brokenly until* MAMA *comes in from the kitchen with the sandwiches*)

MAMA   I didn't know if you take ketchup or not so I— Where's the Doctor?

SHIRLEY   He went home, Mama.

MAMA   He wouldn't get you the audition so you sent him away?

SHIRLEY   No, Mama—he's going to talk to Oscar Miller tomorrow.

(*She bursts into tears and* MAMA *cradles her in her arms.* MAMA *strokes her head*)

MAMA My head examined I should've had . . .

(*FADE OUT:*)

(*FADE IN: A dentist's office. Day.* MAX *is in his white jacket, apart from his patient, mixing a tiny cement solution. He seems very uneasy. In the chair is* OSCAR MILLER, *his mouth open, stuffed with all sorts of dental paraphernalia.*)

MILLER (*says something that cannot be understood*)
MAX What was that, Mr. Miller?
MILLER (*repeats the incoherent phrase*)

(MAX *comes over and removes the saliva drain*)

I said I'm in something of a hurry.
MAX This won't take long.
MILLER Got to be at NBC by four o'clock. They're doing one of my ballets on television tonight.
MAX NBC? You don't say. Open wide, please.

(*starts to work in* MILLER's *mouth*)

Mr. Miller?
MILLER 'Ah?
MAX How does a man like you go about finding new talent?
MILLER Agrsns!
MAX (*taking the drain out of his mouth*) How's that?
MILLER Auditions.

(MAX *puts drain back in his mouth. Examines the tooth carefully*)

MAX (*getting the drill ready*) You must get plenty of people bothering you for auditions all the time, eh?
MILLER (*meaning yes*) 'Ah-ha.
MAX This may hurt a little.

(*He starts to drill the tooth.* MILLER *writhes a little.* MAX *stops the drill a moment*)

Because there's a girl I know . . .

(*drills some more. Stops*)

I think she's a real talent, Mr. Miller.

(*more drilling*)

Not that I know too much about it, you understand.
MILLER   Ah-ha.
MAX   But I think she's good . . . too good. I wouldn't even impose on you like this if I didn't think she had something on the ball. You know what I mean?
MILLER   Ah-hah.
MAX   Open wider, please.

(*He drills some more*)

So I was wondering if I could bring her around sometime to see you.
MILLER   Anrtynr.
MAX (*taking the drain out*)   How's that?
MILLER   I said sure, anytime.
(MAX *puts the drain back in and starts to drill*)
MAX (*mournfully*)   Thanks, Mr. Miller. I sure appreciate it.

(*Dolly in tight on the drill buzzing and DISSOLVE TO: CU of malted machine buzzing behind the counter of the drug store. Pull back and* SHIRLEY *is there not paying much attention to the malted. Her eyes are fastened towards the front of the store, obviously looking for somebody. Her feet, as always, are doing ballet exercises.* FRANCES *comes up behind her*)

FRANCES   Isn't that malted ready *yet?*
SHIRLEY (*still looking off*)   Huh?
FRANCES   Never mind.

(*She takes the metal container off the mixer and tries to pour it into a glass. Nothing flows out.* FRANCES *looks into the container*)

Now, really, Shirley.

SHIRLEY   What's the matter?

FRANCES (*shaking the inverted container a few times until a solid chunk of malted comes out in her hand. She can hold the whole thing like a glass*)   I would say you let it whip a mite too long.

SHIRLEY   I'm sorry, Frances. I guess I'm so anxious to see Max that I—I'll make another one.

FRANCES   Never mind. You stay right where you are—on cloud seven.

(*She leaves.* SHIRLEY *is contrite. She turns and sees* MAX *seated at the counter*)

SHIRLEY   Max!

MAX   A cup of coffee, please.

SHIRLEY   Did you see him? Did you ask him?

MAX   Black.

SHIRLEY   Max, don't torture me. Since last night I've been going crazy. I can't stand it another minute.

MAX   The way you feel about being a big ballet dancer, that's about how much I want you.

SHIRLEY   I'll get your coffee.

(*She goes about serving him coffee*)

MAX   He said okay, Shirley. You can have the audition.

SHIRLEY   You mean it?

MAX   I wish I didn't.

SHIRLEY   Oh, Max, I could kiss you.

MAX   I don't want your kisses for a reason like this.

SHIRLEY   When, Max?

MAX   When you want to kiss me as a husband, that's when.

SHIRLEY   I mean—when is the audition?

MAX   Oh—the audition? He said any time. Any time at all.

SHIRLEY   You didn't make a definite appointment?

MAX   He was in a hurry today. Some television show he's doing on NBC tonight. I didn't get much chance to talk to him.

SHIRLEY   Wait'll I tell Frances. Don't go 'way.

MAX   Don't you think you'd better wait until you see how you make out in the audition before you start telling everybody?

SHIRLEY   I got to tell her I'm leaving, don't I?

MAX   Where you going?

SHIRLEY   NBC.

MAX   Now?

(*Camera dollies in very tight on his face as* MAX's *expression changes from shock to resignation*)

MAX   When else?

(*DISSOLVE TO: Film. RCA building and NBC sign*)

(*DISSOLVE TO: Studio 8G during a break in camera rehearsals. We see cameras around and stagehands, light men, etc., on a long shot*)
(*Dolly in and pick up* OSCAR MILLER *on the floor looking up at the lights on the ceiling. With him are the stage manager and a man from the agency whose name is O'Leary*)

MILLER   There's got to be more lights up there or we don't do the show. It's ridiculous. The Swan Lake number does not take place in a coal mine.

STAGE MANAGER   Yes, Mr. Miller.

(*He exits.* MAX *now sidles up to him hesitantly.* MILLER *is still looking up at the ceiling*)

MAX   Hello, Mr. Miller.

MILLER (*preoccupied*)   Hello, hello . . .

MAX   Guess you're surprised to see me here, eh?

MILLER   Nothing surprises me around this place any more.

(*now he sees* MAX)

The dentist!

MAX   Knew you'd be surprised.

MILLER   Did I leave some of my bridgework in your office?

MAX   Oh, no—nothing like that.

MILLER   By the way—this is Mr. O'Leary. Dr. Binder.

MAX   (*shaking hands*)   Hi, Mr. O'Leary.

MILLER   (*shouting up at the ceiling*)   Put lots more lights up there. It's got to look sunny.

MAX   Incidentally, Mr. Miller—I brought Shirley Kochendorfer with me.

MILLER   That's nice—who?

MAX   The girl for the audition.

MILLER   You don't expect me to audition her now?

MAX   I'd certainly appreciate it, Mr. Miller. Shirley's very excited about it.

MILLER   Look, my dear friend, as a dentist I like you very much. But as an agent—don't bother me, please.

MAX   I'm not asking for myself, Mr. Miller. If it was up to me she'd never put on another pair of ballet shoes in her life. But she's lived her whole life for this moment, Mr. Miller.

MILLER   What kind of a name is that for a ballerina anyway? Shirley Kochendorfer.

MAX   She's willing to change it legally. She'll do anything.

(STAGE MANAGER *re-appears*)

STAGE MANAGER   It'll take about ten minutes to fix that lighting, Mr. Miller.

MILLER   Well, fix it and let's get on with the rehearsal.

(STAGE MANAGER *leaves*)

MAX   You could use those ten minutes to maybe discover a great star.

MILLER   Is she ready now?

MAX   (*pumping* MILLER's *hand*)   I'll never forget this, Mr. Miller. Never. Tell the orchestra to play—

(*He races across the studio to where* SHIRLEY *is waiting, a coat over her costume*)

Now, Shirley!

SHIRLEY   He said it was all right?

MAX   Yes.

SHIRLEY   Oh, Max, I'm so nervous . . .

MAX   You'll knock 'em dead.

SHIRLEY   I love you, Max. I really do.

> (*She kisses him and a moment later the music begins*)
> (SHIRLEY *goes to the center of the studio and does her audition dance*) (*During it keep cutting to* MAX *who enjoys every step and to* MILLER *whose reaction is quite the opposite. Near the end of the dance:*)
> (*DISSOLVE TO: The living room in Brooklyn. Evening. Sound: The doorbell is ringing constantly.* MAMA *emerges from the kitchen with baking flour on her hands*)

MAMA   (*crossing to front door*)   All right, all right, I'm coming.

> (*she opens the door and* MAX *bursts in*)

Doctor Max?

MAX   (*he is visibly upset*)   Is she here?

MAMA   Shirley? Of course not. Tonight is Thursday. She's interpreting.

MAX   No she isn't. Didn't she phone or something?

MAMA   Something happened to Shirley?

MAX   I don't know. Now, please, Mrs. Kochendorfer, don't get excited.

MAMA   Look who is talking! What happened, Doctor Max? You've got to tell her mother.

MAX   This afternoon she had her audition with Oscar Miller.

MAMA   Already?

MAX   You know Shirley. When she makes up her mind to do something. She couldn't wait. It had to be right now.

MAMA   That's Shirley, all right. But tell me, how was the audition?

MAX   I thought she was wonderful.

MAMA   You're not exactly an expert. What did Oscar Miller think?

MAX   He thinks she ought to forget she ever even heard of Pavlova. In plain English he said she was terrible!

MAMA   Yeah, and?

MAX   Mrs. Kochendorfer, you don't seem to understand. He told Shirley she'll never be a good dancer. I wish I could've died right then and there.

MAMA   And that's what's making you so upset? I could have told you long ago that Shirley had everything a ballet dancer needs except one thing. Talent.

MAX   And he didn't pull his punches. He told all this to Shirley right to her face. Like he was deliberately trying to hurt her . . . Wait'll I get him in the chair next time, I'll—

MAMA   So where's Shirley now?

MAX   I wish I knew. We were both standing there talking to Miller and the next minute she's gone. Disappeared. I don't want to alarm you, Mrs. Kochendorfer, but a girl in her state of mind should not be alone tonight.

MAMA   It's possible she went back to her dancing school to work some more on her . . .

MAX   I went to the dancing school. To the drug store. Any place she might possibly be. Then I came here, thinking maybe she came home.

MAMA   Sit down, Max. You look tired.

MAX   What are we going to do?

MAMA   You're going to sit there and worry and I'm going in the kitchen. I've got a cake in the oven. Upside down.

MAX   The whole world is upside down.

MAMA   Relax, Max, please.

(*She goes into kitchen. Max paces nervously until he hears the front door close. He crosses to the foyer and sees* SHIRLEY. *She can't look at him*)

MAX   Hello, Shirley.

SHIRLEY   I didn't expect to find you here.

MAX   (*the lame joke*)   I got bored drinking champagne at the Waldorf Astoria so I thought I'd drop over.

(SHIRLEY *crosses into living room. He follows*)

SHIRLEY   Mama here?

MAX   In the kitchen . . . You like upside down cake?

SHIRLEY   I just ate a little while ago.

MAX   Two hot dogs at Nedick's?

SHIRLEY   Scrambled eggs at Schrafft's.

MAX   That's nourishing.

SHIRLEY   Max, I'm sorry.

MAX   What's to be sorry about?

SHIRLEY   Everything.

MAX   You're not going to let one man's opinion stop you, are you? That's not the Shirley I know. How many stars are there who were once turned down by big producers? Hundreds! Oscar Miller isn't the last word, you know.

SHIRLEY   Maybe not. But he was right about one Shirley Kochendorfer.

MAX   Will you stop it, please?

SHIRLEY   He was, Max. Why kid ourselves now? I'm no dancer and I never will be.

MAX   He was just sore because he didn't want to have an audition today in the first place. He was nervous about his television show, too, which made him extremely irritated. I mean—the way he insulted your dancing was like he wanted to be as mean as he could.

SHIRLEY   He was being kind, Max.

MAX   Kind? If that's kindness I'm going to be awfully kind to him the next time I get him in that chair. I'll—

SHIRLEY   He wanted me to quit, Max. That's why he did it. He saw a girl who had no business in ballet and he wanted to spare me the years of drudgery I would've gone through for nothing. He was really pleading with me not to throw my life away on a thing I could never have . . . I ought to write him a thank you note.

(*She is sniffling*)

MAX   Aw, come on, Shirl. There are millions of wonderful girls who aren't ballet dancers. It's nothing to cry about.

SHIRLEY   I'm not crying about that.

MAX   Something else?

SHIRLEY   Uh-huh . . . Us.

MAX   There's nothing sad about us any more . . . Is there?

(*She nods her head affirmatively, unable to speak*)

You mean you still don't want to marry me?

SHIRLEY I do, Max. I do.

MAX Shirley . . .

SHIRLEY But I can't—now.

MAX Shirley!

(*Phone rings*)

SHIRLEY You'd always have it at the back of your mind that I married you on the rebound. She couldn't be a dancer so she married the second fiddle.

MAX If I'm the third fiddle, I don't care . . .

(*Phone rings*)

SHIRLEY It just isn't fair to a wonderful man like you. Be smart, Max darling. Drop me like a hot potato. Find yourself a girl who's good enough to deserve a prince.

(*Phone rings again*)
(*Mama enters from the kitchen on her way to phone*)

MAMA You don't hear the phone ringing in here? Hello, Shirley dear . . . (*Picks up phone*) Hello . . . Yes, this is the Kochendorfer residence . . . Shirley? Yes, she's my daughter . . . Who is this please? . . . Hold the line . . . (*to Shirley*) It's a gentleman for you, Shirley.

SHIRLEY Who is it?

MAMA A Mr. O'Leary.

SHIRLEY (*puzzled, not recognizing the name*) O'Leary? I don't know any—

MAX Don't you remember, Shirl? He was that fella from the agency who was at the studio today.

SHIRLEY (*to* MAX, *wearily amused*) Maybe he called up to tell me how bad the audition was, too.

MAMA He's hanging on, Shirley.

SHIRLEY I can't speak to anybody now, Mama. Ask him what he wants.

MAMA (*into phone*) Mr. O'Leary, are you there? Would you mind telling me what it's all about? My daughter is indisposed at the moment . . . I see . . . Yes . . . Could you hang on again, please?

(*covering the mouthpiece*)

He says his agency has a cigarette company for a client and he wants to know if you'd be willing to go on TV as the dancing legs of a cigarette package?

MAX (*to* SHIRLEY) What did I tell you? Oscar Miller isn't the only pebble. You're on your way, Shirley.

MAMA Should I tell him that, Shirley? You're on your way?

SHIRLEY I'll speak to him.

(*she takes phone from* MAMA)

Mr. O'Leary, this is Shirley Kochendorfer speaking . . . Yes, my mother gave me your message and I can't tell you how much I appreciate your offer, Mr. O'Leary. Only I'm afraid I'm unavailable . . . Have I got a better offer? I suppose you might call it that . . . No, not from another network. From a prince who's going to give me a house in Flatbush and lots of kids and . . .

(*By this time the camera has panned down slowly from* SHIRLEY's *head to her feet and we find out that while she has been speaking she has been doing her ballet exercises in very small movements*)
(*Fade out*)

THE END

DISCUSSION

1. What similarity do you note between the way in which Shirley manages her job, and the way in which she manages Max?
2. Frances appears at the beginning of the play, but only briefly thereafter. Why is her role nevertheless an important one? (Before answering, look up the definition of the term *foil* in the glossary).
3. Find examples in the play to illustrate Shirley's (a) self confidence, (b) determination, (c) sense of humor, (d) impracticality. How does she change in respect to all or some of these traits by the conclusion of the play?
4. In judging Max's character, why it is important to consider his complete confidence in Shirley's dancing ability?

5. What is amusing about the scene in the dentist's office? How is Max's use of the dentist's drill significant?
6. How are Max and Mama alike in their attitude toward Shirley? How do they differ? What does Mrs. Kochendorfer mean by her questions, "That's the only reason, Doctor? It doesn't look nice"?
7. In view of her long struggle to become a dancing star, does Shirley's abrupt decision to abandon her career seem logical? Why can she now make judgments with a clarity never before possible?
8. Shirley refuses to marry Max after she has been turned down by Oscar Miller, but she agrees to marry him after she herself turns down Mr. O'Leary. Explain these decisions.
9. How are television camera techniques used to maintain the unity of the play? How are they used to sharpen the conflict? Would the play have been as effective as a stage play?

TOPICS FOR WRITING

Native Dancer: An unusual treatment of the popular "success story"
The playwright's use of coincidence

THE OLD LADY SHOWS
HER MEDALS

James M. Barrie

CHARACTERS

Mrs. Dowey
Mrs. Twymley
The Haggerty Woman
Mrs. Mickleham
Mr. Willings
Private Dowey
Dixon

James M. Barrie (1860-1937)

You may already be acquainted with James M. Barrie, for he is the author of the popular fantasy, Peter Pan. *Barrie was born in 1860 in the little Scottish village of Kirriemuir. His early attempts to become a writer were unsuccessful, but the gentleness and warmth of his writing style eventually won him a devoted audience of readers. After his first important novel,* The Little Minister, *was made into a play, Barrie turned his attention almost entirely to the stage. In 1913 he was knighted by the King of England for his writing achievements.*

The Old Lady Shows Her Medals *is Barrie at his best. In this story of the London charwoman who lives on the fringes of other people's lives, he displays the sensitivity to language, the humor, and the sympathetic understanding of people for which he first received widespread acclaim as a writer.*

THE OLD LADY SHOWS HER MEDALS

Three nice old ladies and a criminal, who is even nicer, are discussing the war over a cup of tea. The criminal, who is the hostess, calls it a dish of tea, which shows that she comes from Caledonia; but that is not her crime.

They are all London charwomen, but three of them, including the hostess, are what are called professionally "charwomen and" or simply "ands." An "and" is also a caretaker when required; her name is entered as such in ink in a regis-

*try book, financial transactions take place across a counter
between her and the registrar, and altogether she is of a very
different social status from one who, like* MRS. HAGGERTY, *is
a charwoman but nothing else.* MRS. HAGGERTY, *though present, is not at the party by invitation; having seen* MRS. DOWEY
*buying the winkles, she followed her downstairs, and so has
shuffled into the play and sat down in it against our wish.
We would remove her by force, or at least print her name
in small letters, were it not that she takes offence very readily
and says that nobody respects her. So, as you have slipped in,
you can sit there,* MRS. HAGGERTY; *but keep quiet.*

*There is nothing doing at present in the caretaking way
for* MRS. DOWEY, *our hostess; but this does not damp her,
caretaking being only to such as she an extra financially and
a halo socially. If she had the honour of being served with
an income-tax paper she would probably fill in one of the
nasty little compartments with the words, "Trade—charring;
Profession [if any]—caretaking." This home of hers [from
which, to look after your house, she makes occasionally tem-
porary departures in great style, escorting a barrow] is in one
of those what-care-I streets that you discover only when you
have lost your way; on discovering them, your duty is to
report them to the authorities, who immediately add them
to the map of London. That is why we are now reporting
Friday Street. We shall call it, in the rough sketch drawn
for to-morrow's press, "Street in which the criminal resided";
and you will find* MRS. DOWEY'S *home therein marked with
an X.*

*Her abode really consists of one room, but she maintains
that there are two; so, rather than argue, let us say that there
are two. The other one has no window, and she could not
swish her old skirts in it without knocking something over;
its grandest display is of tin pans and crockery on top of a
dresser which has a lid to it; you have but to whip off the
utensils and raise the lid, and, behold, a bath with hot and
cold.* MRS. DOWEY *is very proud of this possession, and when
she shows it off, as she does perhaps too frequently, she first
signs to you with closed fist [funny old thing that she is] to
approach softly. She then tiptoes to the dresser and pops off*

the lid, as if to take the bath unawares. Then she sucks her lips, and is modest if you have the grace to do the exclamations.

In the real room is a bed, though that is putting the matter too briefly. The fair way to begin, if you love MRS. DOWEY, *is to say to her that it is a pity she has no bed. If she is in her best form she will chuckle, and agree that the want of a bed tries her sore; she will keep you on the hooks, so to speak, as long as she can; and then, with that mouse-like movement again, she will suddenly spring the bed on you. You thought it was a wardrobe, but she brings it down from the wall; and lo, a bed. There is nothing else in her abode [which we now see to contain four rooms—kitchen, pantry, bedroom, and bathroom] that is absolutely a surprise; but it is full of "bits," every one of which has been paid ready money for, and gloated over and tended until it has become part of its owner. Genuine Doweys, the dealers might call them, though there is probably nothing in the place except the bed that would fetch half-a-crown.*

Her home is in the basement, so that the view is restricted to the lower half of persons passing overhead beyond the area stairs. Here at the window MRS. DOWEY *sometimes sits of a summer evening gazing, not sentimentally at a flower-pot which contains one poor bulb, nor yearningly at some tiny speck of sky, but with unholy relish at holes in stockings, and the like, which are revealed to her from her point of vantage. You, gentle reader, may flaunt by, thinking that your finery awes the street, but* MRS. DOWEY *can tell [and does] that your soles are in need of neat repair.*

Also, lower parts being as expressive as the face to those whose view is thus limited, she could swear to scores of the passers-by in a court of law.

These four lively old codgers are having a good time at the tea-table, and wit is flowing free. As you can see by their everyday garments, and by their pails and mops [which are having a little tea-party by themselves in the corner], it is not a gathering by invitations stretching away into yesterday, it is a purely informal affair; so much more attractive, don't you think? than banquets elaborately prearranged. You

*know how they come about, especially in war-time. Very
likely* MRS. DOWEY *met* MRS. TWYMLEY *and* MRS. MICKLEHAM
*quite casually in the street, and meant to do no more than
pass the time of day; then, naturally enough, the word camou-
flage was mentioned, and they got heated, but in the end*
MRS. TWYMLEY *apologised; then, in the odd way in which
one thing leads to another, the winkle man appeared, and*
MRS. DOWEY *remembered that she had that pot of jam and that*
MRS. MICKLEHAM *had stood treat last time; and soon they
were all three descending the area stairs, followed cringingly
by the* HAGGERTY WOMAN.

*They have been extremely merry, and never were four
hard-worked old ladies who deserved it better. All a woman
can do in war-time they do daily and cheerfully, just as their
men-folk are doing it at the Front; and now, with the mops
and pails laid aside, they sprawl gracefully at ease. There is
no intention on their part to consider peace terms until a
decisive victory has been gained in the field* [SARAH ANN
DOWEY], *until the Kaiser is put to the right-about* [EMMA
MICKLEHAM], *and singing very small* [AMELIA TWYMLEY.]

At this tea-party the lady who is to play the part of MRS.
DOWEY *is sure to want to suggest that our heroine has a
secret sorrow, namely, the crime; but you should see us
knocking that idea out of her head!* MRS. DOWEY *knows she
is a criminal, but, unlike the actress, she does not know that
she is about to be found out; and she is, to put it bluntly in
her own Scotch way, the merriest of the whole clanjamfry.
She presses more tea on her guests, but they wave her away
from them in the pretty manner of ladies who know that they
have already had more than enough.*

MRS. DOWEY Just one more winkle, Mrs. Mickleham? [*Indeed
there is only one more.*]

[*But Mrs. Mickleham indicates politely that if she took this
one it would have to swim for it. (The* HAGGERTY WOMAN *takes
it long afterwards when she thinks, erroneously, that no one
is looking.)*]
[MRS. TWYMLEY *is sulky. Evidently some one has contradicted
her. Probably the* HAGGERTY WOMAN.]

MRS. TWYMLEY I say it is so.

THE HAGGERTY WOMAN I say it may be so.

MRS. TWYMLEY I suppose I ought to know: me that has a son a prisoner in Germany. [*She has so obviously scored that all good feeling seems to call upon her to end here. But she continues rather shabbily.*] Being the only lady present that has that proud misfortune. [*The others are stung.*]

MRS. DOWEY My son is fighting in France.

MRS. MICKLEHAM Mine is wounded in two places.

THE HAGGERTY WOMAN Mine is at Salonaiky.

[*The absurd pronunciation of this uneducated person moves the others to mirth.*]

MRS. DOWEY You'll excuse us, Mrs. Haggerty, but the correct pronunciation is Salonikky.

THE HAGGERTY WOMAN [*To cover her confusion.*] I don't think.

[*She feels that even this does not prove her case.*]

And I speak as one that has War Savings Certificates.

MRS. TWYMLEY We all have them.

[*The HAGGERTY WOMAN whimpers, and the other guests regard her with unfeeling disdain.*]

MRS. DOWEY [*To restore cheerfulness.*] Oh, it's a terrible war.

ALL. [*Brightening.*] It is. You may say so.

MRS. DOWEY [*Encouraged.*] What I say is, the men is splendid, but I'm none so easy about the staff. That's your weak point, Mrs. Mickleham.

MRS. MICKLEHAM [*On the defence, but determined to reveal nothing that might be of use to the enemy.*] You may take it from me, the staff's all right.

MRS. DOWEY And very relieved I am to hear you say it.

[*It is here that the HAGGERTY WOMAN has the remaining winkle.*]

MRS. MICKLEHAM You don't understand properly about trench warfare. If I had a map——

MRS. DOWEY [*Wetting her finger to draw lines on the table.*] That's the river Sommy. Now, if we had barrages here——

MRS. TWYMLEY Very soon you would be enfilided. Where's your supports, my lady?

[MRS. DOWEY *is damped.*]

MRS. MICKLEHAM What none of you grasps is that this is a artillery war——

THE HAGGERTY WOMAN [*Strengthened by the winkle.*] I say that the word is Salonaiky.

[*The others purse their lips.*]

MRS. TWYMLEY [*With terrible meaning.*] We'll change the subject. Have you seen this week's *Fashion Chat?* [*She has evidently seen and devoured it herself, and even licked up the crumbs.*] The gabardine with accordion pleats has quite gone out.

MRS. DOWEY [*Her old face sparkling.*] My sakes! You tell me?

MRS. TWYMLEY [*With the touch of haughtiness that comes of great topics.*] The plain smock has come in again, with silk lacing, giving that charming chic effect.

MRS. DOWEY Oho!

MRS. MICKLEHAM I must say I was always partial to the straight line [*Thoughtfully regarding the want of line in* MRS. TWYMLEY'S *person*] though trying to them as is of too friendly a figure.

[*It is here that the* HAGGERTY WOMAN *fingers close unostentatiously upon a piece of sugar.*]

MRS. TWYMLEY [*Sailing into the Empyrean.*] Lady Dolly Kanister was seen conversing across the railings in a dainty *de jou.*

MRS. DOWEY Fine would I have liked to see her.

MRS. TWYMLEY She is equally popular as maid, wife, and munition-worker. Her two children is inset. Lady Pops Babington was married in a tight tulle.

MRS. MICKLEHAM What was her going-away dress?

MRS. TWYMLEY A champagny cream velvet with dreamy corsage.

She's married to Colonel the Hon. Chingford—"Snubs," they called him at Eton.

THE HAGGERTY WOMAN [*Having disposed of the sugar.*] Very likely he'll be sent to Salonaiky.

MRS. MICKLEHAM Wherever he is sent, she'll have the same tremors as the rest of us. She'll be as keen to get the letters wrote with pencils as you or me.

MRS. TWYMLEY Them pencil letters.

MRS. DOWEY [*In her sweet Scotch voice, timidly, afraid she may be going too far.*] And women in enemy lands gets those pencil letters and then stop getting them, the same as ourselves. Let's occasionally think of that.

[*She has gone too far. Chairs are pushed back.*]

THE HAGGERTY WOMAN I ask you!

MRS. MICKLEHAM That's hardly language, Mrs. Dowey.

MRS. DOWEY [*Scared.*] Kindly excuse. I swear to death I'm none of your pacifists.

MRS. MICKLEHAM Freely granted.

MRS. TWYMLEY I've heard of females that have no male relations, and so they have no man-party at the wars. I've heard of them, but I don't mix with them.

MRS. MICKLEHAM What can the likes of us have to say to them? It's not their war.

MRS. DOWEY [*Wistfully.*] They are to be pitied.

MRS. MICKLEHAM But the place for them, Mrs. Dowey, is within doors with the blinds down.

MRS. DOWEY [*Hurriedly.*] That's the place for them.

MRS. MICKLEHAM I saw one of them to-day buying a flag. I thought it was very impudent of her.

MRS. DOWEY [*Meekly.*] So it was.

MRS. MICKLEHAM [*Trying to look modest with indifferent success.*] I had a letter from my son, Percy, yesterday.

MRS. TWYMLEY Alfred sent me his photo.

THE HAGGERTY WOMAN Letters from Salonaiky is less common.

[*Three bosoms heave, but not, alas, MRS. DOWEY's. Nevertheless she doggedly knits her lips.*]

MRS. DOWEY [*The criminal.*] Kenneth writes to me every week. [*There are exclamations. The dauntless old thing holds aloft a packet of letters.*] Look at this. All his.

[*The* HAGGERTY WOMAN *whimpers.*]

MRS. TWYMLEY   Alfred has little time for writing, being a bombardier.

MRS. DOWEY [*Relentlessly.*]   Do your letters begin "Dear mother"?

MRS. TWYMLEY   Generally.

MRS. MICKLEHAM   Invariable.

THE HAGGERTY WOMAN   Every time.

MRS. DOWEY [*Delivering the knock-out blow.*]   Kenneth's begin "Dearest mother."

[*No one can think of the right reply.*]

MRS. TWYMLEY [*Doing her best.*]   A short man, I should say, judging by yourself.

[*She ought to have left it alone.*]

MRS. DOWEY   Six feet two—and a half.

[*The gloom deepens.*]

MRS. MICKLEHAM [*Against her better judgment.*]   A kilty, did you tell me?

MRS. DOWEY   Most certainly. He's in the famous Black Watch.

THE HAGGERTY WOMAN [*Producing her handkerchief.*]   The Surrey Rifles is the famousest.

MRS. MICKLEHAM   There you and the King disagrees, Mrs. Haggerty. His choice is the Buffs, same as my Percy's.

MRS. TWYMLEY [*Magnanimously.*]   Give me the R. H. A. and you can keep all the rest.

MRS. DOWEY   I'm sure I have nothing to say against the Surreys and the R. H. A. and the Buffs; but they are just breeches regiments, I understand.

THE HAGGERTY WOMAN   We can't all be kilties.

MRS. DOWEY [*Crushingly.*]   That's very true.

MRS. TWYMLEY [*It is foolish of her, but she can't help saying it.*] Has your Kenneth great hairy legs?

MRS. DOWEY   Tremendous.

> [*The wicket woman: but let us also say "Poor* SARAH ANN DOWEY." *For at this moment, enter Nemesis. In other words, the less important part of a clergyman appears upon the stair.*]

MRS. MICKLEHAM   It's the reverent gent!

MRS. DOWEY [*Little knowing what he is bringing her.*]   I see he has had his boots heeled.

> [*It may be said of* MR. WILLINGS *that his happy smile always walks in front of him. This smile makes music of his life, it means that once again he has been chosen, in his opinion, as the central figure in romance. No one can well have led a more drab existence, but he will never know it; he will always think of himself, humbly though elatedly, as the chosen of the gods. Of him must it have been originally written that adventures are for the adventurous. He meets them at every street corner. For instance, he assists an old lady off a bus, and asks her if he can be of any further help. She tells him that she wants to know the way to Maddox the butcher's. Then comes the kind triumphant smile; it always comes first, followed by its explanation, "I was there yesterday!" This is the merest sample of the adventures that keep* MR. WILLINGS *up to the mark.*
>
> *Since the war broke out, his zest for life has become almost terrible. He can scarcely lift a newspaper and read of a hero without remembering that he knows some one of the same name. The Soldiers' Rest he is connected with was once a china emporium, and [mark my words], he had bought his tea service at it. Such is life when you are in the thick of it. Sometimes he feels that he is part of a gigantic spy drama. In the course of his extraordinary comings and goings he meets with Great Personages, of course, and is the confidential recipient of secret news. Before imparting the news he does*

not, as you might expect, first smile expansively; on the con-
trary, there comes over his face an awful solemnity, which,
however, means the same thing. When divulging the names of
the personages, he first looks around to make sure that no
suspicious character is about, and then, lowering his voice,
tells you, "I had that from Mr. Farthing himself—he is the
secretary of the Bethnal Green Branch,—h'sh!"

There is a commotion about finding a worthy chair for
the reverent, and there is also some furtive pulling down of
sleeves, but he stands surveying the ladies through his tri-
umphant smile. This amazing man knows that he is about
to score again.]

MR. WILLINGS [*Waving aside the chairs.*]   I thank you. But not at
all. Friends, I have news.

MRS. MICKLEHAM   News?

THE HAGGERTY WOMAN   From the Front?

MRS. TWYMLEY   My Alfred, sir?

[*They are all grown suddenly anxious—all except the hostess,*
who knows that there can never be any news from the Front
for her.]

MR. WILLINGS   I tell you at once that all is well. The news is for
Mrs. Dowey.

[*She stares.*]

MRS. DOWEY   News for me?

MR. WILLINGS   Your son, Mrs. Dowey—he has got five days' leave.
[*She shakes her head slightly, or perhaps it only trembles a little on its*
stem.] Now, now, good news doesn't kill.

MRS. TWYMLEY   We're glad, Mrs. Dowey.

MRS. DOWEY   You're sure?

MR. WILLINGS   Quite sure. He has arrived.

MRS. DOWEY   He is in London?

MR. WILLINGS   He is. I have spoken to him.

MRS. MICKLEHAM   You lucky woman.

[*They might see that she is not looking lucky, but experience has told them how differently these things take people.*]

MR. WILLINGS [*Marvelling more and more as he unfolds his tale.*] Ladies, it is quite a romance. I was in the—— [*He looks around cautiously, but he knows that they are all to be trusted.*] in the Church Army quarters in Central Street, trying to get on the track of one or two of our missing men. Suddenly my eyes—I can't account for it—but suddenly my eyes alighted on a Highlander seated rather drearily on a bench, with his kit at his feet.

THE HAGGERTY WOMAN   A big man?

MR. WILLINGS   A great brawny fellow. [*The* HAGGERTY WOMAN *groans.*] "My friend," I said at once, "welcome back to Blighty." I make a point of calling it Blighty. "I wonder," I said, "if there is anything I can do for you?" He shook his head. "What regiment?" I asked. [*Here* MR. WILLINGS *very properly lowers his voice to a whisper.*] "Black Watch, Fifth Battalion," he said. "Name?" I asked. "Dowey," he said.

MRS. MICKLEHAM   I declare. I do declare.

MR. WILLINGS [*Showing how the thing was done, with the help of a chair.*]   I put my hand on his shoulder as it might be thus. "Kenneth Dowey," I said, "I know your mother."

MRS. DOWEY [*Wetting her lips.*]   What did he say to that?

MR. WILLINGS   He was incredulous. Indeed, he seemed to think I was balmy. But I offered to bring him straight to you. I told him how much you had talked to me about him.

MRS. DOWEY   Bring him here!

MRS. MICKLEHAM   I wonder he needed to be brought.

MR. WILLINGS   He had just arrived, and was bewildered by the great city. He listened to me in the taciturn Scotch way, and then he gave a curious laugh.

MRS. TWYMLEY   Laugh?

MR. WILLINGS [*Whose wild life has brought him into contact with the strangest people.*]   The Scotch, Mrs. Twymley, express their emotions differently from us. With them tears signify a rollicking mood, while merriment denotes that they are plunged in gloom. When I had finished he said at once, "Let us go and see the old lady."

MRS. DOWEY [*Backing, which is the first movement she has made since he began his tale.*]   Is he——coming?

MR. WILLINGS [*Gloriously.*]   He has come. He is up there. I told
him I thought I had better break the joyful news to you.

> [*Three women rush to the window.* MRS. DOWEY *looks at her
> pantry door, but perhaps she remembers that it does not lock
> on the inside. She stands rigid, though her face has gone very
> grey.*]

MRS. DOWEY   Kindly get them to go away.

MR. WILLINGS   Ladies, I think this happy occasion scarcely requires you. [*He is not the man to ask of woman a sacrifice that he is
not prepared to make himself.*] I also am going instantly. [*They all
survey* MRS. DOWEY, *and understand—or think they understand.*]

MRS. TWYMLEY [*Pail and mop in hand.*]   I would thank none for
their company if my Alfred was at the door.

MRS. MICKLEHAM [*Similarly burdened.*]   The same from me. Shall
I send him down, Mrs. Dowey? [*The old lady does not hear her. She
is listening, terrified, for a step on the stairs.*]   Look at the poor,
joyous thing, sir. She has his letters in her hand.

> [*The three women go.* MR. WILLINGS *puts a kind hand on
> MRS. DOWEY's shoulder. He thinks he so thoroughly under-
> stands the situation.*]

MR. WILLINGS   A good son, Mrs. Dowey, to have written to you
so often.

> [*Our old criminal quakes, but she grips the letters more
> tightly.* PRIVATE DOWEY *descends.*]

"Dowey, my friend, there she is, waiting for you, with your letters in
her hand."

DOWEY [*Grimly.*]   "That's great."

> [MR. WILLINGS *ascends the stair without one backward glance,
> like the good gentleman he is; and the DOWEYS are left to-
> gether, with nearly the whole room between them. He is a
> great rough chunk of Scotland, howked out of her not so
> much neatly as liberally; and in his Black Watch uniform, all*

*caked with mud, his kit and nearly all his worldly possessions
on his back, he is an apparition scarcely less fearsome [but
so much less ragged] than those ancestors of his who trotted
with Prince Charlie to Derby. He stands silent, scowling at
the old lady, daring her to raise her head; and she would like
very much to do it, for she longs to have a first glimpse of
her son. When he does speak, it is to jeer at her.]*

"Do you recognize your loving son, missis?" [*"Oh, the fine Scotch
tang of him," she thinks.*] "I'm pleased I wrote so often." [*"Oh, but he's
raized," she thinks.*] *He strides towards her, and seizes the letters
roughly.* "Let's see them."

[*There is a string round the package, and he unties it, and
examines the letters at his leisure with much curiosity. The
envelopes are in order, all addressed in pencil to* MRS. DOWEY,
*with the proud words "Opened by Censor" on them. But the
letter paper inside contains not a word of writing.*]

"Nothing but blank paper! Is this your writing in pencil on the
envelope?" [*She nods, and he gives the matter further consideration.*]
"The covey told me you were a charwoman; so I suppose you
picked the envelopes out of waste-paper baskets, or such like, and then
changed the addresses?" [*She nods again; still she dare not look up,
but she is admiring his legs. When, however, he would cast the letters
into the fire, she flames up with sudden spirit. She clutches them.*]
"Don't you burn them letters, mister."
"They're not real letters."
"They're all I have."
[*He turns to irony.*]   "I thought you had a son?"
"I never had a man nor son nor anything. I just call myself Missis
to give me a standing."
"Well, it's past my seeing through."

[*He turns to look for some explanation from the walls. She
gets a peep at him at last. Oh, what a grandly set-up man!
Oh, the stride of him. Oh, the noble rage of him. Oh, Samson
had been like this before that woman took him in hand.*]

[*He whirls round on her.*] "What made you do it?"

"It was everybody's war, mister, except mine." [*She beats her arms.*] "I wanted it to be my war too."

"You'll need to be plainer. And yet I'm d—d if I care to hear you, you lying old trickster."

[*The words are merely what were to be expected, and so are endurable; but he has moved towards the door.*]

"You're not going already, mister?"

"Yes, I just came to give you an ugly piece of my mind."

[*She holds out her arms longingly.*] "You haven't gave it to me yet."

"You have a cheek!"

[*She gives further proof of it.*] "You wouldn't drink some tea?"

"Me! I tell you I came here for the one purpose of blazing away at you."

[*It is such a roaring negative that it blows her into a chair. But she is up again in a moment, is this spirited old lady.*] "You could drink the tea while you was blazing away. There's winkles."

"Is there?" [*He turns interestedly towards the table, but his proud Scots character checks him, which is just as well, for what she should have said was that there had been winkles.*] "Not me. You're just a common rogue." [*He seats himself far from the table.*] "Now, then, out with it. Sit down!" [*She sits meekly; there is nothing she would not do for him.*] "As you char, I suppose you are on your feet all day."

"I'm more on my knees."

"That's where you should be to me."

"Oh, mister, I'm willing."

"Stop it. Go on, you accomplished liar."

"It's true that my name is Dowey."

"It's enough to make me change mine."

"I've been charring and charring and charring as far back as I mind. I've been in London this twenty years."

"We'll skip your early days. I have an appointment."

"And then when I was old the war broke out."

"How could it affect you?"

"Oh, mister, that's the thing. It didn't affect me. It affected everybody but me. The neighbours looked down on me. Even the posters, on the walls, of the woman saying, 'Go, my boy,' leered at me. I sometimes cried by myself in the dark. You won't have a cup of tea?"

"No."

"Sudden like the idea came to me to pretend I had a son."

"You depraved old limmer! But what in the name of Old Nick made you choose me out of the whole British Army?"

[MRS. DOWEY *giggles. There is little doubt that in her youth she was an accomplished flirt.*] "Maybe, mister, it was because I liked you best."

"Now, now, woman."

"I read one day in the papers, 'In which he was assisted by Private K. Dowey, 5th Battalion, Black Watch.'"

[PRIVATE K. DOWEY *is flattered.*] "Did you, now! Well, I expect that's the only time I was ever in the papers."

[MRS. DOWEY *tries it on again.*] "I didn't choose you for that alone. I read a history of the Black Watch first, to make sure it was the best regiment in the world."

"Anybody could have told you that." [*He is moving about now in better humour, and, meeting the loaf in his stride, he cuts a slice from it. He is hardly aware of this, but* MRS. DOWEY *knows.*] "I like the Scotch voice of you, woman. It drummles on like a hill burn."

"Prosen Water runs by where I was born." [*Flirting again.*] "May be it teached me to speak, mister."

"Canny, woman, canny."

"I read about the Black Watch's ghostly piper that plays proudly when the men of the Black Watch do well, and prouder when they fall."

"There's some foolish story of that kind." [*He has another careless slice off the loaf.*] "But you couldn't have been living here at that time or they would have guessed. I suppose you flitted?"

"Yes, it cost me eleven and sixpence."

"How did you guess the *K* in my name stood for Kenneth?"

"Does it?"

"Umpha."

"An angel whispered it to me in my sleep."

"Well, that's the only angel in the whole black business." [*He chuckles.*]

"You little thought I would turn up!" [*Wheeling suddenly on her.*] "Or did you?"

"I was beginning to weary for a sight of you, Kenneth."
"What word was that?"
"Mister."

[*He helps himself to butter, and she holds out the jam pot to him, but he haughtily rejects it. Do you think she gives in now? Not a bit of it.*]

[*He returns to sarcasm.*] "I hope you're pleased with me now you see me."
"I'm very pleased. Does your folk live in Scotland?"
"Glasgow."
"Both living?"
"Ay."
"Is your mother terrible proud of you?"
"Naturally."
"You'll be going to them?"
"After I've had a skite in London first."
[*The old lady sniffs.*] "So she is in London!"
"Who?"
"Your young lady."
"Are you jealous?"
"Not me."
"You needna be. She's a young thing."
"You surprise me. A beauty, no doubt?"
"You may be sure." [*He tries the jam.*] "She's a titled person. She is equally popular as maid, wife, and munition-worker."

[MRS. DOWEY *remembers* LADY DOLLY KANISTER *so familiar to readers of fashionable gossip, and a very leery expression indeed comes into her face.*]

"Tell me more about her, man."
"She has sent me a lot of things, especially cakes, and a worsted waistcoat, with a loving message on the enclosed card."

[*The old lady is now in a quiver of excitement. She loses control of her arms, which jump excitedly this way and that.*]

"You'll try one of my cakes, mister?"
"Not me."

"They're of my own making."

"No, I thank you."

[*But with a funny little run she is in the pantry and back again. She planks down a cake before him, at sight of which he gapes.*]

"What's the matter? Tell me, oh, tell me mister."

"That's exactly the kind of cake that her ladyship sends me."

[MRS. DOWEY *is now a very glorious old character indeed.*]

"Is the waistcoat right, mister? I hope the Black Watch colours pleased you."

"Wha—t! Was it you?"

"I daredna give my own name, you see, and I was always reading hers in the papers."

[*The badgered man looms over her, terrible for the last time.*]

"Woman, is there no getting rid of you!"

"Are you angry?"

[*He sits down with a groan.*]

"Oh, hell! Give me some tea."

[*She rushes about preparing a meal for him, every bit of her wanting to cry out to every other bit, "Oh, glory, glory, glory!" For a moment she hovers behind his chair. "Kenneth!" she murmurs. "What?" he asks, no longer aware that she is taking a liberty. "Nothing," she says, "just Kenneth," and is off gleefully for the tea-caddy. But when his tea is poured out, and he has drunk a saucerful, the instinct of self-preservation returns to him between two bites.*]

"Don't you be thinking, missis, for one minute that you have got me."

"No, no."

[*On that understanding he unbends.*]

"I have a theatre to-night, followed by a randy-dandy."

"Oho! Kenneth, this is a queer first meeting!"

"It is, woman, oh, it is," guardedly, "and it's also a last meeting."

"Yes, yes."

"So here's to you—you old mop and pail. *Ave atque vale.*"

"What's that?"

"That means Hail and Farewell."

"Are you a scholar?"

"Being Scotch, there's almost nothing I don't know."

"What was you to trade?"

"Carter, glazier, orraman, any rough jobs."

"You're a proper man to look at."

"I'm generally admired."

"She's an enviable woman."

"Who?"

"Your mother."

"Eh? Oh, that was just protecting myself from you. I have neither father nor mother nor wife nor grandmama." [*Bitterly.*] "This party never even knew who his proud parents were."

"Is that." [*Gleaming.*] "Is that true?"

"It's gospel."

"Heaven be praised!"

"Eh? None of that! I was a fool to tell you. But don't think you can take advantage of it. Pass the cake."

"I daresay it's true we'll never meet again, Kenneth, but—but if we do, I wonder where it will be?"

"Not in this world."

"There's no telling." [*Leering ingratiatingly.*] "It might be at Berlin."

"Tod, if I ever get to Berlin, I believe I'll find you there waiting for me!"

"With a cup of tea for you in my hand."

"Yes, and—" [*Heartily.*] "Very good tea too."

[*He has partaken heavily, he is now in high good humour.*]

"Kenneth, we could come back by Paris!"

"All the ladies," slapping his knees, "likes to go to Paris."

"Oh, Kenneth, Kenneth, if just once before I die I could be fitted for a Paris gown with dreamy corsage!"

"You're all alike, old covey. We have a song about it." He sings:

> "Mrs. Gill is very ill,
> Nothing can improve her
> But to see the Tuileries
> And waddle through the Louvre."

[*No song ever had a greater success.* MRS. DOWEY *is doubled up with mirth. When she comes to, when they both come to, for there are a pair of them, she cries:*]

"You must learn me that," and off she goes in song also:

> "Mrs. Dowey's very ill,
> Nothing can improve her."

"Stop!" cries clever Kenneth, and finishes the verse:

> "But dressed up in a Paris gown
> To waddle through the Louvre."

[*They fling back their heads, she points at him, he points at her. She says ecstatically:*]

"Hairy legs!"

[*A mad remark, which brings him to his senses; he remembers who and what she is.*]

"Mind your manners!" [*Rising.*] "Well, thank you for my tea. I must be stepping."

[*Poor* MRS. DOWEY, *he is putting on his kit.*]

"Where are you living?"

[*He sighs.*]

"That's the question. But there's a place called The Hut, where some of the Second Battalion are. They'll take me in. Beggars" [*Bitterly*] "can't be choosers."

"Beggars?"

"I've never been here before. If you knew." [*A shadow coming over him.*] "What it is to be in such a place without a friend. I was crazy with glee, when I got my leave, at the thought of seeing London at last, but after wandering its streets for four hours, I would almost have been glad to be back in the trenches."

[*"If you knew," he has said, but indeed the old lady knows.*]

"That's my quandorum too, Kenneth."

[*He nods sympathetically.*]

"I'm sorry for you, you poor old body." [*Shouldering his kit.*] "But I see no way out for either of us."

[*A cooing voice says, "Do you not?"*]

"Are you at it again!"

[*She knows that it must be now or never. She has left her biggest guns for the end. In her excitement she is rising up and down on her toes.*]

"Kenneth, I've heard that the thing a man on leave longs for more than anything else is a bed with sheets, and a bath."
"You never heard anything truer."
"Go into that pantry, Kenneth Dowey, and lift the dresser-top, and tell me what you see."

[*He goes. There is an awful stillness. He returns, impressed.*]

"It's a kind of a bath!"
"You could do yourself there pretty, half at a time."
"Me?"
"There's a woman through the wall that would be very willing to give me a shakedown till your leave is up."

[*He snorts.*]

"Oh, is there!"

[*She has not got him yet, but there is still one more gun.*]

"Kenneth, look!"

[*With these simple words she lets down the bed. She says no more; an effect like this would be spoilt by language. Fortunately he is not made of stone. He thrills.*]

"My word! That's the dodge we need in the trenches."

"That's your bed, Kenneth."

"Mine?" [*He grins at her.*] "You queer old divert. What can make you so keen to be burdened by a lump like me?"

"He! he! he! he!"

"I tell you, I'm the commonest kind of man."

"I'm just the commonest kind of old wife myself."

"I've been a kick-about all my life, and I'm no great shakes at the war."

"Yes, you are. How many Germans have you killed?"

"Just two for certain, and there was no glory in it. It was just because they wanted my shirt."

"Your shirt?"

"Well, they said it was their shirt."

"Have you took prisoners?"

"I once took half a dozen, but that was a poor affair too."

"How could one man take half a dozen?"

"Just in the usual way. I surrounded them."

"Kenneth, you're just my ideal."

"You're easily pleased."

[*He turns again to the bed.*] "Let's see how the thing works." [*He kneads the mattress with his fist, and the result is so satisfactory that he puts down his kit.*]

"Old lady, if you really want me, I'll bide."

"Oh! oh! oh! oh!"

[*Her joy is so demonstrative that he has to drop a word of warning.*]

"But, mind you, I don't accept you as a relation. For your personal glory, you can go on pretending to the neighbours; but the best I can say for you is that you're on your probation. I'm a cautious character, and we must see how you'll turn out."

"Yes, Kenneth."

"And now, I think, for that bath. My theatre begins at six-thirty. A cove I met on a 'bus is going with me."

[*She is a little alarmed.*]

"You're sure you'll come back?"

"Yes, yes." [*Handsomely.*] "I leave my kit in pledge."

"You won't liquor up too freely, Kenneth?"

"You're the first" [*Chuckling*] "to care whether I do or not." [*Nothing she has said has pleased the lonely man so much as this.*] "I promise. Tod, I'm beginning to look forward to being awakened in the morning by hearing you cry, 'Get up, you lazy swine.' I've kind of envied men that had womenfolk with the right to say that."

[*He is passing to the bathroom when a diverting notion strikes him.*]

"What is it, Kenneth?"

"The theatre. It would be showier if I took a lady."

[MRS. DOWEY *feels a thumping at her breast.*]

"Kenneth, tell me this instant what you mean. Don't keep me on the jumps."

[*He turns her round.*]

"No, it couldn't be done."

"Was it me you were thinking of?"

"Just for the moment." [*Regretfully.*] "But you have no style."

[*She catches hold of him by the sleeve.*]

"Not in this, of course. But, oh, Kenneth, if you saw me in my merino! It's laced up the back in the very latest."

"Hum." [*Doubtfully*.] "But let's see it."

[*It is produced from a drawer, to which the old lady runs with almost indecent haste. The connoisseur examines it critically.*]

"Looks none so bad. Have you a bit of chiffon for the neck? It's not bombs nor Kaisers nor Tipperary that men in the trenches think of, it's chiffon."

"I swear I have, Kenneth. And I have a bangle, and a muff, and gloves."

"Ay, ay." [*He considers.*] "Do you think you could give your face less of a homely look?"

"I'm sure I could."

"Then you can have a try. But, mind you, I promise nothing. All will depend on the effect."

[*He goes onto the pantry, and the old lady is left alone. Not alone, for she is ringed round by entrancing hopes and dreadful fears. They beam on her and jeer at her, they pull her this way and that; with difficulty she breaks through them and rushes to her pail, hot water, soap, and a looking-glass. Our last glimpse of her for this evening shows her staring (not discontentedly) at her soft old face, licking her palm, and pressing it to her hair. Her eyes are sparking.*]

[*One evening a few days later* MRS. TWYMLEY *and* MRS. MICKLEHAM *are in* MRS. DOWEY'S *house, awaiting that lady's return from some fashionable dissipation. They have undoubtedly been discussing the war, for the first words we catch are:*]

MRS. MICKLEHAM   I tell you flat, Amelia, I bows no knee to junkerdom.

MRS. TWYMLEY   Sitting here by the fire, you and me, as one to another, what do you think will happen after the war? Are we to go back to being as we were?

MRS. MICKLEHAM   Speaking for myself, Amelia, not me. The war has wakened me up to a understanding of my own importance that is really astonishing.

MRS. TWYMLEY   Same here. Instead of being the poor worms the like of you and me thought we was, we turns out to be visible departments of a great and haughty empire.

> [*They are well under weigh, and with a little luck we might now hear their views on various passing problems of the day, such as the neglect of science in our public schools. But in comes the* HAGGERTY WOMAN, *and spoils everything. She is attired, like them, in her best, but the effect of her is that her clothes have gone out for a walk, leaving her at home.*]

MRS. MICKLEHAM   [*With deep distaste.*]   Here's that submarine again.

> [*The* HAGGERTY WOMAN *cringes to them, but gets no encouragement.*]

THE HAGGERTY WOMAN   It's a terrible war.
MRS. TWYMLEY   Is that so?
THE HAGGERTY WOMAN   I wonder what will happen when it ends?
MRS. MICKLEHAM   I have no idea.

> [*The intruder produces her handkerchief, but does not use it. After all, she is in her best.*]

THE HAGGERTY WOMAN   Are they not back yet?

> [*Perfect ladies must reply to a direct question.*]

MRS. MICKLEHAM   No. [*Icily.*]   We have been waiting this half hour. They are at the theatre again.
THE HAGGERTY WOMAN   You tell me! I just popped in with an insignificant present for him, as his leave is up.
MRS. TWYMLEY   The same errand brought us.
THE HAGGERTY WOMAN   My present is cigarettes.

> [*They have no intention of telling her what their presents are, but the secret leaps from them.*]

MRS. MICKLEHAM So is mine.
MRS. TWYMLEY Mine too.

[*Triumph of the* HAGGERTY WOMAN. *But it is short-lived.*]

MRS. MICKLEHAM Mine has gold tips.
MRS. TWYMLEY So has mine.

[*The* HAGGERTY WOMAN *need not say a word. You have only to look at her to know that her cigarettes are not gold-tipped. She tries to brazen it out, which is so often a mistake.*]

THE HAGGERTY WOMAN What care I? Mine is Exquisytos.

[*No wonder they titter.*]

MRS. MICKLEHAM Excuse us, Mrs. Haggerty (if that's your name), but the word is Exquiseetos.
THE HAGGERTY WOMAN Much obliged. [*Weeps.*]
MRS. MICKLEHAM I think I heard a taxi.
MRS. TWYMLEY It will be her third this week.

[*They peer through the blind. They are so excited that rank is forgotten.*]

THE HAGGERTY WOMAN What is she in?
MRS. MICKLEHAM A new astrakhan jacket he gave her, with Venus sleeves.
THE HAGGERTY WOMAN Has she sold her gabardine coat?
MRS. MICKLEHAM Not her! She has them both at the theatre, warm night though it is. She's wearing the astrakhan, and carrying the gabardine, flung careless-like over her arm.
THE HAGGERTY WOMAN I saw her strutting about with him yesterday, looking as if she thought the two of them made a procession.
MRS. TWYMLEY Hsh! [*Peeping.*] Strike me dead, if she's not coming mincing down the stair, hooked on his arm!

[*Indeed it is thus that* MRS. DOWEY *enters. Perhaps she had seen shadows lurking on the blind, and at once hooked on to* KENNETH *to impress the visitors. She is quite capable of it.*]

[*Now we see what* KENNETH *saw that afternoon five days
ago when he emerged from the bathroom and found the old
trembler awaiting his inspection. Here are the muff and the
gloves and the chiffon, and such a kind old bonnet that it
makes you laugh at once; I don't know how to describe it,
but it is trimmed with a kiss, as bonnets should be when the
wearer is old and frail. We must take the merino for granted
until she steps out of the astrakhan. She is dressed up to the
nines, there is no doubt about it. Yes, but is her face less
homely? Above all, has she style? The answer is in a stout
affirmative. Ask* KENNETH. *He knows. Many a time he has had
to go behind a door to roar hilariously at the old lady. He
has thought of her as a lark to tell his mates about by and by;
but for some reason that he cannot fathom, he knows now
that he will never do that.*]

MRS. DOWEY   Kenneth. [*Affecting surprise.*] We have visitors!
DOWEY   Your servant, ladies.

[*He is no longer mud-caked and dour. A very smart figure is
this* PRIVATE DOWEY, *and he winks engagingly at the visitors,
like one who knows that for jolly company you cannot easily
beat charwomen. The pleasantries that he and they have
exchanged this week! The sauce he has given them. The wit
of* MRS. MICKLEHAM'S *retorts. The badinage of* MRS. TWYMLEY.
The neat giggles of the HAGGERTY WOMAN. *There has been
nothing like it since you took the countess in to dinner.*]

MRS. TWYMLEY   We should apologise. We're not meaning to stay.
MRS. DOWEY   You are very welcome. Just wait [*The ostentation of
this!*] till I get out of my astrakhan—and my muff—and my gloves—
and [*It is the bonnet's turn now*] my Excelsior.

[*At last we see her in the merino (a triumph).*]

MRS. MICKLEHAM   You've given her a glory time, Mr. Dowey.
DOWEY   It's her that has given it to me, missis.
MRS. DOWEY   Hey! hey! hey! hey! He just pampers me. [*Waggling
her fists.*] The Lord forgive us, but this being the last night, we had

a sit-down supper at a restaurant! [*Vehemently.*] I swear by God that we had champagny wine. [*There is a dead stillness, and she knows very well what it means, she has even prepared it.*] And to them as doubts my word—here's the cork.

> [*She places the cork, in its lovely gold drapery, upon the table.*]

MRS. MICKLEHAM I'm sure!

MRS. TWYMLEY I would thank you, Mrs. Dowey, not to say a word against my Alfred.

MRS. DOWEY Me!

DOWEY Come, come, ladies. [*In the masterful way that is so hard for women to resist.*] If you say another word, I'll kiss the lot of you.

> [*There is a moment of pleased confusion.*]

MRS. MICKLEHAM Really, them sodgers!

THE HAGGERTY WOMAN The kilties is the worst!

MRS. TWYMLEY I'm sure. [*Heartily.*] We don't grudge you your treats, Mrs. Dowey; and sorry we are that this is the end.

DOWEY Yes, it's the end. [*With a troubled look at his old lady.*] I must be off in ten minutes.

> [*The little soul is too gallant to break down in company. She hurries into the pantry and shuts the door.*]

MRS. MICKLEHAM Poor thing! But we must run, for you'll be having some last words to say to her.

DOWEY I kept her out long on purpose so as to have less time to say them in.

> [*He more than half wishes that he could make a bolt to a public-house.*]

MRS. TWYMLEY It's the best way. [*In the important affairs of life there is not much that any one can teach a charwoman.*] Just a mere nothing, to wish you well, Mr. Dowey.

> [*All three present him with the cigarettes.*]

MRS. MICKLEHAM   A scraping, as one might say.

THE HAGGERTY WOMAN   The heart [*Enigmatically*] is warm though it may not be gold-tipped.

DOWEY   You bricks!

THE LADIES   Good luck, cocky.

DOWEY   The same to you. And if see a sodger man up there in a kilt, he is one that is going back with me. Tell him not to come down, but—but to give me till the last minute, and then to whistle.

> [*It is quite a grave man who is left alone, thinking what to do next. He tries a horse laugh, but that proves of no help. He says "Hell!" to himself, but it is equally ineffective. Then he opens the pantry door and calls.*]

"Old lady."

> [*She comes timidly to the door, her hand up as if to ward off a blow.*]

"Is it time?"

> [*An encouraging voice answers her.*]

"No, no, not yet. I've left word for Dixon to whistle when go I must."

"All is ended."

"Now, then, you promised to be gay. We were to help one another."

"Yes, Kenneth."

"It's bad for me, but it's worse for you."

"The men have medals to win, you see."

"The women have their medals, too." [*He knows she likes him to order her about, so he tries it again.*]

"Come here. No, I'll come to you." [*He stands gaping at her wonderingly. He has no power of words, nor does he quite know what he would like to say.*] "God!"

"What is it, Kenneth?"

"You're a woman."

"I had near forgot it."

[*He wishes he was at the station with* DIXON. DIXON *is sure to have a bottle in his pocket. They will be roaring a song presently. But in the meantime—there is that son business. Blethers, the whole thing of course—or mostly blethers. But it's the way to please her.*]

"Have you noticed you have never called me son?"

"Have I noticed it! I was feared, Kenneth. You said I was on probation."

"And so you were. Well, the probation's ended." [*He laughs uncomfortably.*]

"The like of me! But if you want me you can have me."

"Kenneth, will I do?"

"Woman." [*Artfully gay.*] "Don't be so forward. Wait till I have proposed."

"Propose for a mother?"

"What for no?" [*In the grand style.*] "Mrs. Dowey you queer carl, you spunky tiddy, have I your permission to ask you the most important question a neglected orphan can ask of an old lady?"

[*She bubbles with mirth. Who could help it, the man has such a way with him?*]

"None of your sauce, Kenneth."

"For a long time, Mrs. Dowey, you cannot have been unaware of my sonnish feelings for you."

"Wait till I get my mop to you!"

"And if you're not willing to be my mother, I swear I'll never ask another."

[*The old divert pulls him down to her and strokes his hair.*]

"Was I a well-behaved infant, mother?"

"Not you, sonny, you were a rampaging rogue."

"Was I slow in learning to walk?"

"The quickest in our street. He! he! he!" [*She starts up.*] "Was that the whistle?"

"No, no. See here. In taking me over you have, in a manner of speaking, joined the Black Watch."

"I like to think that, Kenneth."

"Then you must behave so that the ghost piper can be proud of you. 'Tion!" [*She stands bravely at attention.*] "That's the style. Now listen. I've sent in your name as being my nearest of kin, and your allowance will be coming to you weekly in the usual way."

"Hey! hey! hey! Is it wicked, Kenneth?"

"I'll take the responsibility for it in both worlds. You see, I want you to be safeguarded in case anything hap——"

"Kenneth!"

"'Tion! Have no fear. I'll come back, covered with mud and medals. Mind you have that cup of tea waiting for me." [*He is listening for the whistle. He pulls her on to his knee.*]

"Hey! hey! hey! hey!"

"What fun we'll have writing to one another! Real letters this time!"

"Yes."

"It would be a good plan if you began the first letter as soon as I've gone."

"I will."

"I hope Lady Dolly will go on sending me cakes."

"You may be sure."

[*He ties his scarf around her neck.*]

"You must have been a bonny thing when you were young."

"Away with you!"

"That scarf sets you fine."

"Blue was always my colour."

[*The whistle sounds.*]

"Old lady, you are what Blighty means to me now."

[*She hides in the pantry again. She is out of sight to us, but she does something that makes* PRIVATE DOWEY *take off his bonnet. Then he shoulders his equipment and departs. That is he laughing coarsely with* DIXON.

[*We have one last glimpse of the old lady—a month or two after* KENNETH's *death in action. It would be rosemary to us to see her in her black dress, of which she is very proud; but let us rather peep at her in the familiar garments that make a third to her mop and pail. It is early morning, and she is having a look at her medals before setting off on the daily round. They are in a drawer, with the scarf covering them, and on the scarf a piece of lavender. First, the black frock, which she carries in her arms like a baby. Then her War Savings Certificates,* KENNETH's *bonnet, a thin packet of real letters, and the famous champagne cork. She kisses the letters, but she does not blub over them. She strokes the dress, and waggles her head over the certificates and presses the bonnet to her cheeks, and rubs the tinsel of the cork carefully with her apron. She is a tremulous old 'un; yet she exults, for she owns all these things, and also the penny flag on her breast. She puts them away in the drawer, the scarf over them, the lavender on the scarf. Her air of triumph well becomes her. She lifts the pail and the mop, and slouches off gamely to the day's toil.*]

THE END

DISCUSSION

1. When does the nature of Mrs. Dowey's "crime" first become clear? What is the playwright's purpose in withholding this information as long as he does?
2. What were Mrs. Dowey's motives for committing the crime? Is she the only "criminal" in the play? Explain.
3. How do the early conversations of the charwomen foreshadow events that occur later in the play?
4. Describe Mrs. Dowey's living quarters. How do they reflect her personality? What do you learn about Mrs. Dowey from her attitude toward personal possessions?
5. Trace the course of the relationship between Mrs. Dowey and Kenneth. How does it begin? How does it change?
6. Account for Mrs. Dowey's success in winning Kenneth's affection. Despite differences in manner, how are these two characters basically alike?
7. Which characters undergo little or no change of outlook during the course of the play? Why are they nevertheless important to the story?
8. What is the function of the brief, final scene? Would dialogue have improved it? Would the play have been as satisfying to you without it?

9. Cite instances of Barrie's humor. How does he gently but consistently satirize the standards of British "class society"?
10. What is unusual about Barrie's stage directions? How does he clearly reveal his own attitudes toward the characters whom he is portraying?
11. What is the theme of this play? Does Barrie have something to say about life which is as true today as it was in 1916, when the play was first performed? Explain.

TOPICS FOR WRITING

It has been said that plays by Barrie appeal more to the emotions than to the intellect. Discuss whether or not you feel that this is an apt description of *The Old Lady Shows Her Medals.*
Explain why the role of Mrs. Dowey requires the talents of an extremely competent actress.

NOTES

p. 217   Caledonia: Scotland
p. 217   charwomen: cleaning women
p. 218   winkles: small shellfish
p. 218   damp: discourage
p. 220   the Kaiser: German ruler during World War I
p. 222   Sommy: Mrs. Dowey's mispronunciation of the French river Somme
p. 222   enfilided: Mrs. Twymley's mispronunciation of the military term "enfiladed," meaning "raked by gunfire."
p. 222   *de jou* (French): play dress
p. 224   Black Watch: a well-known British army regiment (also the Surrey Rifles, the Buffs, and the R.H.A.)
p. 225   Nemesis: goddess of vengeance, according to ancient mythology
p. 227   Blighty (British slang): home
p. 229   Prince Charlie: Pretender to the British throne in the eighteenth century
p. 229   raized: irritated
p. 229   covey: slang for fellow or man
p. 231   limmer (Scotch): rascal
p. 231   canny (Scotch): shrewd
p. 231   flitted: moved
p. 232   skite (Scotch): a pleasant time

p. 234 randy-dandy: a noisy spree
p. 234 orraman (Scotch): odd-job man
p. 236 quandorum: Mrs. Dowey's mispronunciation of the word "quandary," meaning "problem."
p. 237 divert: slang for an odd or unusual person
p. 239 junkerdom: Mrs. Mickleham means the might of Germany
p. 241 astrakhan: fur

TO BOBOLINK,
FOR HER SPIRIT

William Inge

CHARACTERS

Renaldo
Fritz
Nellie
Bobolink
Gretchen
Annamarie

William Inge (1913-)

William Inge first attracted public attention in 1950 for his dramatic play, Come Back Little Sheba. *Since then, he has won the New York Drama Critics Award, the Pulitzer Prize, and the Donaldson Award. Many of his plays have gone on road tours, and some have been adapted for the movies. These include* Picnic, Bus Stop, *and* The Dark at the Top of the Stairs. *In 1961 he received an Oscar for the best screenplay of the year.*

Inge was born in 1913 in Independence, Kansas. Before becoming a playwright he served as a teacher and as a drama critic. To Bobolink, for Her Spirit *is one of Inge's earliest short plays. In its portrayal of an individual who cannot adjust to reality, it anticipates a theme which he has repeated, with variations, in many of his later works.*

TO BOBOLINK,
FOR HER SPIRIT

Every day the weather permits, a group of autograph hunters assembles outside the 21 Club in New York. The size of the group varies from day to day and seems to depend upon the number and magnitude of the movie stars reported to be inside. It is an oddly assorted group, most of them teen-agers, but sometimes middle-aged women are included. The ring-leader of today's group is BOBOLINK BOWEN, *a woman probably in her early thirties, who is so fat that her body, in silhouette, would form an almost perfect circle.* BOBOLINK *has the fat woman's usual disposition, stolidly complacent and happy. Her lips usually are formed in a grin of guzzling contentment. Her hair is short and kinky; she wears thick-lensed glasses that reduce her eyes to the size of buttonholes, and her clothes by necessity are simple: a man's coat-style sweater, saddle shoes and bobbysocks and bare legs that swell at the calves like bowling pins.* NELLIE, *a starved and eager woman in her late twenties, is* BOBOLINK's *dependable stand-by. The two young boys,* RENALDO *and* FRITZ, *are friends; the two young girls,* GRETCHEN *and* ANNAMARIE, *are friends also. They are people without any personal attraction they could possibly lay claim to, and so must find in others attributes they want and lack in themselves.* ANNAMARIE, *in her dress, has tried to emulate one of her favorite film stars; she wears exotic sun glasses, a complicated coiffure and exciting shoes with straps, bows and platform soles. The group has been standing around for over an hour. They have learned to handle these periods of waiting like patients in a rest home; they talk idly with one another, move restlessly about in a limited space.* GRETCHEN *knits,* FRITZ *is working a cross-word puzzle. Behind them stands the* DOORMAN, *a man of rigid and calculated dignity, dressed in a colorful uniform. He holds his head high and keeps it turned away from the autograph seekers as though to disclaim any association with them.*

RENALDO   I heard Lana Turner was in this joint last week. Man, wouldn't that be something?

FRITZ   Just imagine walking down the street one day and . . plop! all of a sudden there's Lana Turner . . . just outa the blue. Man, I'd drop my teeth.

NELLIE (*Making a claim that* BOBOLINK *would be too proud to make for herself*)   Bobolink here's got Lana Turner's autograph. Haven't you, Bobby?

BOBOLINK   Lana's no better'n anyone else.

FRITZ (*Impressed; to* BOBOLINK)   No foolin'? You got Lana Turner's autograph?

BOBOLINK (*Proving it with her autograph book*)   Think I was lying to you?

FRITZ (*To* RENALDO) Look, Ronny, she's got it.

NELLIE Oh, Bobolink's got 'em all.

BOBOLINK (*She always holds her own*) I got all of 'em that's worth gettin'.

GRETCHEN My girl friend saw her. My girl friend goes out to California every summer. Her folks are real wealthy. She saw Lana Turner on the beach one day and she just goes up to her and says, "Hi, Lana" . . . just like that. And Lana smiles back and says, "Hi!"

BOBOLINK Sure, she's not stuck-up. Now Katharine Hepburn's stuck-up, but Lana Turner's not at all. The best ones never are stuck-up.

FRITZ (*Addressing the* DOORMAN, *who stands with rigid dignity*) Hey, mister, how long's Perry Como been inside?

(*The* DOORMAN *does not respond*)

BOBOLINK (*To* FRITZ) Hey, don't you know anything? Those guys don't pay no attention to movie stars. They see so many of 'em they get sick of 'em. You can't find out anything from him.

FRITZ Are we sure Perry Como's there?

BOBOLINK (*Impatiently*) I told you I seen him, didn't I? Well, what more do you want? I was up there on the corner waitin' for a bus. Nellie here nudges me and says, "Hey, ain't that Perry Como goin' into the 21 Club?" And I looked and sure enough. There was a guy goin' in, had on the same kinda suit Perry Como had on last week over at the Paramount. Looked exactly like him.

FRITZ But are you sure it was him?

BOBOLINK Look, boy, you're never sure of anything in this world, don't you know that?

FRITZ We been waiting here over an hour.

BOBOLINK No one's asking you to stay. I waited outside the Stork Club three hours one night, three whole hours, and it was snowin'. Someone told me Elizabeth Taylor was inside and I wanted her autograph. It wasn't Elizabeth Taylor at all. Just some college girl trying to make out she was Elizabeth Taylor. I was sore, but what the heck!

NELLIE Besides, you never know what's going to happen in this racket; like the time we was waitin' outside the St. Regis for Ronald Colman, and shoot! Who cares about Ronald Colman . . .

RENALDO He's famous.

NELLIE Not very. Anyway, we was waitin' for his autograph and . . .

BOBOLINK (*Taking over*) Oh, yeh, and we'd been waiting for Ronald Colman all night and we was just about to give up and go home and then what do you think happened?

(*She's going to build up suspense by making them guess*)

NELLIE That was the best luck we ever had, wasn't it, Bobby?

BOBOLINK Well, we was just about to give up and go home when a taxi draws up at the curb and Van Johnson and Peter Lawford get out, and we got 'em both, right there on the same spot.

(*This is an impressive story. The others are a little awed*)

GRETCHEN No foolin'! You got Van Johnson and Peter Lawford?

BOBOLINK (*She produces her autograph book proudly*) And both at the same time!

NELLIE (*Producing her own evidence*) I got 'em, too.

BOBOLINK See what Peter Lawford wrote? "All my love to Bobolink." I told him that was my name.

NELLIE And he said the same thing on mine, but my name's Nellie. They're both just as cute in real life as they are in pictures, aren't they, Bobby?

BOBOLINK Not a bit stuck-up.

(*An elaborately dressed couple appears in the doorway coming out of the restaurant. The woman wears a dress of dramatic cut and an exotic hat. Their manner is ridiculously aloof and they make quite a thing of ignoring the autograph hounds*)

FRITZ (*Nudging* RENALDO) Hey, who's that?

(*They all look*)

GRETCHEN Looks like Rosalind Russell, don't it?

BOBOLINK Naw, that ain't Rosalind Russell. I seen Rosalind Russell. She's real tall.

ANNAMARIE Isn't she stunning? Don't you just love that dress?
GRETCHEN I bet that dress cost two or three hundred dollars.
ANNAMARIE 'Course it did. Probably cost more than that.

(BOBOLINK *is studying the woman, trying to decide who she is.
The woman and her escort now stand at the curb waiting for
the* DOORMAN *to hail them a cab. The hounds are gaping at
them*)

FRITZ (*Approaching the glamorous woman*) Miss, can I have
your autograph?

(*The woman is a little surprised. She looks questioningly at
her escort, who gives her an indulgent smile. So the woman,
a little mystified, signs her name to* FRITZ's *book. Then she
and her escort disappear in a cab.* FRITZ *studies the signature.
The others flock around him to see who it is, but* BOBOLINK *is
not as quickly curious as the others*)

ALL Who is she? Hey, let's see. It's not Rosalind Russell, is it?
If I missed Rosalind Russell, I could kill myself. Let's see.
FRITZ I'm trying to make it out. (*He attempts a pronunciation of
the name*) Irina Nechibidikoff.
BOBOLINK (*Emphatically*) Russian!
FRITZ Hey, she may be someone famous.
BOBOLINK Whoever heard of Irina Nechibidikoff?
ANNAMARIE Maybe she's a famous dancer.
BOBOLINK So what? She's not in the movies, is she? With a name
like that.
GRETCHEN Maybe she's a famous singer.
FRITZ Anyway, I got her, whoever she is.
BOBOLINK I'm waitin' here for Perry Como. I come for Perry
Como, and I'm gonna stay till I *get* Perry Como.
NELLIE (*To the others*) Bobby always finishes up what she starts
out to do.
BOBOLINK You tell the world I do. And I'm not leavin' here with-
out Perry Como's autograph. I been trailin' him for two years. I got
Bing Crosby; I got Frank Sinatra; I got Van Johnson and Peter Law-
ford and Jimmy Stewart and Tyrone Power . . .

NELLIE Tell 'em about the time you got Tyrone Power, Bobby.

BOBOLINK Now I mean to get Perry Como. He's not my favorite or anything, but I want to get his autograph.

NELLIE Tyrone Power's your real favorite, isn't he, Bobolink?

BOBOLINK (*With modest adoration*) Yah. Tyrone's a real guy.

NELLIE (*To the others*) Bobbie's president of the Tyrone Power Fan Club up in Irvington. (*The others are impressed*) Go on, Bobbie, tell 'em about Tyrone.

BOBOLINK (*This is too sacred to be treated lightly and* BOBOLINK *is capable of dramatizing her modesty*) No, Nellie, I don't think it's right a person should go around boasting about things like that.

NELLIE Tell 'em, Bobby. If you don', I will. (BOBOLINK, *after all, can't stop her*) Bobby's too modest about it, I think. But Tyrone Power shook her hand and told her personally that he was very indebted to her . . .

BOBOLINK I met him at the train; don't forget that, Nellie.

NELLIE As president of the Tyrone Power Fan Club in Irvington, she met his train at the Pennsylvania Station when he came in from Hollywood.

BOBOLINK And I had to fight the man at the gate to let me pass.

NELLIE That's right. She did. See, it wasn't supposed to be known that Tyrone was on that train, but the Pasadena Fan Club had wired us he was coming, so Bobby and I met him at the train to welcome him to New York, didn't we, Bobby?

BOBOLINK We didn't want him t'arrive in town all alone.

NELLIE 'Course not. So we went down to the station together. The man at the gate wouldn't let us through, but Bobby got by him, didn't you, Bobby? I had to stay behind, but Bobby got through and got right on the train, didn't you, Bobby?

BOBOLINK And I hunted all through them cars till I found him. He was still packing his things and he was in a hurry.

NELLIE But he wasn't stuck-up, was he, Bobby?

BOBOLINK (*This is sacred to her*) No, he wasn't stuck-up at all. I introduced myself as the president of the Irvington Fan Club, and told him we had forty-three members and met once a week to discuss his career.

NELLIE And he was very pleased, wasn't he, Bobby?

BOBOLINK Of course he was. And I told him us fans was awful glad he didn't marry Lana Turner 'cause, although our club don't have anything personal against Lana Turner, we never did think she was the right sort for Tyrone. And I told him that in just those words.

NELLIE   And she isn't. I mean, I like Lana Turner and I think she's awfully pretty and of course she's awful famous, but she isn't the right sort of girl for Tyrone at all.

GRETCHEN   And you got his autograph?

BOBOLINK   'Course I got his autograph, silly. Nellie did, too. And he gave me lots of his autographs to give to other club members, but he made me promise not to give them to anyone else. (*She displays her proudest acquisition*) Just club members. Then he told me to call him Tyrone, and he said he was very indebted to me. See what he wrote?

FRITZ   (*Reading the inscription aloud*) "To Bobolink, for her faithful enthusiasm and spirit." Gee!

BOBOLINK   Then he had his secretary give me a picture and he autographed it, too. It just says, "With gratitude, Tyrone." Then he shook my hand and he said he wished he could come to Irvington to visit the fan club, but he was going to be terribly busy in New York, he wouldn't have a minute to spare, and then he had to get back to Hollywood to make another picture.

ANNAMARIE   (*To* NELLIE)   Did you meet him?

NELLIE   No, but I saw him. He came hurrying through the gate with his coat collar turned up so no one would recognize him. I called out, "Hi, Tyrone! I'm a friend of Bobolink," but he started running.

BOBOLINK   He didn't want people to know who he was. Sometimes they get mobbed by fans and get their clothes ripped off and even get hurt. I wouldn't want anything like that to happen to Tyrone.

(*Another couple appear in entrance way. The young man is dapper and handsome and the girl is pretty and expensively dressed. The haughty* DOORMAN *starts hailing a cab*)

RENALDO   Hey, who's this?

GRETCHEN   Is this Perry Como?

BOBOLINK   (*With a look*)   No, that ain't Perry Como.

NELLIE   She looks familiar, don't she? I bet she's in pictures.

BOBOLINK   (*After a moment's study*)   No, she ain't in pictures.

FRITZ   They might be somebody. They might be somebody we haven't heard about yet. (*The couple stand at the curb now.* FRITZ *approaches them*) Mister, can I have your autograph?

ANNAMARIE (*To the girl*) Are you in pictures?

(*The girl smiles tolerantly and shakes her head no*)

GRETCHEN Go on and sign anyway, will you please?
ANNAMARIE I bet you're both in pictures and just don't wanta admit it. C'mon and give us your autograph.

> (*The young man and the girl smile at each other and sign the books, while the* DOORMAN *hails a cab. But this is small-time stuff for* BOBOLINK. *She has the dignity of her past career to think of. She stays back, leaning against the grill fence surrounding the club, with a look of superior calm on her face.* NELLIE *stays by her side*)

NELLIE I don't think they're anyone famous, do you, Bobolink?
BOBOLINK 'Course not. I can tell the famous ones. I can tell.
NELLIE Sure you can, Bobby.

> (*The couple go off in a cab. The* DOORMAN *returns to his position by the doorway. The young autograph seekers start studying the names that have been inscribed in their books*)

BOBOLINK They might be famous *one* day . . . I said they *might* be . . . But I don't have time to waste on people that *might* be famous.
NELLIE 'Course not.

> (*They stand quietly, removed from the others now*)

FRITZ (*Reading his new acquisitions*) Frederick Bischoff and Mary Milton. Who are they?
ANNAMARIE Yah, who are they?
GRETCHEK I bet she models. I think I seen her picture once in an ad for hair remover. Yah, that was her. I know it was. It was a picture showed her with one arm stretched over her head so you could see she didn't have no hair under her arm and was smiling real pretty.
ANNAMARIE He's probably just a model, too. He was kinda cute, though.
BOBOLINK (*Personally to* NELLIE, *in appraisal of her colleagues*) These are just kids, Nellie.

NELLIE   Yah.

FRITZ   Isn't anyone famous ever coming outa there?

RENALDO   (*To* BOBOLINK)   Are you sure you saw Perry Como go inside?

BOBOLINK   I said Perry Como was inside, didn't I? If you don't believe me, you don't have to.

NELLIE   Bobolink knows a lot more about these things than you kids do. She spotted Perry Como two blocks away and Bobolink don't make mistakes.

RENALDO   O.K. O.K. Don't get sore.

NELLIE   You might remember that Bobolink is president of the Tyrone Power Fan Club.

FRITZ   We wasn't doubtin' your word. C'mon, Renaldo. Let's wait.

GRETCHEN   Let's wait a little longer, Annamarie.

ANNAMARIE   I gotta get home for supper, Gretchen.

GRETCHEN   Let's wait.

FRITZ   (*To* RENALDO)   Let's wait.

(They resume their positions of patient attendance)

C U R T A I N

D I S C U S S I O N

1. Where, in the introductory stage notes, does Inge clarify Bobo-link's problem? Do you feel that such clarification is necessary for readers of the play? Why?

2. As an autograph enthusiast, what are Bobolink's standards? Why, for example, does she express disinterest in stars of the dance? Why is Tyrone Power a "real guy"?

3. How does Bobolink differ from her companions? In what respect is she very much like the doorman of the "21" Club?

4. What does Bobolink's manner of speech reveal about her?

5. What is ironic about Bobolink's contempt for stars who are "stuck-up"? What is equally ironic about her comment: "I don't have time to waste on people that *might* be famous"?

6. Why is Inge's use of the term "career" appropriate as it is applied to Bobolink? What makes you certain that the highlight of Bobo-link's career was just an incidental moment in Tyrone Power's?

7. There is only one reference to the family obligations of the autograph seekers. What do you conclude?
8. Which of the several stars mentioned in the play are not as well-known today as they were in 1949 when the play was first written? How is this significant?
9. Why is it noteworthy that the story ends as it began, with Bobolink and her friends standing in "patient attendance"?
10. How does Inge hold your interest in his play, despite the fact that there is no strong *rising action* or clear-cut climax?

TOPICS FOR WRITING

Write a character analysis of Bobolink
Discuss why people idolize entertainers

THE DEVIL AND
DANIEL WEBSTER

Stephen Vincent Benét

CHARACTERS

Jabez Stone
Mary Stone
Daniel Webster
Mr. Scratch
The Fiddler
Justice Hathorne
Justice Hathorne's Clerk
King Philip
Teach
Walter Butler
Simon Girty
Dale
Men and Women of Cross Corners, New Hampshire

Stephen Vincent Benét (1898-1943)

Stephen Vincent Benét is best remembered today for The Devil and Daniel Webster *and for his book-length poem about the Civil War,* John Brown's Body. *For this poem he received a Pulitzer Prize in 1928. Benét wrote several books of poetry during his lifetime, publishing the first when he was only seventeen years old. His writing reveals an interest in the history of America, and a firm understanding of its heritage.*

Benét based The Devil and Daniel Webster *on an old German legend about a magician who bargained with the devil and was dragged off to Hell twenty-four years later. The character Jabez Stone suggests the theme of the play in the opening scene, when he confides to his wife: "A man can't always be proud of everything . . . Mary. There's some things a man does, or might do—when he has to make his way."*

THE DEVIL AND DANIEL WEBSTER

The scene is the main room of a New Hampshire farmhouse in 1841, a big comfortable room that hasn't yet developed the stuffiness of a front-parlor. A door, right, leads to the kitchen—a door, left, to the outside. There is a fireplace, right. Windows, in center, show a glimpse of summer landscape. Most of the furniture has been cleared away for the dance which follows the wedding of JABEZ *and* MARY STONE,

*but there is a settle or bench by the fireplace, a table, left,
with some wedding presents upon it, at least three chairs by
the table, and a cider barrel on which the* FIDDLER *sits, in
front of the table. Near the table, against the side-wall, there
is a cupboard where there are glasses and a jug. There is a
clock.*

*A country wedding has been in progress—the wedding
of* JABEZ *and* MARY STONE. *He is a husky young farmer,
around twenty-eight or thirty. The bride is in her early
twenties. He is dressed in stiff, store clothes but not ridiculously—they are of good quality and he looks important.
The bride is in a simple white or cream wedding-dress and
may carry a small, stiff bouquet of country flowers.*

*Now the wedding is over and the guests are dancing.
The* FIDDLER *is perched on the cider barrel. He plays and calls
square-dance figures. The guests include the recognizable
types of a small New England town, doctor, lawyer, store-
keeper, old maid, schoolteacher, farmer, etc. There is an air
of prosperity and hearty country mirth about the whole affair.*

At rise, JABEZ *and* MARY *are up left center, receiving
the congratulations of a few last guests who talk to them and
pass on to the dance. The others are dancing. There is a buzz
of conversation that follows the tune of the dance-music.*

FIRST WOMAN   Right nice wedding.

FIRST MAN   Handsome couple.

SECOND WOMAN (*passing through crowd with dish of oyster-stew*)
Oysters for supper!

SECOND MAN (*passing cake*)   And layer-cake—layer-cake——

AN OLD MAN (*hobbling toward cider barrel*)   Makes me feel
young again! Oh, by jingo!

AN OLD WOMAN (*pursuing him*)   Henry, Henry, you've been drinking cider!

FIDDLER   Set to your partners! Dosy-do!

WOMAN   Mary and Jabez.

MEN   Jabez and Mary.

A WOMAN   Where's the State Senator?

A MAN   Where's the lucky bride? (*With cries of "Mary—Jabez—
strike it up, Fiddler—make room for the bride and groom," the* CROWD

drags MARY *and* JABEZ, *pleased but embarrassed, into the center of the room and* MARY *and* JABEZ *do a little solo-dance, while the* CROWD *claps, applauds and makes various remarks.*)

A MAN   Handsome steppers!

A WOMAN   She's pretty as a picture.

A SECOND MAN   Cut your pigeon-wing, Jabez!

THE OLD MAN   Young again, young again, that's the way I feel! (*He tries to cut a pigeon-wing himself.*)

THE OLD WOMAN   Henry, Henry, careful of your rheumatiz!

A THIRD WOMAN   Makes me feel all teary—seeing them so happy. (*The solo-dance ends, the music stops for a moment.*)

THE OLD MAN (*gossiping to a neighbor*)   Wonder where he got it all—Stones was always poor.

HIS NEIGHBOR   Ain't poor now—makes you wonder just a mite.

A THIRD MAN   Don't begrudge it to him—but I wonder where he got it.

THE OLD MAN (*starting to whisper*)   Let me tell you something—

THE OLD WOMAN (*quickly*)   Henry, Henry, don't you start to gossip. (*She drags him away.*)

FIDDLER (*cutting in*)   Set to your partners! Scratch for corn! (*The dance resumes, but as it does so, the* CROWD *chants back and forth.*)

WOMEN   Gossip's got a sharp tooth.

MEN   Gossip's got a mean tooth.

WOMEN   She's a lucky woman. They're a lucky pair.

MEN   That's true as gospel. But I wonder where he got it.

WOMEN   Money, land and riches.

MEN   Just came out of nowhere.

WOMEN *and* MEN (*together*)   Wonder where he got it all— But that's his business.

FIDDLER   Left and right—grand chain! (*The dance rises to a pitch of ecstasy with the final figure—the fiddle squeaks and stops. The dancers mop their brows.*)

FIRST MAN   Whew! Ain't danced like that since I was knee-high to a grasshopper!

SECOND MAN   Play us "The Portland Fancy," fiddler!

THIRD MAN   No, wait a minute, neighbor. Let's hear from the happy pair! Hey, Jabez!

FOURTH MAN   Let's hear from the State Senator! (*They crowd around* JABEZ *and push him up on the settle.*)

OLD MAN   Might as well. It's the last time he'll have the last word!

OLD WOMAN   Now, Henry Banks, you ought to be ashamed of yourself!

OLD MAN   Told you so, Jabez!

THE CROWD   Speech!

JABEZ (*embarrassed*)   Neighbors—friends—I'm not much of a speaker—spite of your 'lecting me to State Senate——

THE CROWD   That's the ticket, Jabez. Smart man, Jabez. I voted for ye. Go ahead, Senator, you're doing fine.

JABEZ   But we're certainly glad to have you here—me and Mary. And we want to thank you for coming and——

A VOICE   Vote the Whig ticket!

ANOTHER VOICE   Hooray for Daniel Webster!

JABEZ   And I'm glad Hi Foster said that, for those are my sentiments, too. Mr. Webster has promised to honor us with his presence here tonight.

THE CROWD   Hurray for Dan'l! Hurray for the greatest man in the U. S.!

JABEZ   And when he comes, I know we'll give him a real New Hampshire welcome.

THE CROWD   Sure we will—Webster forever—and to hell with Henry Clay!

JABEZ   And meanwhile—well, there's Mary and me (*takes her hand*)—and, if you folks don't have a good time, well, we won't feel right about getting married at all. Because I know I've been lucky—and I hope she feels that way, too. And, well, we're going to be happy or bust a trace! (*He wipes his brow to terrific applause. He and* MARY *look at each other.*)

A WOMAN (*in kitchen doorway*)   Come and get the cider, folks! (*The* CROWD *begins to drift away—a few to the kitchen—a few toward the door that leads to the outside. They furnish a shifting background to the next little scene, where* MARY *and* JABEZ *are left alone by the fireplace.*)

JABEZ   Mary.

MARY   Mr. Stone.

JABEZ   Mary.

MARY   My husband.

JABEZ   That's a big word, husband.

MARY   It's a good word.

JABEZ   Are you happy, Mary?

MARY   Yes. So happy, I'm afraid.

JABEZ   Afraid?

MARY   I suppose it happens to every girl—just for a minute. It's like spring turning into summer. You want it to be summer. But the spring was sweet. (*Dismissing the mood.*) I'm sorry. Forgive me. It just came and went, like something cold. As if we'd been too lucky.

JABEZ   We can't be too lucky, Mary. Not you and me.

MARY   (*rather mischievously*)   If you say so, Mr. Stone. But you don't even know what sort of housekeeper I am. And Aunt Hepsy says—

JABEZ   Bother your Aunt Hepsy! There's just you and me and that's all that matters in the world.

MARY   And you don't know something else——

JABEZ   What's that?

MARY   How proud I am of you. Ever since I was a little girl. Ever since you carried my books. Oh, I'm sorry for women who can't be proud of their men. It must be a lonely feeling.

JABEZ   (*uncomfortably*)   A man can't always be proud of everything, Mary. There's some things a man does, or might do—when he has to make his way.

MARY   (*laughing*)   I know—terrible things—like being the best farmer in the county and the best State Senator——

JABEZ   (*quietly*)   And a few things, besides. But you remember one thing, Mary, whatever happens. It was all for you. And nothing's going to happen. Because he hasn't come yet—and he would have come if it was wrong.

MARY   But it's wonderful to have Mr. Webster come to us.

JABEZ   I wasn't thinking about Mr. Webster. (*He takes both her hands.*) Mary, I've got something to tell you. I should have told you before, but I couldn't seem to bear it. Only, now that it's all right, I can. Ten years ago——

A VOICE (*from off stage*)   Dan'l! Dan'l Webster! (JABEZ *drops* MARY's *hands and looks around. The* CROWD *begins to mill and gather toward the door. Others rush in from the kitchen.*)

ANOTHER VOICE   Black Dan'l! He's come!

ANOTHER VOICE   Three cheers for the greatest man in the U. S.!

ANOTHER VOICE   Three cheers for Daniel Webster! (*And, to the cheering and applause of the crowd,* DANIEL WEBSTER *enters and stands for a moment upstage, in the familiar pose, his head thrown back, his attitude leonine. He stops the cheering of the crowd with a gesture.*)

WEBSTER   Neighbors—old friends—it does me good to hear you. But don't cheer me—I'm not running for President this summer. (*A laugh from the* CROWD.) I'm here on a better errand—to pay my humble respects to a most charming lady and her very fortunate spouse. (*There is the twang of a fiddlestring breaking.*)

FIDDLER   'Tarnation! Busted a string!

A VOICE   He's always bustin' strings. (WEBSTER *blinks at the interruption but goes on.*)

WEBSTER   We're proud of State Senator Stone in these parts—we know what he's done. Ten years ago he started out with a patch of land that was mostly rocks and mortgages and now—well, you've only to look around you. I don't know that I've ever seen a likelier farm, not even at Marshfield—and I hope, before I die, I'll have the privilege of shaking his hand as Governor of this State. I don't know how he's done it—I couldn't have done it myself. But I know this—Jabez Stone wears no man's collar. (*At this statement there is a discordant squeak from the fiddle and* JABEZ *looks embarrassed.* WEBSTER *knits his brows.*) And what's more, if I know Jabez, he never will. But I didn't come here to talk politics—I came to kiss the bride. (*He does so among great applause. He shakes hands with* JABEZ.) Congratulations, Stone— you're a lucky man. And now, if our friend in the corner will give us a tune on his fiddle—— (*The* CROWD *presses forward to meet the great man. He shakes hands with several.*)

A MAN   Remember me, Mr. Webster? Saw ye up at the State House at Concord.

ANOTHER MAN   Glad to see ye, Mr. Webster. I voted for ye ten times. (WEBSTER *receives their homage politely, but his mind is still on music.*)

WEBSTER (*a trifle irritated*)   I said, if our friend in the corner would give us a tune on his fiddle——

FIDDLER (*passionately, flinging the fiddle down*)   Hell's delight— excuse me, Mr. Webster. But the very devil's got into that fiddle of mine. She was doing all right up to just a minute ago. But now I've tuned her and tuned her and she won't play a note I want. (*And, at this point,* MR. SCRATCH *makes his appearance. He has entered unobserved, and mixed with the crowd while all eyes were upon* DANIEL WEBSTER. *He is, of course, the devil—a New England devil, dressed like a rather shabby attorney but with something just a little wrong in clothes and appearance. For one thing, he wears black gloves on his hands. He carries a large black tin box, like a botanist's collecting-box, under one arm. Now he slips through the crowd and taps the* FIDDLER *on the shoulder.*)

SCRATCH (*insinuatingly*) Maybe you need some rosin on your bow, fiddler?

FIDDLER Maybe I do and maybe I don't. (*Turns and confronts the stranger.*) But who are you? I don't remember seeing you before.

SCRATCH Oh, I'm just a friend—a humble friend of the bridegroom's. (*He walks toward* JABEZ. *Apologetically.*) I'm afraid I came in the wrong way, Mr. Stone. You've improved the place so much since I last saw it that I hardly knew the front door. But, I assure you, I came as fast as I could.

JABEZ (*obviously shocked*) It—It doesn't matter. (*With a great effort.*) Mary—Mr. Webster—this is a—a friend of mine from Boston —a legal friend. I didn't expect him today but——

SCRATCH Oh, my dear Mr. Stone—an occasion like this—I wouldn't miss it for the world. (*He bows.*) Charmed, Mrs. Stone. Delighted, Mr. Webster. But—don't let me break up the merriment of the meeting. (*He turns back toward the table and the* FIDDLER.)

FIDDLER (*with a grudge, to* SCRATCH) Boston lawyer, eh?

SCRATCH You might call me that.

FIDDLER (*tapping the tin box with his bow*) And what have you got in that big tin box of yours? Lawpapers?

SCRATCH Oh—curiosities for the most part. I'm a collector, too.

FIDDLER Don't hold much with Boston curiosities, myself. And you know about fiddling too, do you? Know all about it?

SCRATCH Oh—— (*A deprecatory shrug.*)

FIDDLER Don't shrug your shoulders at me—I ain't no Frenchman. Telling me I needed more rosin!

MARY (*trying to stop the quarrel*) Isaac—please——

FIDDLER Sorry, Mary—Mrs. Stone. But I been playing the fiddle at Cross Corners weddings for twenty-five years. And now here comes a stranger from Boston and tells me I need more rosin!

SCRATCH But, my good friend——

FIDDLER Rosin indeed! Here—play it yourself then and see what you can make of it! (*He thrusts the fiddle at* SCRATCH. *The latter stiffens, slowly lays his black collecting-box on the table, and takes the fiddle.*)

SCRATCH (*with feigned embarrassment*) But really, I—— (*He bows toward* JABEZ.) Shall I—Mr. Senator? (JABEZ *makes a helpless gesture of assent.*)

MARY (*to* JABEZ) Mr. Stone—Mr. Stone—are you ill?

JABEZ No—no—but I feel—it's hot——

WEBSTER (*chuckling*) Don't you fret, Mrs. Stone. I've got the right medicine for him. (*He pulls a flask from his pocket.*) Ten-year-old Medford, Stone—I buy it by the keg down at Marshfield. Here—— (*He tries to give some of the rum to* JABEZ.)

JABEZ No—(*he turns*)—Mary—Mr. Webster—— (*But he cannot explain. With a burst.*) Oh, let him play—let him play! Don't you see he's bound to? Don't you see there's nothing we can do? (*A rustle of discomfort among the guests.* SCRATCH *draws the bow across the fiddle in a horrible discord.*)

FIDDLER (*triumphantly*) I told you so, stranger. The devil's in that fiddle!

SCRATCH I'm afraid it needs special tuning. (*Draws the bow in a second discord.*) There—that's better. (*Grinning.*) And now for this happy—this very happy occasion—in tribute to the bride and groom —I'll play something appropriate—a song of young love——

MARY Oh, Jabez—Mr. Webster—stop him! Do you see his hands? He's playing with gloves on his hands. (WEBSTER *starts forward, but, even as he does so,* SCRATCH *begins to play and all freeze as* SCRATCH *goes on with the extremely inappropriate song that follows. At first his manner is oily and mocking—it is not till he reaches the line "The devil took the words away" that he really becomes terrifying and the crowd starts to be afraid.*)

SCRATCH (*accompanying himself fantastically*)

> Young William was a thriving boy.
> (Listen to my doleful tale.)
> Young Mary Clark was all his joy.
> (Listen to my doleful tale.)
> He swore he'd love her all his life.
> She swore she'd be his loving wife.
> But William found a gambler's den
> And drank with livery-stable men.
> He played the cards, he played the dice.
> He would not listen to advice.
> And when in church he tried to pray,
> The devil took the words away.

(SCRATCH, *still playing, starts to march across the stage.*)

The devil got him by the toe
And so, alas, he had to go.
"Young Mary Clark, young Mary Clark,
I now must go into the dark."

(*These last two verses have been directed at* JABEZ, SCRATCH *continues, now turning on* MARY.)

Young Mary lay upon her bed.
"Alas my Will-i-am is dead."
He came to her a bleeding ghost——

(*He rushes at* MARY *but* WEBSTER *stands between them.*)

WEBSTER Stop! Stop! You miserable wretch—can't you see that you're frightening Mrs. Stone? (*He wrenches the fiddle out of* SCRATCH's *hands and tosses it aside.*) And now, sir—out of this house!

SCRATCH (*facing him*) You're a bold man, Mr. Webster. Too bold for your own good, perhaps. And anyhow, it wasn't my fiddle. It belonged to—— (*He wheels and sees the* FIDDLER *tampering with the collecting-box that has been left on the table.*) Idiot! What are you doing with my collecting-box? (*He rushes for the* FIDDLER *and chases him round the table, but the* FIDDLER *is just one jump ahead.*)

FIDDLER Boston lawyer, eh? Well, I don't think so. I think you've got something in that box of yours you're afraid to show. And, by jingo—— (*He throws open the lid of the box. The lights wink and there is a clap of thunder. All eyes stare upward. Something has flown out of the box. But what?* FIDDLER, *with relief.*) Why, 'tain't nothing but a moth.

MARY A white moth—a flying thing.

WEBSTER A common moth—*telea polyphemus*——

THE CROWD A moth—just a moth—a moth——

FIDDLER (*terrified*) But it ain't. It ain't no common moth! I seen it! And it's got a death's-head on it! (*He strikes at the invisible object with his bow to drive it away.*)

VOICE OF THE MOTH Help me, neighbors! Help me!

WEBSTER What's that? It wails like a lost soul.

MARY A lost soul.

THE CROWD   A lost soul—lost—in darkness—in the darkness.

VOICE OF THE MOTH   Help me, neighbors!

FIDDLER   It sounds like Miser Stevens.

JABEZ   Miser Stevens!

THE CROWD   The Miser—Miser Stevens—a lost soul—lost.

FIDDLER (*frantically*)   It sounds like Miser Stevens—and you had him in your box. But it can't be. He ain't dead.

JABEZ   He ain't dead—I tell you he ain't dead! He was just as spry and mean as a woodchuck Tuesday.

THE CROWD   Miser Stevens—soul of Miser Stevens—but he ain't dead.

SCRATCH (*dominating them*)   Listen! (*A bell off stage begins to toll a knell, slowly, solemnly.*)

MARY   The bell—the church bell—the bell that rang at my wedding.

WEBSTER   The church bell—the passing bell.

JABEZ   The funeral bell.

THE CROWD   The bell—the passing bell—Miser Stevens—dead.

VOICE OF THE MOTH   Help me, neighbors, help me! I sold my soul to the devil. But I'm not the first or the last. Help me. Help Jabez Stone!

SCRATCH   Ah, would you! (*He catches the moth in his red bandanna, stuffs it back into his collecting-box, and shuts the lid with a snap.*)

VOICE OF THE MOTH (*fading*)   Lost—lost forever, forever. Lost, like Jabez Stone. (*The* CROWD *turns on* JABEZ. *They read his secret in his face.*)

THE CROWD   Jabez Stone—Jabez Stone—answer us—answer us.

MARY   Tell them, dear—answer them—you are good—you are brave—you are innocent. (*But the* CROWD *is all pointing hands and horrified eyes.*)

THE CROWD   Jabez Stone—Jabez Stone. Who's your friend in black, Jabez Stone? (*They point to* SCRATCH.)

WEBSTER   Answer them, Mr. State Senator.

THE CROWD   Jabez Stone—Jabez Stone. Where did you get your money, Jabez Stone? (SCRATCH *grins and taps his collecting-box.* JABEZ *cannot speak.*)

JABEZ   I—I—— (*He stops.*)

THE CROWD   Jabez Stone—Jabez Stone. What was the price you paid for it, Jabez Stone?

JABEZ (*looking around wildly*)   Help me, neighbors! Help me!

(*This cracks the built-up tension and sends the* CROWD *over the edge into fanaticism.*)

A WOMAN'S VOICE (*high and hysterical*)   He's sold his soul to the devil! (*She points to* JABEZ.)

OTHER VOICES   To the devil!

THE CROWD   He's sold his soul to the devil! The devil himself! The devil's playing the fiddle! The devil's come for his own!

JABEZ (*appealing*)   But, neighbors—I didn't know—I didn't mean—oh, help me!

THE CROWD (*inexorably*)   He's sold his soul to the devil!

SCRATCH (*grinning*)   To the devil!

THE CROWD   He's sold his soul to the devil! There's no help left for him, neighbors! Run, hide, hurry, before we're caught! He's a lost soul—Jabez Stone—he's the devil's own! Run, hide, hasten! (*They stream across the stage like a flurry of bats, the cannier picking up the wedding-presents they have given to take along with them.* MR. SCRATCH *drives them out into the night, fiddle in hand, and follows them.* JABEZ *and* MARY *are left with* WEBSTER. JABEZ *has sunk into a chair, beaten, with his head in his hands.* MARY *is trying to comfort him.* WEBSTER *looks at them for a moment and shakes his head, sadly. As he crosses to exit to the porch, his hand drops for a moment on* JABEZ'S *shoulder, but* JABEZ *makes no sign.* WEBSTER *exits.* JABEZ *lifts his head.*)

MARY (*comforting him*)   My dear—my dear——

JABEZ   I—it's all true, Mary. All true. You must hurry.

MARY   Hurry?

JABEZ   Hurry after them—back to the village—back to your folks. Mr. Webster will take you—you'll be safe with Mr. Webster. You see, it's all true and he'll be back in a minute. (*With a shudder.*) The other one. (*He groans.*) I've got until twelve o'clock. That's the contract. But there isn't much time.

MARY   Are you telling me to run away from you, Mr. Stone?

JABEZ   You don't understand, Mary. It's true.

MARY   We made some promises to each other. Maybe you've forgotten them. But I haven't. I said, it's for better or worse. It's for better or worse. I said, in sickness or in health. Well, that covers the ground, Mr. Stone.

JABEZ   But, Mary, you must—I command you.

MARY   "For thy people shall be my people and thy God my God." (*Quietly.*) That was Ruth, in the Book. I always like the name of Ruth—always liked the thought of her. I always thought—I'll call a child Ruth, some time. I guess that was just a girl's notion. (*She breaks.*) But, oh, Jabez—why?

JABEZ   It started years ago, Mary. I guess I was a youngster then—guess I must have been. A youngster with a lot of ambitions and no way in the world to get there. I wanted city clothes and a big white house—I wanted to be State Senator and have people look up to me. But all I got on the farm was a crop of stones. You could work all day and all night but that was all you got.

MARY   (*softly*)   It was pretty—that hill-farm, Jabez. You could look all the way across the valley.

JABEZ   Pretty? It was fever and ague—it was stones and blight. If I had a horse, he got colic—if I planted garden-truck, the wood-chucks ate it. I'd lie awake nights and try to figure out a way to get somewhere—but there wasn't any way. And all the time you were growing up, in the town. I couldn't ask you to marry me and take you to a place like that.

MARY   Do you think it's the place makes the difference to a woman? I'd—I'd have kept your house. I'd have stroked the cat and fed the chickens and seen you wiped your shoes on the mat. I wouldn't have asked for more. Oh, Jabez—why didn't you tell me?

JABEZ   It happened before I could. Just an average day—you know—just an average day. But there was a mean east wind and a mean small rain. Well, I was plowing, and the share broke clean off on a rock where there hadn't been any rock the day before. I didn't have money for a new one—I didn't have money to get it mended. So I said it and I said loud, "I'll sell my soul for about two cents," I said. (*He stops.* MARY *stares at him.*) Well, that's all there is to it, I guess. He came along that afternoon—that fellow from Boston—and the dog looked at him and ran away. Well, I had to make it more than two cents, but he was agreeable to that. So I pricked my thumb with a pin and signed the paper. It felt hot when you touched it, that paper. I keep remembering that (*He pauses*). And it's all come true and he's kept his part of the bargain. I got the riches and I've married you. And, oh, God Almighty, what shall I do?

MARY   Let us run away! Let us creep and hide!

JABEZ   You can't run away from the devil—I've seen his horses. Miser Stevens tried to run away.

MARY   Let us pray—let us pray to the God of Mercy that He redeem us.

JABEZ   I can't pray, Mary. The words just burn in my heart.

MARY I won't let you go! I won't! There must be someone who could help us. I'll get the judge and the squire——

JABEZ Who'll take a case against old Scratch? Who'll face the devil himself and do him brown? There isn't a lawyer in the world who'd dare do that. (WEBSTER *appears in the doorway*.)

WEBSTER Good evening, neighbors. Did you say something about lawyers——

MARY Mr. Webster!

JABEZ Dan'l Webster! But I thought——

WEBSTER You'll excuse me for leaving you for a moment. I was just taking a stroll on the porch, in the cool of the evening. Fine summer evening, too.

JABEZ Well, it might be, I guess, but that kind of depends on the circumstances.

WEBSTER H'm. Yes. I happened to overhear a little of your conversation. I gather you're in trouble, Neighbor Stone.

JABEZ Sore trouble.

WEBSTER (*delicately*) Suit of law case, I understand.

JABEZ You might call it that, Mr. Webster. Kind of a mortgage case, in a way.

MARY Oh, Jabez!

WEBSTER Mortgage case. Well, I don't generally plead now, except before the Supreme Court, but this case of yours presents some very unusual features and I never deserted a neighbor in trouble yet. So, if I can be of any assistance——

MARY Oh, Mr. Webster, will you help him?

JABEZ It's a terrible lot to ask you. But—well, you see, there's Mary. And, if you could see your way to it——

WEBSTER I will.

MARY (*weeping with relief*) Oh, Mr. Webster!

WEBSTER There, there, Mrs. Stone. After all, if two New Hampshire men aren't a match for the devil, we might as well give the country back to the Indians. When is he coming, Jabez?

JABEZ Twelve o'clock. The time's getting late.

WEBSTER Then I'd better refresh my memory. The—er—mortgage was for a definite term of years?

JABEZ Ten years.

WEBSTER And it falls due——?

JABEZ Tonight. Oh, I can't see how I came to be such a fool!

WEBSTER No use crying over spilt milk, Stone. We've got to get you out of it, now. But tell me one thing. Did you sign this precious document of your own free will?

JABEZ   Yes, it was my own free will. I can't deny that.

WEBSTER   H'm, that's a trifle unfortunate. But we'll see.

MARY   Oh, Mr. Webster, can you save him? Can you?

WEBSTER   I shall do my best, madam. That's all you can ever say till you see what the jury looks like.

MARY   But even you, Mr. Webster—oh, I know you're Secretary of State—I know you're a great man—I know you've done wonderful things. But it's different—fighting the devil!

WEBSTER   (*towering*)   I've fought John C. Calhoun, madam. And I've fought Henry Clay. And, by the great shade of Andrew Jackson, I'd fight ten thousand devils to save a New Hampshire man!

JABEZ   You hear, Mary?

MARY   Yes. And I trust Mr. Webster. But—oh, there must be some way that I can help!

WEBSTER   There is one, madam, and a hard one. As Mr. Stone's counsel, I must formally request your withdrawal.

MARY · No.

WEBSTER   Madam, think for a moment. You cannot help Mr. Stone—since you are his wife, your testimony would be prejudiced. And frankly, madam, in a very few moments this is going to be no place for a lady.

MARY   But I can't—I can't leave him—I can't bear it!

JABEZ   You must go, Mary. You must.

WEBSTER   Pray, madam—you can help us with your prayers. Are the prayers of the innocent unavailing?

MARY   Oh, I'll pray—I'll pray. But a woman's more than a praying machine, whatever men think. And how do I know?

WEBSTER   Trust me, Mrs. Stone. (MARY *turns to go, and, with one hand on* JABEZ' *shoulder, as she moves to the door, says the following prayer:*)

MARY

Now may there be a blessing and a light betwixt thee and me, forever.

For, as Ruth unto Naomi, so do I cleave unto thee.

Set me as a seal upon thy heart, as a seal upon thine arm, for love is strong as death.

Many waters cannot quench love, neither can the floods drown
it.

As Ruth unto Naomi, so do I cleave unto thee.

The Lord watch between thee and me when we are absent,
one from the other.

Amen. Amen. (*She goes out.*)

WEBSTER   Amen.

JABEZ   Thank you, Mr. Webster. She ought to go. But I couldn't
have made her do it.

WEBSTER   Well, Stone—I know ladies—and I wouldn't be surprised if she's still got her ear to the keyhole. But she's best out of
this night's business. How long have we got to wait?

JABEZ   (*beginning to be terrified again*)   Not long—not long.

WEBSTER   Then I'll just get out the jug, with your permission,
Stone. Somehow or other, waiting's wonderfully shorter with a jug.
(*He crosses to the cupboard, gets out jug and glasses, pours himself
a drink.*) Ten-year-old Medford. There's nothing like it. I saw an
inchworm take a drop of it once and he stood right up on his hind
legs and bit a bee. Come—try a nip.

JABEZ   There's no joy in it for me.

WEBSTER   Oh, come, man, come! Just because you've sold your
soul to the devil, that needn't make you a teetotaller. (*He laughs and
passes the jug to* JABEZ *who tries to pour from it. But at that moment
the clock whirs and begins to strike the three-quarters, and* JABEZ
spills the liquor.)

JABEZ   Oh, God!

WEBSTER   Never mind—it's a nervous feeling, waiting for a trial
to begin. I remember my first case——

JABEZ   'Taint that. (*He turns to* WEBSTER.) Mr. Webster—Mr.
Webster—for God's sake harness your horses and get away from this
place as fast as you can!

WEBSTER   (*placidly*)   You've brought me a long way, neighbor, to
tell me you don't like my company.

JABEZ   I've brought you the devil's own way. I can see it all, now.
He's after both of us—him and his damn collecting-box! Well, he can
have me, if he likes—I don't say I relish it but I made the bargain.
But you're the whole United States! He can't get you, Mr. Webster—
he mustn't get you!

WEBSTER   I'm obliged to you, Neighbor Stone. It's kindly thought
of. But there's a jug on the table and a case in hand. And I never left
a jug or a case half-finished in my life. (*There is a knock at the door.*
JABEZ *gives a cry.*) Ah, I thought your clock was a trifle slow, Neighbor Stone. Come in! (SCRATCH *enters from the night.*)

SCRATCH   Mr. Webster! This *is* a pleasure!

WEBSTER   Attorney of record for Jabez Stone. Might I ask your
name?

SCRATCH   I've gone by a good many. Perhaps Scratch will do for
the evening. I'm often called that in these regions. May I? (*He sits
at the table and pours a drink from the jug. The liquor steams as it
pours into the glass while* JABEZ *watches, terrified.* SCRATCH *grins,
toasting* WEBSTER *and* JABEZ *silently in the liquor. Then he becomes
businesslike. To* WEBSTER.) And now I call upon you, as a law-abiding
citizen, to assist me in taking possession of my property.

WEBSTER   Not so fast, Mr. Scratch. Produce your evidence, if you
have it. (SCRATCH *takes out a black pocketbook and examines papers.*)

SCRATCH   Slattery—Stanley—Stone. (*Takes out a deed*). There,
Mr. Webster. All open and above board and in due and legal form.
Our firm has its reputation to consider—we deal only in the one way.

WEBSTER   (*taking deed and looking it over*)   H'm. This appears—
I say, it appears—to be properly drawn. But, of course, we contest the
signature. (*Tosses it back, contemptuously*).

SCRATCH   (*suddenly turning on* JABEZ *and shooting a finger at him.*)
Is that your signature?

JABEZ   (*wearily*)   You know damn well it is.

WEBSTER   (*angrily*)   Keep quiet, Stone. (*To* SCRATCH.) But that is
a minor matter. This precious document isn't worth the paper it's
written on. The law permits no traffic in human flesh.

SCRATCH   Oh, my dear Mr. Webster! Courts in every State in the
Union have held that human flesh is property and recoverable. Read
your Fugitive Slave Act. Or, shall I cite Brander versus McRae?

WEBSTER   But, in the case of the State of Maryland versus Four
Barrels of Bourbon——

SCRATCH   That was overruled, as you know, sir. North Carolina
versus Jenkins and Co.

WEBSTER   (*unwillingly*)   You seem to have an excellent acquaintance with the law, sir.

SCRATCH   Sir, that is no fault of mine. Where I come from, we
have always gotten the pick of the Bar.

WEBSTER (*changing his note, heartily*) Well, come now, sir. There's no need to make hay and oats of a trifling matter when we're both sensible men. Surely we can settle this little difficulty out of court. My client is quite prepared to offer a compromise. (SCRATCH *smiles.*) A very substantial compromise. (SCRATCH *smiles more broadly, slowing shaking his head.*) Hang it, man, we offer ten thousand dollars! (SCRATCH *signs* "No".) Twenty thousand—thirty—name your figure! I'll raise it if I have to mortgage Marshfield!

SCRATCH Quite useless, Mr. Webster. There is only one thing I want from you—the execution of my contract.

WEBSTER But this is absurd. Mr. Stone is now a State Senator. The property has greatly increased in value!

SCRATCH The principle of *caveat emptor* still holds, Mr. Webster. (*He yawns and looks at the clock.*) And now, if you have no further arguments to adduce—I'm rather pressed for time—(*He rises briskly as if to take* JABEZ *into custody.*)

WEBSTER (*thundering*) Pressed or not, you shall not have this man. Mr. Stone is an American citizen and no American citizen may be forced into the service of a foreign prince. We fought England for that, in '12, and we'll fight all hell for it again!

SCRATCH Foreign? And who calls me a foreigner?

WEBSTER Well, I never yet heard of the dev—of your claiming American citizenship?

SCRATCH And who with better right? When the first wrong was done to the first Indian, I was there. When the first slaver put out for the Congo, I stood on her deck. Am I not in your books and stories and beliefs, from the first settlements on? Am I not spoken of, still, in every church in New England? 'Tis true, the North claims me for a Southerner and the South for a Northerner, but I am neither. I am merely an honest American like yourself—and of the best descent—for, to tell the truth, Mr. Webster, though I don't like to boast of it, my name is older in the country than yours.

WEBSTER Aha! Then I stand on the Constitution! I demand a trial for my client!

SCRATCH The case is hardly one for an ordinary jury—and indeed, the lateness of the hour——

WEBSTER Let it be any court you choose, so it is an American judge and an American jury. Let it be the quick or the dead, I'll abide the issue.

SCRATCH The quick or the dead! You have said it! (*He points his*

*finger at the place where the jury is to appear. There is a clap of
thunder and a flash of light. The stage blacks out completely. All that
can be seen is the face of* SCRATCH, *lit with a ghastly green light as he
recites the invocation that summons the* JURY. *As, one by one, the
important* JURYMEN *are mentioned, they appear.*)

I summon the jury Mr. Webster demands.
From churchyard mould and gallows grave,
Brimstone pit and burning gulf,
I summon them!
Dastard, liar, scoundrel, knave,
I summon them! Appear!
There's Simon Girty, the renegade,
The haunter of the forest glade
Who joined with Indian and wolf
To hunt the pioneer.
The stains upon his hunting-shirt
Are not the blood of the deer.
There's Walter Butler, the loyalist,
Who carried a firebrand in his fist
Of massacre and shame.
King Philip's eye is wild and bright.
They slew him in the great Swamp Fight,
But still, with terror and affright,
The land recalls his name.
Blackbeard Teach, the pirate fell,
Smeet the strangler, hot from hell,
Dale, who broke men on the wheel,
Morton, of the tarnished steel,
I summon them, I summon them
From their tormented flame!
Quick or dead, quick or dead,
Broken heart and bitter head,
True Americans, each one,
Traitor and disloyal son,
Cankered earth and twisted tree,
Outcasts of eternity,
Twelve great sinners, tried and true,
For the work they are to do!

I summon them, I summon them!
Appear, appear, appear!

(*The* JURY *has now taken its place in the box*—WALTER
BUTLER *in the place of foreman. They are eerily lit and so
made-up as to suggest the unearthly. They sit stiffly in their
box. At first, when one moves, all move, in stylized gestures.
It is not till the end of* WEBSTER's *speech that they begin to
show any trace of humanity. They speak rhythmically, and,
at first, in low, eerie voices.*)

JABEZ (*seeing them, horrified*) A jury of the dead!

JURY Of the dead!

JABEZ A jury of the damned!

JURY Of the damned!

SCRATCH Are you content with the jury, Mr. Webster?

WEBSTER Quite content. Though I miss General Arnold from the
company.

SCRATCH Benedict Arnold is engaged upon other business. Ah,
you asked for a justice, I believe. (*He points his finger and* JUSTICE
HATHORNE, *a tall, lean, terrifying Puritan, appears, followed by his*
CLERK.) Justice Hathorne is a jurist of experience. He presided at the
Salem witch-trials. There were others who repented of the business
later. But not he, not he!

HATHORNE Repent of such notable wonders and undertakings?
Nay, hang them, hang them all! (*He takes his place on the bench.
The* CLERK, *an ominous little man with clawlike hands, takes his place.
The room has now been transformed into a courtroom.*)

CLERK (*in a gabble of ritual*) Oyes, oyes, oyes. All ye who have
business with this honorable court of special session this night, step
forward!

HATHORNE (*with gavel*) Call the first case.

CLERK The World, the Flesh and the Devil versus Jabez Stone.

HATHORNE Who appears for the plaintiff?

SCRATCH I, Your Honor.

HATHORNE And for the defendant?

WEBSTER I.

JURY The case—the case—he'll have little luck with this case.

HATHORNE The case will proceed.

WEBSTER   Your Honor, I move to dismiss this case on the grounds of improper jurisdiction.

HATHORNE   Motion denied.

WEBSTER   On the grounds of insufficient evidence.

HATHORNE   Motion denied.

JURY   Motion denied—denied. Motion denied.

WEBSTER   I will take an exception.

HATHORNE   There are no exceptions in this court.

JURY   No exceptions—no exceptions in this court. It's a bad case, Daniel Webster—a losing case.

WEBSTER   Your Honor——

HATHORNE   The prosecution will proceed——

SCRATCH   Your Honor—gentlemen of the jury. This is a plain, straightforward case. It need not detain us long.

JURY   Detain us long—it will not detain us long.

SCRATCH   It concerns one thing alone—the transference, barter and sale of a certain piece of property, to wit, his soul, by Jabez Stone, farmer, of Cross Corners, New Hampshire. That transference, barter or sale is attested by a deed. I offer that deed in evidence and mark it Exhibit A.

WEBSTER   I object.

HATHORNE   Objection denied. Mark it Exhibit A. (SCRATCH *hands the deed—an ominous and impressive document—to the* CLERK *who hands it to* HATHORNE. HATHORNE *hands it back to the* CLERK *who stamps it. All very fast and with mechanical gestures.*)

JURY   Exhibit A—mark it Exhibit A. (SCRATCH *takes the deed from the* CLERK *and offers it to the* JURY, *who pass it rapidly among them, hardly looking at it, and hand it back to* SCRATCH.) We know the deed—the deed—it burns in our fingers—we do not have to see the deed. It's a losing case.

SCRATCH   It offers incontestable evidence of the truth of the prosecution's claim. I shall now call Jabez Stone to the witness-stand.

JURY   (*hungrily*)   Jabez Stone to the witness-stand, Jabez Stone. He's a fine, fat fellow, Jabez Stone. He'll fry like a batter-cake, once we get him where we want him.

WEBSTER   Your Honor, I move that this jury be discharged for flagrant and open bias!

HATHORNE   Motion denied.

WEBSTER   Exception.

HATHORNE   Exception denied.

JURY His motion's always denied. He thinks himself smart and clever—lawyer Webster. But his motion's always denied.

WEBSTER Your Honor! (*He chokes with anger.*)

CLERK (*advancing*) Jabez Stone to the witness-stand!

JURY Jabez Stone—Jabez Stone. (WEBSTER *gives* JABEZ *an encouraging pat on the back, and* JABEZ *takes his place in the witness-stand, very scared.*)

CLERK (*offering a black book*) Do you solemnly swear—testify—so help you—and it's no good for we don't care what you testify?

JABEZ I do.

SCRATCH What's your name?

JABEZ Jabez Stone.

SCRATCH Occupation?

JABEZ Farmer.

SCRATCH Residence?

JABEZ Cross Corners, New Hampshire. (*These three questions are very fast and mechanical on the part of* SCRATCH. *He is absolutely sure of victory and just going through a form.*)

JURY A farmer—he'll farm in hell—we'll see that he farms in hell.

SCRATCH Now, Jabez Stone, answer me. You'd better, you know. You haven't got a chance and there'll be a cooler place by the fire for you.

WEBSTER I protest! This is intimidation! This mocks all justice!

HATHORNE The protest is irrelevant, incompetent and immaterial. We have our own justice. The protest is denied.

JURY Irrelevant, incompetent and immaterial—we have our own justice—oh, ho, Daniel Webster! (*The* JURY's *eyes fix upon* WEBSTER *for an instant, hungrily.*)

SCRATCH Did you or did you not sign this document?

JABEZ Oh, I signed it! You know I signed it. And, if I have to go to hell for it, I'll go! (*A sigh sweeps over the* JURY.)

JURY One of us—one of us now—we'll save a place by the fire for you, Jabez Stone.

SCRATCH The prosecution rests.

HATHORNE Remove the prisoner.

WEBSTER But I wish to cross-examine—I wish to prove——

HATHORNE There will be no cross-examination. We have our own justice. You may speak, if you like. But be brief.

JURY Brief—be very brief—we're weary of earth—incompetent, irrelevant and immaterial—they say he's a smart man, Webster, but he's lost his case tonight—be very brief—we have our own justice here. (WEBSTER *stares around him like a baited bull. Can't find words.*)

MARY'S VOICE (*from off stage*) Set me as a seal upon thy heart, as a seal upon thine arm, for love is strong as death——

JURY (*loudly*) A seal!—ha, ha—a burning seal!

MARY'S VOICE Love is strong——

JURY (*drowning her out*) Death is stronger than love. Set the seal upon Daniel Webster—the burning seal of the lost. Make him one of us—one of the damned—one with Jabez Stone! (*The* JURY'S *eyes all fix upon* WEBSTER. *The* CLERK *advances as if to take him into custody. But* WEBSTER *silences them all with a great gesture.*)

WEBSTER
Be still!
I was going to thunder and roar. I shall not do that.
I was going to denounce and defy. I shall not do that.
You have judged this man already with your abominable justice.
See that you defend it. For I shall not speak of this man.
You are demons now, but once you were men. I shall speak
    to every one of you.
Of common things I speak, of small things and common.
The freshness of morning to the young, the taste of food to
    the hungry, the day's toil, the rest by the fire, the quiet sleep.
These are good things.
But without freedom they sicken, without freedom they are
    nothing.
Freedom is the bread and the morning and the risen sun.
It was for freedom we came in the boats and the ships. It was
    for freedom we came.
It has been a long journey, a hard one, a bitter one.
But, out of the wrong and the right, the sufferings and the
    starvations, there is a new thing, a free thing.
The traitors in their treachery, the wise in their wisdom, the
    valiant in their courage—all, all have played a part.
It may not be denied in hell nor shall hell prevail against it.
Have you forgotten this? (*He turns to the* JURY.) Have you
    forgotten the forest?

GIRTY (*as in a dream*) The forest, the rustle of the forest, the free forest.

WEBSTER (*to* KING PHILIP) Have you forgotten your lost nation?

KING PHILIP My lost nation—my fires in the wood—my warriors.

WEBSTER (*to* TEACH) Have you forgotten the sea and the way of ships?

TEACH The sea—and the swift ships sailing—the blue sea.

JURY Forgotten—remembered—forgotten yet remembered.

WEBSTER You were men once. Have you forgotten?

JURY We were men once. We have not thought of it nor remembered. But we were men.

WEBSTER

Now here is this man with good and evil in his heart.

Do you know him? He is your brother. Will you take the law of the oppressor and bind him down?

It is not for him that I speak. It is for all of you.

There is sadness in being a man but it is a proud thing, too.

There is failure and despair on the journey—the endless journey of mankind.

We are tricked and trapped—we stumble into the pit—but, out of the pit, we rise again.

No demon that was ever foaled can know the inwardness of that—only men—bewildered men.

They have broken freedom with their hands and cast her out from the nations—yet shall she live while man lives.

She shall live in the blood and the heart—she shall live in the earth of this country—she shall not be broken.

When the whips of the oppressors are broken and their names forgotten and destroyed.

I see you, mighty, shining, liberty, liberty! I see free men walking and talking under a free star.

God save the United States and the men who have made her free.

The defense rests.

JURY (*exultantly*) We were men—we were free—we were men —we have not forgotten—our children—our children shall follow and be free.

HATHORNE (*rapping with gavel*) The jury will retire to consider its verdict.

BUTLER (*rising*) There is no need. The jury has heard Mr. Webster. We find for the defendant, Jabez Stone!

JURY   Not guilty!

SCRATCH   (*in a screech, rushing forward*)   But, Your Honor——
(*But, even as he does so, there is a flash and a thunderclap, the stage
blacks out again, and when the lights come on,* JUDGE *and* JURY *are
gone. The yellow light of dawn lights the windows.*)

JABEZ   They're gone and it's morning—Mary, Mary!

MARY   (*in doorway*)   My love—my dear. (*She rushes to him.
Meanwhile* SCRATCH *has been collecting his papers and trying to sneak
out. But* WEBSTER *catches him.*)

WEBSTER   Just a minute, Mr. Scratch. I'll have that paper first, if
you please. (*He takes the deed and tears it*). And, now, sir, I'll have
you!

SCRATCH   Come, come, Mr. Webster. This sort of thing is ridic—
ouch—is ridiculous. If you're worried about the costs of the case,
naturally, I'd be glad to pay.

WEBSTER   And so you shall! First of all, you'll promise and cove-
nant never to bother Jabez Stone or any other New Hampshire man
from now till doomsday. For any hell we want to raise in this State,
we can raise ourselves, without any help from you.

SCRATCH   Ouch! Well, they never did run very big to the barrel
but—ouch—I agree!

WEBSTER   See you keep to the bargain! And then—well, I've got
a ram named Goliath. He can butt through an iron door. I'd like to
turn you loose in his field and see what he could do to you. (SCRATCH
trembles.) But that would be hard on the ram. So we'll just call in the
neighbors and give you a shivaree.

SCRATCH   Mr. Webster—please—oh——

WEBSTER   Neighbors! Neighbors! Come in and see what a long-
barrelled, slab-sided, lantern-jawed, fortune-telling note-shaver I've got
by the scruff of the neck! Bring on your kettles and your pans! (*A
noise and murmur outside.*) Bring on your muskets and your flails!

JABEZ   We'll drive him out of New Hampshire!

MARY   We'll drive old Scratch away! (*The* CROWD *rushes in, with
muskets, flails, brooms, etc. They pursue* SCRATCH *around the stage,
chanting.*)

THE CROWD

> We'll drive him out of New Hampshire!
> We'll drive old Scratch away!

Forever and a day, boys,
Forever and a day!
(*They finally catch* SCRATCH *between two of them and fling him out of the door, bodily.*)

A MAN Three cheers for Dan'l Webster!

ANOTHER MAN Three cheers for Daniel Webster! He's licked the devil!

WEBSTER (*moving to center stage, and joining* JABEZ' *hands and* MARY's) And whom God hath joined let no man put asunder. (*He kisses* MARY *and turns, dusting his hands.*) Well, that job's done. I hope there's pie for breakfast, Neighbor Stone. (*And, as some of the women, dancing, bring in pies from the kitchen*)

THE CURTAIN FALLS

DISCUSSION

1. What important facts do you learn from the opening conversations of the wedding guests? How does the clipped, rhythmic pattern of these conversations help to establish the atmosphere of the play?

2. When does Jabez first indicate that he is not as "lucky" as he seems? Why does he choose this particular moment to do so?

3. Explain the presence of Daniel Webster at Jabez's wedding party. Contrast the arrival of Webster to the arrival of Mr. Scratch. How do the two men differ in manner? In their effect upon the crowd? What opposing forces do Webster and Scratch represent?

4. What lies behind the fiddler's dilemma?

5. Account for the readiness with which the guests accept the "evidence" of Jabez's guilt. Does their behavior here seem consistent with their behavior elsewhere in the play?

6. How does Jabez explain his motives for making a pact with the devil? In what respects has he both underestimated Mary and deluded himself?

7. What are Webster's motives for coming to Jabez's defense, despite the seeming hopelessness of the case?

8. Contrast Mary's prayer to the devil's earlier song. How does Mary's prayer anticipate the outcome of the conflict? Why does Benét interject excerpts from this prayer into the trial proceedings? Is

there any similarity between Mary Stone and Ruth of the Biblical story?

9. Explain the humor of the devil's comment to Webster: "I am an honest American like yourself—and of the best descent . . ." How is the devil's selection of a jury a commentary on his character? Refer to the characteristics of each member of the jury, by way of explanation.

10. Why does Webster mention that he "miss(es) General Arnold from the company"?

11. Evaluate Webster's performance as lawyer for the defense. Why do his chances of winning the case at first seem slight? When do you first sense that his chances are improving?

12. Why is Webster's final plea to the jury effective? How does this plea underscore the theme of the play?

13. What is Benét's purpose in using poetry instead of prose for some portions of the play?

TOPICS FOR WRITING

Discuss the reasons why, in your estimation, the story of a man's dealings with the devil has been popular in one form or another with countless generations of readers.

Explain the techniques by which Benét creates an atmosphere of fantasy in *The Devil and Daniel Webster*.

Write a character study of Daniel Webster, Mr. Scratch, Mary, or Jabez Stone

NOTES

p. 268   Whig: a political party which opposed the Democratic party between 1834 and 1855. Daniel Webster was a leader of this party.

p. 281   *caveat emptor* (Latin): Let the buyer beware. Scratch means that Jabez has made a bargain for which there is now no recourse.

p. 283   oyes: a cry used in a court of law to command silence.

p. 288   shivaree: a mock serenade in which the participants use pots, pans, spoons, and kettles as musical instruments.

SAMMY

Ken Hughes

CHARACTERS

Sammy
Radio Commentator

SAMMY was first produced on BBC Television on March 26, 1958.

Ken Hughes (1923-   )

Ken Hughes, who was born in Liverpool, England, began his literary career as a re-wind boy in the motion picture industry. He later served as a director of feature and documentary films. In addition to his television and movie work, Hughes has written two novels, High Wray *and* The Long Echo.

In 1958, Hughes earned the award of best script of the year for Sammy, *a television play about a man's struggle to avert the consequences of his own actions.* Sammy *first appeared on British television, starring Anthony Newley. It was subsequently produced for television in the United States, with Mickey Rooney in the title role.*

SAMMY

FADE IN

1. INT. LIVING-ROOM OF SAMMY ELLERMAN'S APARTMENT.

It is about 3 p.m. on a sunny afternoon. The window curtains drift gently in the breeze, and through the open window come the sounds of the city. A few newspapers are scattered on a divan. A cheap radio stands on a small table near fireplace.

*A table is centre with telephone on long cord. Right of the
table stands a chest of drawers. There are empty bottles of
beer, a glass with dog ends in it, and racing forms. In the
right foreground there is an armchair, worn but still has a
certain elegance and beauty.*

2. INT. LIVING-ROOM OF SAMMY ELLERMAN'S BED-
   ROOM.

As we move into bedroom, we see SAMMY *hunched up among
bed-clothes. He wears underpants and a singlet. On the bedroom table stands a cheap alarm clock, a bottle of influenza
mixture, an empty water jug, and a bottle of codeine tablets.
The time by the clock is three o'clock. Suddenly the clock
goes off: the alarm rings furiously runs slowly down and then
stops.* SAMMY *unwinds himself in the bed, lifts his head from
the pillow and lies on his back staring at the ceiling. He
raises into a sitting position and pulls blanket around him.
Takes two codeine tablets, as there is no water in the jug
he rises and walks slowly out into living-room.*

CUT TO

3. INT. LIVING-ROOM.

SAMMY *crosses R. into kitchen.*

CUT TO

4. INT. KITCHEN.

SAMMY *comes to sink, takes water then stares into mirror.
Then fills kettle. When* SAMMY *has filled kettle he moves to
stove and puts kettle on. Then moves out into living-room.*

CUT TO

5. INT. LIVING-ROOM.

*He walks across room to radio L., switches it on and moves
back into bedroom.*

6. INT. BEDROOM.

We see SAMMY *seated on his bed and dressing, and hear the race commentary in the living-room:*

RADIO COMMENTATOR . . . here at Newmarket for the two-year-old event of the season, and it's a perfect day for racing on this famous broad heath, beautiful turf, a cloudless sky, and a line-up of horses that is going to make the result of this race anybody's guess!

The commentary continues (as below) as SAMMY *pulls on his pants and sits on the edge of the bed. He shivers, wipes his face, and takes a swig from the medicine bottle like a man attacking a whisky bottle. He makes a wry face and belches. Then picking up his shirt he goes into the living-room, pulling it on.*

. . . And now as they canter down past us towards the starting gate, this is how they will line up: Jacko, owned by Captain Howell, trained by Richard Lewitt and ridden by Ron Easton. Fillibuster, from Lord Beresford's stables, trained by Harry Macdowell and ridden by Jackie White. Royal Train, the favourite, owned by Arthur Becker and ridden by Tom West. People's Choice, also from the Howell stable and ridden by 16-year-old Peter Winston. Lucky Lucy, owned by Sir John Rutherford, trained by Arthur Locke, ridden by Tony Arison. Mother's Boy, owned by Major Ruskin, trained by Ron Harris, ridden by Eddie Leroy. Uncle Tom, owned by Tom Williams, trained by Richard Lewitt and ridden by new-comer Harry Jones . . . Breakaway, owned by Mr. Lyle, trained by John Abbot, and ridden by Tim Leaston.

CUT TO

7. INT. LIVING-ROOM.

SAMMY *comes from bedroom, crosses to radio and sits.*

RADIO COMMENTATOR (cont.) . . . Wendle Red ridden by Jock Summerfield, and Geordie, owned by Major Johns, trained by Matt Lewitt and ridden by Paddy O'Niel.

SAMMY *sits by the phone, turns the radio low, and picks up the receiver.*

SAMMY (*on phone*) Hallo . . . Oh, hallo.

He reaches for a cigarette in a packet on the table, balances the phone on his shoulder.

Lousy. I dunno, feels like double pneumonia to me. Yes, he came around this morning. Of course he did, but I got to get up once in a while.

He leans forward, turns up the radio to make sure he isn't missing anything. He listens to the radio anxiously.

RADIO COMMENTATOR . . . The white flag is up and they're under starter's orders, all pretty well in line: Wendle Red a bit behind . . .
SAMMY Look, Patsy, let me call you back, will you? I . . . All right so it's important but it can keep for five minutes, can't it? I'll call you back in five minutes, where are you? Piccadilly Circus Underground!! What are you doing there, why aren't you at work? What? Oh, Patsy, I don't know what you're talking about. Call me back in five minutes, will you? No, there isn't anyone here! I just want to listen to the radio. A Race! A Race! What do you think? 'Listen with Mother?' (*He turns up the radio.*) . . . But, Patsy, I . . . Patsy! Ring me back, will you?

He slams down phone and listens with tension and anxiety.

RADIO COMMENTATOR . . . and THEY'RE OFF!!! with Breakaway first to break the line, Royal Train close in behind, with Fillibuster and People's Choice right up there making up ground, and Wendle Red, Geordie . .

SAMMY *makes a beckoning gesture with his finger-tips.*

SAMMY So Jacko . . . where's Jacko?
RADIO COMMENTATOR . . . and last of all is Jacko.
SAMMY . . . 'last of all is Jacko!'

RADIO COMMENTATOR . . . Now it's Royal Train taking the lead with Breakaway in second place. Fillibuster a length behind and Wendle Red moving up smoothly . . .

SAMMY What about Jacko!

RADIO COMMENTATOR And now Jacko is coming up fast on the inside . . .

> SAMMY *wipes his mouth, lights a cigarette but lights the wrong end. The* RADIO COMMENTATOR *begins to get excited.*

. . . Two furlongs to go and it's Royal Train still in the lead, with Fillibuster challenging and Jacko . . . Jacko now third with People's Choice fourth and Wendle Red. And now here's Jacko up on the inside and drawing level with Fillibuster . . . a furlong to go and it's Royal Train, Jacko . . . Fillibuster now third . . .

> *The phone rings.* SAMMY *glances irritably at the phone but lets it ring.*

. . . and it's *Royal Train* and Jacko neck and neck . . . 100 yards to go and it's Jacko in the lead by half a length from Royal Train who's being ridden all out. Fillibuster a length behind and People's Choice still fourth . . .

> *The phone still rings.* SAMMY *grabs the phone, slams down the receiver. By this time, he is sweating blood. He rubs his knuckles against his teeth, and rolls the cigarette into a ball as he strains every nerve and muscle with the race.*

. . . Fifty yards to go and it's still Jacko, yes Jacko's going really well.

> SAMMY *leans forward, his eyes widen frantically.*

SAMMY Come on—come on—stay with it!

RADIO COMMENTATOR But here's Royal Train cutting loose, he's going ahead with a terrific finishing burst . . .

> SAMMY *grips the radio frantically, turns the volume full up.*

SAMMY No!

RADIO COMMENTATOR   It's Royal Train!!! Royal Train by, I should say, half a length from Jacko second, Fillibuster third, then People's Choice, Wendle Red and Breakaway. A magnificent finishing effort by Jockey Tom West. So that's the result—first Royal Train by half a length . . . second.

> SAMMY *switches off the radio savagely. He sits with his head in his hands, his eyes closed. Then slowly raises his head and stares across the room, a man deeply and seriously worried. The phone rings. He turns, looks at the phone, picks it up slowly; puts it to his ear.*

SAMMY   Yes. Who? No. You got the wrong number.

> *He slams the phone down and sits hunched on the edge of the chair. Kettle whistles. He looks up towards the kitchen, then slowly rises and crosses towards the kitchen.*

CUT TO

8. INT. KITCHEN.

> SAMMY *enters, turns off the gas beneath the steaming and whistling kettle, and stands there, leaning on the gas stove, staring at the kettle.*

SAMMY   And I had to play it to win! Fifty quid to win and it comes in *second!* (*He slams a saucepan lid down on top of the stove.*)

> *The phone rings.*

Oh, for crying out loud! (*He returns to the living-room.*)

9. INT. LIVING-ROOM.

> SAMMY *enters, picks up the telephone.*

SAMMY   *Hallo!* Oh, hallo, Patsy, no it's all right, it's over now.

> *He sits down, puts a cigarette in his mouth, hardly listening to what* PATSY *is saying.*

Yes . . . Why, you taken the day off or something?

He takes the unlighted cigarette from his mouth.

You did *what?* (*He puts a hand to forehead . . . more trouble.*) Oh,
Patsy, for Pete's sake . . . sure I know . . . yes, yes, I'm sure I did,
but . . . Look, Patsy, I said a lot of things. No, I'm not going back on
my word, Patsy, it's just that . . . well, you picked a bad time, a bad
time, Patsy. (*He listens as she talks.*) Then you'll have to go back
home . . . Patsy, I *know* I said that but I didn't think you were going
to pack a bag and come tearing up to town . . . and I tell you, *you
can't come here!* Look, I don't want to get slung out a here. Oh,
don't do that. Please. Of course I do. All right, 'I love you,' now will
you please go and find yourself a room somewhere . . . Then go home,
then! But don't make it my responsibility, I got troubles enough of
my own . . . trouble is trouble. What's the difference what sort of
trouble? (*Pause.*) You got two hundred quid? Then you can't help
me. (*Pause.*) Sure I want to see you but not right *now*, I don't know,
later on sometime. Four o'clock all right, where? Okay, I'll see you
there. No, I'm not going any place . . . Patsy, there isn't anyone here,
no girls, no nothing, now will you please hang up. Four o'clock, yes.
All right. Good-bye. (*He puts the phone down, then rises.*) At a time
like *this!*

> *He moves to window, gets newspaper from chest of drawers,
> then moves to table, sits and then dials phone.*

Hallo, this is Mr. Ellerman. B-6478. What's the score on the three-
thirty at Sandown? That's right, Ellerman. What do you mean, you
can't accept any more bets from me. I . . . certainly I know I'm over
my credit limit but you're not talking to one of your two bob punters
now, you know! I shall talk to Mr. Conner himself about *this*. Oh,
he wants to talk to *me?* Well, that suits me, put him on . . . Well,
now, Joe, there's a funny thing, I was about to give *you* a call. I look
in my little book just now and I find I owe you, how much is it, let
me see . . . (CONNER *tells him.*) . . . That's right, two hundred.
Weeeeeell I really ought to settle up with you, oughtn't I? How long
has it been? Two months? *Six* months! Well, well, how time flies. Well,
I'll be passing your office Saturday, I could drop the money in then.

SAMMY *listens as* CONNER *lays down the law.*

Tonight! By *six o'clock!* You must be kidding, Joe. Where can I lay
hands on two hundred nicker this time of day. The banks close at
three, you know. (*His forced smile freezes.*) Oh, now, Joe, don't be
like that. But, Joe, you . . . *What do you think? I got two hundred
under the bed or something?* Shouting, who's shouting? (*He listens.*)
Now, look here, don't you threaten me, I could go to the law, you
know. A man has a right to protect himself. (*Pause.*) Barney Thompson, what about him? Sure I know he's in hospital, he got done up last
week, everyone knows that. Twenty stitches—twenty-five stitches?
So who's counting? He owed you a *hundred* quid. And I owe you two
hundred . . . Certainly I can multiply!! Look, Joe, Mr. Conner, I'm
sick. I got a fever, I got a temperature of a hundred and seven. You're
right, *I should be dead.* How can I come to your office? I can't even
cross the room. Oh. You'll send someone round here . . . by six o'clock.
(*He listens.*) Now, look, Joe, listen, give me a couple of days, a day,
tomorrow, I'll have it for you tomorrow I swear. Two hundred in cash,
on the nose, ten o'clock in your office . . . Joe, give me a chance, I
tell you I couldn't raise that much dough by six o'clock! Joe . . . *listen
to me . . . Give me a break . . . I'll get it for you . . . Joe . . . Joe, are
you there . . . Hallo! Hallo! Hallo!* (*He looks at dead phone in his
hand, puts it down gently.*) Oh, my Gawd.

> *He rises and moves across room. Suddenly he comes face to
> face with himself in a mirror. He moves closer, stares at him-
> self, dishevelled, sweaty and scared. He puts his trembling
> finger-tips to his face and touches the skin.*

Oh . . . no . . .

> *His hands shake, he covers his mouth, he walks away and
> flops helplessly into the antique chair and stares aimlessly
> about him. He glances at his watch.*

Six o'clock yet.

> *He rubs his face, thinks hard for a moment, then with sudden
> decision gets up and goes to the phone and dials. He searches*

*feverishly through the notebook for a phone number. Finding
it he picks up the phone and dials.*

Hallo . . . is Mr. Ellerman there? It's his brother Sammy. (*He holds on,
waiting anxiously, conscious of the time.*) Two hundred nicker in three
hours, he must be mad! Lou? Sammy.

*There is an awkward pause from which we gather that Lou's
reception is unfriendly.*

How are you, Lou boy? All right. Becky. Good, good. And the kids?
. . . Great . . . another one . . . well, well, well, you're the boy, Lou,
ha, ha, ha. What do I want? Well, as a matter of fact, I was going
to ask you to do me a small favour, Lou. (*Pause.*) Well, not very
much, I mean with you doing so well and . . . (*Pause.*) Two hundred.
(*Pause.*) Now, wait a minute, Lou, would I come to you if I wasn't
dead stuck. I'm in trouble, Lou, real trouble. If I don't have it by six
o'clock they're going to cut me up. What's the difference how I come
to owe it? I owe it. (*Pause.*) Lou, do me a favour, no sermons. Yes,
yes, yes, yes, I know what Pappa always said, sure, sure, sure you'd
make good and I'd make bad. Sure, sure . . . yes, you offered to make
me a partner. I just don't see myself in the grocery business, that's all.
Okay, okay, so make me a partner now and advance me two hundred
on account. Lou, you don't seem to understand, they've got the finger
on me. (*Pause.*) Lou, this is your brother, your own flesh and blood.
If you won't do it for me do it for Mama. May she rest in peace! Lou,
you gotta believe me, I'm, I'm so scared. They don't mess around,
these boys and I don't like razors! Every time I go to the barber's
I come out in a cold sweat. Believe me, Lou, I'll never ask you for
another penny as long as I breathe . . . on my life, not another penny.
(*Pause. He lowers his voice, talks quietly.*) Lou, just let me have a
hundred. Maybe with a hundred, they'll only bash half my face in!
Lou, listen to me, this is your brother Sammy. Remember me? Who
was it took the blame when you heaved a rock at that copper in Pedro
Street? Ah . . . aha . . . and who was it sorted out Maxie Abrahams
when he was going to kick your face in? Okay, okay, okay, so do *me*
a favour, huh, Lou? (*Pause.*) Twenty-five!!! *What are you trying to
do, Lou, see me get killed!* (*Pause.*) Okay. All right, Lou. Thanks for
nothing. Good luck to you, Lou. May you live so long! And as for your

twenty-five quid I tell you what you do. You take it and buy Becky a new fox fur. *And I hope she strangles herself with it!!!*

> *There are tears in* SAMMY's *eyes as he slams the phone down. He appeals to the empty room.*

My own brother. My own brother! At a time like this a man should have such a brother!!

> *He gets up, stalks around desperately worried. He glances at his watch.*

Quarter to four.

> *He feels in his pocket for a dog end, enters the bedroom.*

CUT TO

10. INT. BEDROOM.

He feels in his pocket for cigarettes, finds none, takes a dog end from the ashtray, lights it, sits on the bed puffing it. It tastes horrible. He stubs it out, coughing. Then, as he sits there he notices the cardboard boxes stacked in the corner. He goes over to them and opens one up. From it he takes an eight-inch plastic doll, fully dressed. He looks at it for a moment. Slowly an idea comes to him. With sudden resolution he enters the living-room.

CUT TO

11. INT. LIVING-ROOM.
SAMMY *picks up the phone, looks through his notebook, finds a number, dials it. As he waits for the number to ring he examines the doll in his hand.*

SAMMY   Is Mr. Anderson there, please? Sam Ellerman.

> *A pause, he looks at the doll, lifts its skirt, looks underneath, shrugs.*

Mr. Anderson. How are you? Fine, fine. Business? Good, glad to hear it. Mr. Anderson, I got the very merchandise you're looking for. British made, unbreakable, washable, every one in perfect condition . . . (*The head falls off the doll.*) . . . Oh, great! What are they? Dolls, Mr. Anderson. No, no, no, no, no, *Dolls*, not *Poles*. Sure I know this ain't Christmas, but the kids always want a doll. Wait till you see them, Mr. Anderson, all happy and smiling, and every one a squeaker. Here, listen.

> *He tips the doll up near the mouthpiece. The doll doesn't utter a word.*

(*Sotto*): Oh, my life. (*He puts his own voice near the mouthpiece.*) 'Mama.' There! Hear *that*, Mr. Anderson, and to *you*, sixty bob a dozen. I got a gross, you can have the whole lot for thirty quid . . . You *got* dolls! Two thousand of 'em! Can't shift 'em. Twenty-five quid, I'm giving them away. Hmm. Okay so you don't want dolls. What do you want, Mr. Anderson? (*Pause.*) Chair? What chair? . . . (*He listens.*) Yes, I remember, you came up here for a drink Derby Day. You and that blonde. What was her name? . . . Sylvia, that's right. Boy, did we have a time! Ha, ha . . . Whatever became of that old slag? Oh . . . you *did*. Congratulations. The chair? . . . oh, the *chair!*

> *He looks across at the antique chair, eyes it lovingly.*

Oh, it's a beautiful chair, all right. Eighteenth-century. They don't make 'em like that any more. But, look here, Mr. Anderson, you got a big wholesale business, there must be something you need. The chair? What about the chair? (*He listens, frowns.*) I'm sorry, Mr. Anderson, that chair isn't for sale. You're telling me it's worth a lot of money, but it's worth more than money to me, Mr. Anderson. My mother died in that chair, God rest her soul. Five years she sat in it, never got out of it, day or night. Arthritis. Then she died, sitting right there. (*A reverent pause as he looks at the chair.*) It's the only possession I got in the world. I wouldn't part with it not if you was to offer me twenty pounds. (*Pause.*) Fifty pounds!

> *He struggles with his conscience, looks at the chair.*

I'm sorry, Mr. Anderson. Not *that* chair. Not my mother's chair. You must know how a man feels about his mother's chair. I tell you what, though, maybe I could get you one like it. I see. Well, there must be something I can do for you. I know a geezer got plastic raincoats at ten bob each. You've got two thousand, and you can't shift 'em. What are you doing, saving them up for a rainy day? Look, Mr. Anderson, I'll level with you. I'm in a dead shtuch, anything you could throw my way . . . American whisky? How much do you want? Hmmm. Well, I'll do what I can. What are you offering, Mr. Anderson? Twenty-five bob a bottle? Blimey, it's only thirty-five bob retail . . . Thirty-two bob or it isn't worth my while. Are you kidding? All right, thirty bob, I'll meet you half-way. Right, I'll call you back. Oh, and Mr. Anderson, this'll have to be a cash transaction, I mean you understand, what with the merchandise being maybe a little on the warm side, checks and all that . . . that's very kind of you. Good-bye.

> *He rings off, rubs his mouth thoughtfully, then starts to search through his notebook.*

Tony, Tailor, Tex? Trumans, Teresa . . . 'Teresa,' I wonder what she's doing now? Yeah, I bet she is. (*Back to book.*) Taxi . . . ah, Ted . . . (*He picks up the phone, dials.*) 'Teresa,' hmm, ha! . . . Ted? Sammy. American whisky, got any? Now, now, now, now, Ted, don't give me that. Thirty bob a bottle!!! Do me a favour. Twenty-five bob and I haven't got time to mess around! Twenty-seven bob, take it or leave it. Right. That's four doz., that's—er—forty-eight times twenty-seven, seven eights, one, two five, six, that's *sixty-two quid*. Quite correct, and sixteen shillings. I'll send someone around with a cheque right away. What do you mean? 'No, thank you?' You want cash! Then let's forget the whole deal, I just thought I'd put a little business your way. So I was wrong. So long, Ted.

> *He turns the dial of the phone, holds it there a second, re-leases it, then puts the receiver to his ear.*

Hallo . . . hallo . . . who's that? You still on the line? Look, I'm trying to make a call, do you mind . . . what? So who does business in *cash* these days? It's not the principle, Ted boy, it's the *money*. What do you mean, *twenty-five quid cash* and a cheque for the balance??? Ted, I'm surprised at you, I really am. (*He thinks hard.*) All right, if that's the way you do business, that's fine by me, but it's the last time. I'll have someone come around to your place in half an hour. Yes, twenty-five quid, I heard you the first time.

He rings off, rises, looks at his watch, dials another number, looks for a cigarette, finds none, so trailing the phone, he crosses to chest of drawers for fags, then comes to table.

(*On phone*) Harry? Sammy. Want to make a tenner? Got a couple of messages I want you to run. I said a tenner, didn't I? Have I ever twisted you. Now, listen. You got your car? Good. Now . . . what? No, no, nothing like that. This is straight business. Cash and carry. Okay, now get round here fast.

He rings off. He is beginning to sweat a little. He glances at his watch, then gets up, goes into the bedroom.

CUT TO

12. INT. BEDROOM.

SAMMY Oh, blimey . . .

He takes a wallet from his jacket, the contents are two ten-shilling notes, a few visiting cards and other rubbish. He thinks hard. Totters back to the living-room.

CUT TO

13. INT. LIVING-ROOM.

He totters across to mantelpiece. He picks up a vase, tips it on to the table. Out comes a screwed-up note, some foreign coins and a button. He unravels the note.

SAMMY A thousand francs. I wonder if Harry's going to Boulogne this year?

He stands thinking hard, looks at the phone, then makes up his mind and goes over to it. He picks up the phone, dials a number. Meanwhile, he straightens out a dog end and searches for a match.

SAMMY Hallo, Cosmo? Sammy Ellerman. Look, there's a girl in there. Patsy Miller, blonde, about twenty-three, she's got a suitcase. Can I speak to her? Patsy? Sammy. Listen, you got any money? That's no good, I mean *money!* Your Post Office book? . . . Oh, now I wouldn't want to touch that . . . how much you got in there? Four pounds three and elevenpence! What you been doing, Patsy, saving up to get married or something? Oh, now, now, now, Patsy, I didn't mean it . . . it was a joke. Oh, Patsy, don't start that again . . . Oh, dear, oh, dear . . . look, you go and have another cup of tea. Yes, yes, I'll be along about five. All right. You all right now? There's a good girl. Good-bye. (*He puts the phone down.*) Oy—women! (*He thinks hard.*) Twenty-five quid . . . Twenty-five quid . . .

He moves to antique chair and sits. He stops suddenly, rises and moves to phone in background, stares at the phone, goes through a moment of decision then picks up the phone, dials a number. There is a short pause. He hesitates, then speaks.

Hallo. Can I speak to Mr. Ellerman, please? It's his brother Sammy. INSERT OF CLOCK: *the clock says quarter to five.*

                                                                    CUT TO

14. INT. LIVING-ROOM.

SAMMY *crosses to phone.*

SAMMY Come on, Harry boy . . . Blimey, what's he doing, picking flowers or something!

The phone rings. He grabs it.

Harry! Where you been? I'm doing my *nut* here! What you mean you can't get it all in the car? Well, put it in the boot then. Blimey, I dunno! Now listen. You know Anderson's, off the Euston Road . . .

wait a minute . . . (*He refers to notebook.*) 37 Dalton Street. Get that booze round there fast, ask for Mr. Anderson in person, give him the stuff and collect *Seventy-Two Pounds Cash. Cash,* understand. Don't let him fob you off with no kite. What? Yes, yes, you can take your tenner out of that; blimey, you don't trust no one, do you. Then get on the blower right away . . . and Harry . . . *don't dawdle!*

> *He rings off, sits, searches through his notebook, picks up phone, dials a number.*

Hallo. Morrie? Sammy Ellerman. Fine, great. Say, Morrie, weather's not been too good lately, lot of rain about, must be quite a call for raincoats these days, especially plastic ones. Seventy-two bob a gross. All right, all right, so it hasn't rained for three weeks, seventy bob! Certainly I know Anderson's got them for seventy-two bob a gross, at *that* price she should be lumbered with them. Sixty-six bob? Do me a favour. Sixty-eight, and you won't get 'em any cheaper, anywhere in London. Okay, so we're having a heatwave, you've got connections in Manchester, haven't you? It's a deal. How many, twelve gross? Right. I'll have 'em round to you in twenty minutes. Oh, and Morrie. Strictly cash, eh? What do you mean, thirty-eight pounds cash or a cheque for forty-one? What kind of a deal is that? Okay, okay, okay, I haven't got time to quibble. Twenty minutes, okay?

> *He flashes the rest, dials another number.*

Mr. Anderson, please.
> *As he waits he makes rapid calculations on a sheet of paper.*
> INSERT OF FIGURES DUPLICATE TABLE. *The paper is covered in figures but in the centre he has blocked out the following:*

For whisky	£	72
To Harry	—	10
		62
For Raincoats	+	38
Cash in Hand		100

Back to SAMMY.

Mr. Anderson. That stuff'll be with you in ten minutes. Bourbon. Eighty-five per cent, okay? Now, didn't you mention something about raincoats, you couldn't shift 'em you said. Well, I'm not surprised, the weather being what it is. Hottest summer we've had for ninety years it said in the paper this morning. I'll give you fifty-five bob a gross for them. Fifty-six bob as a personal favour. Fifty-seven and that's my last offer. Right. I'll take twelve gross. Let me see, twelve sevens are . . . eighty-four, twelve fives, what are twelve fives . . . thank you, sixty . . . that's thirty-four pounds four shillings. I can't give you a cheque, Mr. Anderson, how can I, I'm *here* and you're *there*. Oh! Well, that makes it a little tricky as those other goods will be arriving any minute now. My man's there already, is he . . . hmmm. Well, you'd better put him on, I'll tell him not to unload the stuff. Eh? Well, that's not very businesslike of you, Mr. A. I'll put a cheque in the post tonight. Can I speak to my man, anyway? Thank you. Harry? Listen. This idiot's giving you twelve gross of raincoats. Take them to . . . (*Refers to book.*) Morrie Fine, Kentish Town Road, you know, just past the Three Blind Fiddlers, and collect . . . let me see—thirty-eight nicker in *hard*, then phone me back and don't forget to pick up the lolly for the booze. Seventy-two quid, right. What do you mean you didn't know there was going to be all this running around, you're getting paid, aren' you. *And hurry up!*

SAMMY *rings off. Makes notes, goes through his book.*

Baker, Bermondsey, Boxing Club, Board of Trade . . . (*His eyes light up.*) Board of Trade! (*He shrugs.*) No, dodgy mob . . . Beckman . . . *Beckman.*

He goes to pick up the phone when it rings.

Hallo! . . . Oh, hallo, Patsy, look, Patsy, not right now, I'm busy. I know I said five, so it's quarter-past . . . Well, you'll have to wait. And if I ain't there by quarter-past six, don't wait for me cos I won't be coming.

He flashes the rest, gets the dialling tone, dials again, then realises he has forgotten the number.

Oh . . . (*He rings off, looks in his book.*) Blimey, I've never worked so hard in my life!

> *He glances at his watch, selects another name, wipes the sweat from his face, dials feverishly.*

Can I speak to Mr. Davies, please. Yes, yes, I'll wait.

> *He puts the dog end in his mouth, searches for a match, puts the phone down, rushes into the kitchen.*

CUT TO

15. INT. KITCHEN.

> *He rushes in, lights the automatic pilot, lights the dog end, nearly burns his eyebrows off, rushes back to phone.*

CUT TO

16. INT. LIVING-ROOM.

> *He picks up the phone.*

SAMMY Mr. Davies, sorry I was on the other phone. You may not remember me, Mr. Davies, my name is Ellerman. I, er, hear you had a little visit from the cops last night. Tch, tch. Closed it down, tch, tch. Getting so you can't earn an honest living these days. When are you opening another club, Mr. Davies? Tomorrow night! And good *luck* to you! Is there anything you need . . . cutlery, tablecloths, ashtrays . . . glasses? You mean to *drink* from? Very essential in a night club. You've been quoted *nineteen* bob a dozen? Tch. tch. A liberty! Fifteen bob a dozen's my price, Mr. Davies . . . Fine. How many? Six gross. Fine. Anything else? No. All right, Mr. Davies, you can expect a delivery within twenty minutes. Oh, believe me, Sam Ellerman doesn't hang round . . .

> *He rings off, sits, looks at his book, dials a number.*

. . . Hallo, General Kitchenware? Mr. er . . . (*Looks at book.*) Price, please . . . Oh, Mr. Price? My name is Ellerman, I'm purchasing some equipment for Mr. Davies who, as you probably know, is opening a new club. Now, we shall need a number of things, a charcoal range, a large gas oven, three . . . no, four cake mixers, three electric toasters, oh, and six gross of glasses. Could I drop in tomorrow morning and see what you have? Fine. Good-bye, Mr. Price . . . oh . . . Mr. Price, I nearly forgot. We're having a little press reception tonight and we're a bit short of glasses: you know what the press are, they draw the line at drinking out of bottles . . . ha, ha . . . I'd say we need about two dozen . . . What is your price, Mr. er . . . Price? Nineteen bob a dozen. Well, that seems very reasonable. Could I send the van around for them now . . . two dozen, yes, that's all . . . of course, now I come to think of it, the driver might as well pick up the lot, if you have them in stock . . . you have? . . . well, that'll save an extra journey tomorrow . . . *six gross*, yes . . . Good, and I will be around in the morning to look over the kitchen equipment. Hmm? My dear Mr. Price, my van driver hasn't got the time to come back here and pick up a cheque for a mere sixty-eight quid—er—pounds. Put it down to our account . . . will you? Thank you so much. Good-bye.

> *He rings off, wipes sweat from his face, looks at watch. The phone rings.*

(*Phone*): . . . Hallo! . . . *Harry!* Where are you? Get the money? Good, now listen carefully, in fact, you'd better write it down. Go to this address. Now, now, now, Harry, don't be like that. I'm paying you a tenner, aren't I? That's good money for an afternoon's work. Do you know how much a bus driver makes? Nine pounds, thirteen shillings and sixpence a week. Not an *afternoon*, Harry, but a *week!* And him with a wife and four kids to support. Have you got a wife and four kids, Harry? Well, there you *are*, then. You're quids in, boy! So stop beefing and get on with it . . . The General Kitchenware Company at . . . (*He refers to the book.*) . . . 6a Charing Cross Road. Are you getting this all down? Good. See a Mr. Price. Collect six gross of glasses. No, no, no, you don't give him any money! Nit! Oh, dear, oh, dear, oh, dear. Just sign for them. *Well, use a false name, then!!* Blimey! Then take the glasses to the Capitol Club in Bruton Street, that's off Bond Street, you may have a little trouble finding it cos it doesn't open till tomorrow. See a Mr. Davies, *personal*. Give him the gear, collect . . . let me see . . . six gross at fifteen bob . . . one hundred and eight shillings . . . that's nine pounds times six . . . that's fifty-four pounds. Okay? Oh, and Harry, how much cash you got on you now?

> *He listens as* HARRY *counts.*

Ninety-eight pounds fifteen!! Harry, have you been in the *boozer?* What do you mean petrol? When you hire a car it's supposed to have petrol *in it,* isn't it? All right, all right, never mind, so you're making a couple of quid on the side, you should live so long. Now get moving and phone me when you get to the club.

> *He rings off, rubs his hair, wipes his mouth, looks at his watch.*

Half-past already. (*He makes frantic calculations on paper.*)

INSERT THE PAPER, COVERED IN FIGURES:

For whisky	£72	0	0
To Harry	— 10		
	62		
For Raincoats	+ 38		
	100		
Petrol (Sundries)	— 1	5	0
	98	15	0
Capitol Club			
Glasses	+ 54		
Cash in Hand	£152	15	0

Back to SAMMY.
He stares at paper, throws the pencil down.

Fifty quid to go. (*He looks at watch.*) And half an hour left.

> SAMMY *gets up, starts thumbing through his book.*

Let's start again at the beginning. A. Acton, Anderson . . . no, we've worked *him*. Albert. Amalgamated Export Company, no, too straight. Alperton. B. Bristol . . . (*He paces through into kitchen.*)

CUT TO

17. INT. KITCHEN.

> SAMMY *drinks milk.*
> *There is the sound of kids shouting and running upstairs. He moves back into living-room as the factory hooter sounds.*

CUT TO

18. INT. LIVING-ROOM.

> *He crosses L. to table.*

> SAMMY   Dervis, Dalton . . .

> *He dials number. Child starts piano practice upstairs. He glares up at ceiling.*

Dalton's Garage? Mr. West? He's gone home? . . . No, no, it's all right. (*He rings off. Goes through notebook.*)

> *The piano practice continues. He dials, misdials, dials again, getting increasingly flustered.*

Hallo, is Mr. Forbes there? Hr. Ellerman. No, *Ellerman* . . . *Ellerman!* (*He glares in despair at the ceiling.*) E—L—L—E—R—M—— No, M. M. for *Mother*, A—N—*Ellerman!* What? I want to speak to Mr. Forbes. He's *what!!* In Switzerland. *No, no, never mind!*

> *He slams the phone down, turns the pages of his book, then glares wildly up at the ceiling.*

Shuttup, will you!!! Shuuttuuup!

> *He returns to his book, finds a number, starts to dial. As he does so, someone overhead bangs heavily on the floor as if telling him to shut up.*

Oh, my Gawd!

> *He holds his head in his hands. Near to tears he begins to turn the pages of the book. He isn't really looking at it, just turning the pages. Suddenly he throws the book down, buries his head in hands, pressing the palms against his temples. The room is suddenly strangely quiet. After a pause, the phone rings. He looks at it, lets it ring for a bit, then picks it up. He answers quietly, his voice now a little hoarse with talking. He is thoroughly dejected and spiritless.*

Yes. Oh, hallo, Harry. You got it? How much you got altogether? A hundred fifty-three pounds? Yeh, that's about right. (*He sits, thinking.*) Huh? No . . . no. I got nothing else for you. Maybe I can stall Conner off with that much. You're telling *me* he won't settle for a hundred fifty but what else can I do, lad? (*Pause.*) Well, you'd better get over here. Huh? A tenner? You keep your tenner, you earned it. What time is it? Twenty to six. You're a little fast. Okay, boy, see you back here.

> *Puts phone down. Sits there staring blankly into the dark corners of the room. His eyes shift slowly around, unseeing, tired eyes. Suddenly they alight on one object and stay there. He stares blankly at it for a long time. It is his mother's chair. The evening sun filters through the curtains and casts a shaft of dusty light around the chair. The rest of the room grows darker. Slowly, SAMMY gets up, walks over to the chair. Then slowly he stares at the chair, as if seeing the image of his mother still sitting there, then he sits. Buries his face against the fabric, closes his eyes. A faint, muffled sob comes from his throat. Then slowly he raises his eyes, looks at the chair, comes to his feet. He moves away and we next hear dialling tone and then his voice.*

SAMMY'S VOICE (*Out of shot*)   Hallo. Mr. Anderson. Sammy Ellerman . . . about that chair.

The Camera slowly moves down to the chair.

FADE OUT

FADE IN VERY FAINT

19. INT. LIVING-ROOM.

*The sun has gone down, the room is almost in darkness.
Where the elegant chair once stood is now a conspicuous
empty space.* SAMMY *stands at the window, staring into the
spreading darkness. The phone rings.* SAMMY *moves to table
and sits, then slowly picks up the phone. He speaks quietly.*

SAMMY   Hallo. Oh, hallo, Patsy. Yes, I know. I'm sorry, but I've
got to wait here till six. No, I'm all right. I . . . I'll be there just after
six, I promise. Hmm? Yes, I was worried . . . a business matter but
it's all right now. No, I've got to wait till a friend of mine gets here
with some money. He should *be* here by now. Then we'll go to a
movie or something. Yes, I don't mind. I *like* a good Western. Tonight?
I don't know. I guess you'd better go back home. It wouldn't be right
for you to come here. I mean . . . well, it's all right for *some* girls, but
not you. You're a nice girl, Patsy, and . . . well, I wouldn't want us
to do anything that would spoil it . . . you know what I mean? Well,
I . . . we'll talk about that later . . . we'll talk about a lot of things.
Yes, maybe we'll talk about that, too . . . A job? . . . You're right, it's
about time I *did*. This sort of life . . . living from one day to the next,
it wears you down . . . Sure . . . of course I do. Yes, I'll be there. It's
five to now, say in about ten minutes. All right. Good-bye, Patsy.

He puts the phone down. Looks at his watch.

Come on, Harry boy, what's keeping you? (*Pause.*) It's like one of
them little white mice in one of them wheels . . . the faster you run,
the faster you don't get no place. (*He chuckles cynically.*)

There is the sound of steps on the stairs outside, then a single tap at the door. SAMMY *breathes with relief.*

And about *time!* (*He goes to the door.*) What *kept* you? I thought you'd never get here in time . . .

    20. EXT. LIVING-ROOM DOOR.
    SAMMY *opens the door.*

MAN'S VOICE It's six o'clock, Sammy!
SAMMY Oh . . . now . . . now wait a minute!

He gestures helplessly in the empty air. He looks at his watch. His hands are shaking.

It's not six yet . . . look . . . another five minutes.

There is no answer. SAMMY *puts a trembling hand to his mouth, looks at his watch.*

I got a guy coming with the money . . . all of it . . . I swear . . . two hundred, like Joe said . . . he should be here by now . . . you're too early . . . it's five to six, look . . . (*Pointing to watch*) look . . . five to . . . five minutes . . . it's never wrong.

From an upstairs radio we hear the six pips, followed by an announcer's voice:

ANNOUNCER This is the BBC Home Service. Here is the Six O'Clock News, etc. . . . .
MAN'S VOICE You got a cheap watch, Sammy.

Two men in overcoats enter the room. The door slams.
    21. INT. LIVING-ROOM.

SAMMY *No! No!*

There is a sudden scuffle, the sound of blows, a sharp cry of pain. The two men stand there for a second, then turn and walk swiftly back to the door. They go out and slam the door behind them. There is the sound of hurried steps on the stairs. Someone bangs on the door.

HARRY   Sammy? Sammy, you there? It's me, Harry. I got the money. Sammy?

> *The handle is turned. The door opens.* HARRY's *feet appear in the doorway, his shadow spreads out across the carpet. He stops dead.*

Oh, my Gawd!

> *He turns and belts down the stairs, leaving door open.*

(*Off*) Help! Quick! Someone . . . get the police. Get an ambulance.

> *Curious voices converse.* (*Off screen.*) *A* LANDLADY *demands to know what's going on.*

VOICE LANDLADY   What's going on (etc. . . . .).

> *We see* SAMMY *crawling to table, his face hidden, whimpering quietly to himself.*

SAMMY   Mama . . . mama, mama, mama . . .

FADE OUT

DISCUSSION

1. What are the earliest indications of Sammy's character and of the type of world that he inhabits?
2. By what means does the playwright "bring to life" people you never see, and whose voices you never hear? From the information provided, how would you describe the personality of (a) Patsy, (b) Sammy's brother, Lou, (c) Mr. Anderson, (d) Joe Conner?
3. What parallels can be drawn between the opening description of a horse race and Sammy's situation in the play?

4. Examine Sammy's reactions to the people with whom he converses. How do these reactions vary? Why?
5. What is signified by Sammy's switch from "Joe" to "Mr. Conner" in the middle of his conversation with the book maker?
6. At what moment in the play do you first sense what the outcome will be?
7. Cite evidences of Sammy's growing tension. How do the constant shifts of scene, from bedroom, to living room, to kitchen, point up this tension?
8. Interpret the scene in which Sammy confronts himself in the mirror and then exclaims, "Oh . . . no . . ."
9. What proof does the playwright offer of Sammy's resourcefulness and ingenuity? How is this noteworthy?
10. What incident represents Sammy's final loss of integrity? How has the playwright prepared for this incident? Could it be called the climax of the play? Why?
11. What change do you observe in Sammy's manner as section nineteen begins? How is this change explainable?
12. How is the ending of the play ironic? Do you feel sympathy for Sammy, or only contempt? Give reasons for your answer.

TOPICS FOR WRITING

Analyze the use of stage lighting (sections 1, 18, and 19)

Discuss the means by which the playwright builds suspense

Contrast Sammy to his brother, Lou

Show how the following quotation from the play applies to its central character: "It's like one of them little white mice in one of them wheels . . . the faster you run, the faster you don't get no place."

NOTES

p. 294   singlet: chiefly British, a kind of undershirt worn by men
p. 298   quid (British slang): a sovereign (worth about four dollars in American money)

THE THINKING HEART

Excerpt—Act II, Last Scene

George H. Faulkner

THE THINKING HEART

CHARACTERS

Abraham Lincoln
Tinker
Chandler
Narrator

THE THINKING HEART was first presented on the "Kraft Television Theatre" on February 11, 1954 on NBC under the direction of Fielder Cook.

George H. Faulkner (1903-1957)

In countless essays, novels, biographies, and plays, writers have reminded us of Lincoln's wisdom as a statesman, and of the gentle understanding with which he administered to his people's needs. George H. Faulkner's portrayal of Lincoln in The Thinking Heart *is certainly among the finest. Setting his story in the shabby interior of a Washington telegraph office, Faulkner reveals the torment of Lincoln's private moments as Civil War president.*

Faulkner was born in Winooski, Vermont, in 1903. His early writing experience included publicity work for Paramount Pictures, and radio scriptwriting. Later, he wrote many outstanding plays for television.

The Thinking Heart *was a full-hour production when it first appeared on the Kraft Television Theatre in 1954. The excerpt that appears here is the last scene of Act II, but it is, as you will see, a complete one-act play in itself.*

THE THINKING HEART

> *Music: Martial in tone, hits in full Crossfade to film shot of marching men in Civil War uniforms, narrative image Number 12*
> *Crossfade to narrator over marching men*

NARRATOR

The color of the ground was in him, the red earth;
The smell and smack of elemental things:

The rectitude and patience of the cliff:
The good-will of the rain that loves all leaves:
The courage of the bird that dares the sea:
The gladness of the wind that shakes the corn;
The undelaying justice of the light . . .
Action followed thought and feeling.
And action led to bloody war. For Lincoln, war meant torment. And
waiting . . . waiting . . . waiting . . . In the Federal army telegraph
office at Washington . . .

> *Fade out above*

> *Fade in, close-up of a chattering telegraph key, then our view
> broadens to encompass the office of the Union army's chief
> telegraph operator, in the War Department Building. It is
> late at night. The key chatters, under. Other similar Morse-
> code keys are heard in an outer office, off screen, muted,
> throughout scene, occasionally. We see* CHARLES TINKER, *the
> chief operator, at the table on which the instrument is chat-
> tering. Then we see* LINCOLN. *He is lying on a decrepit horse-
> hair sofa which is placed under a high Washington-like
> window. Perhaps there is an indication of bitter weather
> outside. The sofa is too short. Or* LINCOLN *is too long. His
> feet are hiked up at one end, and he is asleep. He has a
> woolen shawl over him. He is awakened by the noise of*
> TINKER's *key . . .*

LINCOLN   Mr. Tinker!

TINKER (*rather old, in uniform but with collar open*)   Yes, Mr.
President?

LINCOLN   Is it from General Burnside?

TINKER   No, sir. Routine. From Harper's Ferry. A Colonel Ferris
asks for more blankets. Says it's cold in Virginia.

> (*The key stops.* TINKER *sends "Message Received"*)

LINCOLN   Reckon I could loan him *this.*

> (*Throws woolen shawl off*)

But then I guess he'd need a couple more—

> (LINCOLN *sits up, peers down at his coat lapel. Very carefully, with exaggerated interest, he takes a case of spectacles out of his pocket, puts on the glasses, looks down at his lapel. He carefully seizes, between his thumb and forefinger, an insect . . .*)

LINCOLN (*announces, solemnly*) Charlie—I have taken a prisoner.

TINKER Here, sir?

LINCOLN (*rising and carrying his captive for examination to the telegraph desk, which is lighted by a kerosene light*) No, here. Poor little critter! Know what they call him, Charlie?

TINKER (*dubiously*) Looks to me like—

LINCOLN (*interrupts*) That's what *you* think. I looked it up, because I have encountered blood relatives of this little tike ever since I can remember. This persistent and persnickety mite is called *cimex lectularius*, by folks who know how to pronounce it.

TINKER (*peering, over spectacles*) I still think he looks like a bed-bug.

LINCOLN That's what he is, Charlie, that's what he is. But he's the runt of the litter, I expect. Sort of a citified *cimex*. Back on the Sangamon, in Illinois, his like grow to three inches long, not countin' the horns and tail.

TINKER (*playing up, this is an old game for two fairly old men*) I hear tell, Mr. Lincoln, that down N'Orleans way they have such-like bugs that can carry off a pair of fire tongs, two to a tong.

LINCOLN (*going along with it*) Mr. Tinker, back in Hardin County, Kentucky, where I was born, we had fellers like this that used to *chew up* fire tongs, regular. And then spit out tupenny nails. We used to train 'em to tack shingles onto roofs . . .

> (*The two men look at each other, under the oil lamp, across the desk. And they burst into laughter. The laughter dies rather quickly, as both realize the reason for* LINCOLN's *vigil tonight . . .*)

LINCOLN (*regarding bug closely*) If it weren't so cold out, Charles, I'd loose little *cimex* through the window. As it is—

(*He lets the insect go with an upward lift and fling of his arms*)

—go back to your bed, bug . . . companion of my bosom!

TINKER   Mr. Lincoln, I have complained to Secretary Stanton a hundred times about that old couch of yours—

LINCOLN   Mr. Stanton has other things to worry over.

(*Suddenly serious*)

There hasn't been anything at all from Fredericksburg since I fell asleep?

TINKER   Nothing, Mr. President. Burnside has crossed the Rappahannock. He is attacking—that is, he *was* attacking, this afternoon. Nothing since.

(LINCOLN *slumps, tiredly, into old, broken-down, easy chair opposite* TINKER'S *table-desk. This chair was reserved for him. Like the old sofa*)

LINCOLN   Seems to me I spend about five times as many hours here in the War Office as I do anywhere else in town. Where's Mr. Stanton?

TINKER   Gone home, sir. He'll be back at dawn.

LINCOLN   Poor old curmudgeon! He doesn't like me, much. And, between you and me, Charlie—I don't so much like him.

(*We see* CHARLIE'S *face. It is evident that* CHARLIE *agrees with* MR. LINCOLN'S *opinion of Secretary of War Stanton*)

LINCOLN   (*tired, tired*)   But he's a *worker*. My land! Such a worker! And he usually talks good sense. Have you ever noticed how often people don't seem to do that any more, Charlie?

TINKER   (*a little warily*)   Yes, Mr. Lincoln. I . . . I have.

LINCOLN   Stanton may be pig-headed. But even when he's wrong, he has reasons. In a pig-headed sort of way.

(*He realizes he is talking perhaps too much to a subordinate of Stanton*)

I . . . I guess I'm . . . pretty well tuckered out, myself. I don't talk much . . . good sense, late at night.

TINKER (*positive affirmation, intense loyalty*) To me, Mr. President, you *do*. Shouldn't you . . . go home, sir?

LINCOLN Not before I get some word from General Burnside at Fredericksburg. Meantime . . . well, I like it here. Mr. Tinker, it's a pleasure to sit in this old chair and listen to those keys rattle out there —and know I'm among men who *work* for a living . . . not just talk, talk, talk . . . as they do over yonder on the hill . . .

(*The key starts to chatter*)

LINCOLN Tinker!

TINKER (*after listening for a second or two*) Nothing, sir. Message for General Halleck. Concerning promotions. Chandler will take it down, outside. And reply.

(*The key stops*)

LINCOLN Do I . . . do I get in your way here, Charles?

TINKER No, sir. We like to have you in here with us.

LINCOLN I know you do. I'm sure of that, and it—well, it comforts me. This is just about the only place in Washington where I can let loose and act as if I were back home in Springfield—or out on the circuit, lawyerin' again . . .

(LINCOLN *leans back in his chair and starts to put his feet up on* TINKER's *desk-table. The key opens up . . .* LINCOLN *pulls his feet down, all attention. The message is very brief. It stops*)

TINKER Sorry, sir. Nothing. Have you had any supper, Mr. President?

LINCOLN No, Charlie. Things have sort of piled up on me all day long, over yonder. Maybe you could do something about a bite to eat?

TINKER I have, Mr. President. Sent an orderly half an hour ago for sandwiches and coffee. Guess I better go see what's happened to him.

(*Tinker gets up, starts to leave*)

LINCOLN   What about the key?

TINKER   Chandler's desk outside is a duplicate, sir. A duplicate key. If anything comes through from Fredericksburg, he can give it to you. But I'll only be a minute—you need *food*, Mr. President.

LINCOLN   Charlie, I swear telegraphers are my favorite folks. They know I've got human *insides* in spite of all the evidence to the contrary *outside*.

> (*Calls*)

Don't be long, now . . .

> (TINKER *exits.* LINCOLN *regards the telegraph sender and receiver*)

LINCOLN

Ambrose Burnside! Deep in your whiskers!
Why are you silent, why are you dumb?
And why did I choose *you*, from all the others?
I know. Yes, I know so well, too well—
Because the politicians whispered in my ear
"He's McClellan's friend, the *West Point* friend:
Be kind to friends of George McClellan,
For McClellan still has partisans . . . and power" . . .

> (*He strikes desk in momentary anger*)

Why! Why! I needed a *man*
Not a friend of a friend of railroads in New York.
I've been weak again, for the hundredth time
And now I fret, and now *we* suffer—
And those poor devils there beyond the river . . .

> (*He turns from the desk, goes to window, looking out on a desolate winter landscape*)

On the Rappahannock, now, it's over and done.
There on the Virginia hills beyond the stream
Hundreds have died and still are dying slowly—
And it's cold in Virginia, December cold.

I've seen the battle-ground on fresh and tidy maps
With never a smirch of dry, brown blood . . .
There's a hill called *Marye's Hill,*
Up beyond the river, and in the marrow of my bone
I know young men are taken hardly there,
Dribbling a lively, unlived youth away
Between living and dying, *between ice and flame—*

> (*With a start,* LINCOLN *draws back from the window, starting
> back as if he has seen a ghost. He begins pacing the floor . . .*)

Ice and flame? Why flame—and ice?
Why should I so often think on *opposites*
In such a bitter, stabbing thrust of thought?
Why must that eternal desperate paradox—
The damnable mystic mirror image
Of all things made in earth or heav'n—
Clutch me tight in ever-double clamps of iron
And shake my mind until it reels
In sick wide captive spirals down the night:
Fire and ice . . . life and death . . . good and evil—
If they *are* the same, my work's a random cheat
And the savor of God's unholy Godless jest
Is the taste of ashes on a burning hill . . .
I'll not believe it. 'Twas Jack Kelso's doom—

> (*He paces up and down for a moment*)

I remember now. The last despatch.
It was clear and *dry* below the stream,
Burnside said. How often have I seen the like
Where other hills meet other rivers:
The winter fields, still high in grassy sedge,
But sere and yellow-grey and dry—
Like tinder ready for the careless match.
Such fields will *burn,* and burning must . . .

> (*We hear, and then see, close-up. Quickly, dramatically, in a
> sudden purposeful shift of camera emphasis, the telegraph
> key going in a vehement chatter. The soliloquy is abruptly*

broken off. LINCOLN *goes to* TINKER's *desk. He is piteously helpless . . .*)

LINCOLN (*leaning over chattering key, desperately*) What are you saying! What is it? What is it? *Chandler!* Chandler, come in here!

(CHANDLER, *another operator, younger, enters. Goes to* TINKER's *desk. The key stops, momentarily*)

CHANDLER   It's from Burnside, sir. I caught the first of it, outside.
LINCOLN   Yes, young man?
CHANDLER   Bad news, sir, I'm afraid

(*The key starts again. Stops quickly*)

LINCOLN   From General Burnside, himself?
CHANDLER   No, sir, an aide, Colonel Hardwick. He just identified himself.
LINCOLN (*controlling his voice*)   Read it to me as it comes, Chandler, if you will?

(*Key starts again, stops*)

CHANDLER (*without emotion, like a television air force type*) General Burnside reports, sir, he is utterly defeated.

(*Pause. Key sounds*)

Attack on Marye's Hill repulsed, sir, with heavy loss by artillery fire from sunken road.

(*Key . . . Pause*)

Meagher's Irish Brigade destroyed on Marye's Hill.

(*Key . . . Pause*)

Attempts to relieve Meagher rendered futile by fire in dry sedge-grass on the hill . . .

LINCOLN (*close-up. Unspoken thought*) The flame, the flame! I saw the flame! From the window, there—

(*Key chatters, briefly*)

CHANDLER (*almost bored*) Burnside has retreated across the Rappahannock, sir, to the north.

(*Key*)

Weather is worsening. Very cold. Freezing sleet.

(*Key*)

River crossing makes necessary abandonment of wounded on Marye's Hill. Losses exceed twelve thousand men. Comprehensive report in morning, sir.

(*Key stops*)
(*We see* LINCOLN, *who has been bending intently over telegraph desk. He straightens up*)

LINCOLN (*aloud, but as if to himself*) Those who were burned in the flame on the hill, and yet lived for a while—why, then, this night they'll freeze to death . . . there on the hill . . . on Marye's Hill in the ice . . . fire and ice . . . fire and ice . . .
TINKER (*off screen*) Mr. President, sir!
LINCOLN (*wearily, after a pause, turns to door*) Yes, Charlie?
TINKER (*coming on*) I've brought the sandwiches, sir . . .

(*Sees* LINCOLN'S *face*)

You—you've had the news?
LINCOLN (*struggling for control*) Yes. I . . . I don't think I'll want anything to eat, Charlie. Thank you.

(*Music is under.* LINCOLN *takes up his shawl from the side of couch. The camera watches him as he walks slowly off, putting the shawl over his shoulders and clutching it about him, huddled over. He turns at door*)

LINCOLN   Thank you, Charlie. Thank you.

Black-out
Music resolves
End of Act

DISCUSSION

1. Study the author's use of *figurative language* at the beginning of the play. What does he suggest about Lincoln's character by his references to (a) the cliff, (b) the rain, (c) the bird, (d) the wind, (e) the light?

2. How do you learn quite early in the play that Lincoln is neither concerned for his own comfort, nor impressed with his own self-importance?

3. Interpret Lincoln's behavior during the brief "bedbug" incident. How does this incident suggest the theme of the play?

4. How are the allusions to Secretary of War Stanton indicative of Lincoln's outlook as Civil War president?

5. How does the line beginning, "Mr. Tinker, it's a pleasure to sit in this old chair . . ." help to explain Lincoln's presence in the telegraph office? What other explanations for his presence become apparent by the end of the play?

6. Find examples of the courtesy with which Lincoln and Tinker address one another. What is the significance?

7. Why is Tinker's departure from the telegraph office essential to the development of the plot? How does the playwright arrange for this departure without making it seem forced or unnatural?

8. What changes do you observe in Lincoln's behavior, once he is alone? How may these changes be explained?

9. Both Lincoln's *soliloquy* and the introductory comments of the narrator are written in poetic form rather than in prose. Why do you think the playwright chose poetry for these portions of the play?

10. What is the probable explanation for Lincoln's insistence, "I *saw* the flame!" Do the repeated references to flame, fire, and burning assume symbolic significance? Explain.

11. How does the periodic ticking of the telegraph add to the dramatic intensity of the play?

12. Why is the ending effective? Why might the ending have been less effective, had the report from Burnside been a favorable one?

13. What is the connection between the title of the play and its theme?

TOPICS FOR WRITING

Discuss the function of the narrator.
Discuss the function of the soliloquy as a dramatic technique.

THE RISING OF THE MOON

Lady Augusta Gregory

Reprinted by permission of Putnam & Co. Ltd.

A fee for each and every performance is payable in advance. Inquiries in regard to performances by amateurs should be addressed to Samuel French, Inc., 25 West 45th Street, New York City.

CHARACTERS

Sergeant
Policeman X
Policeman B
A Ragged Man

Lady Augusta Gregory (1859-1932)

Lady Augusta Gregory was born in 1859 in the County of Galway, Ireland. She wrote a total of thirty-one plays during her lifetime, twenty-nine of which were performed in the famed Abbey Theatre, where she herself was a director for many years. Lady Gregory was one of several influential Irish playwrights who helped to dispel the notion that sentimentality and buffoonery are an inevitable part of the Irish character.

In The Rising of the Moon, Lady Gregory dramatizes the typical conflict of loyalties that developed during the years when Ireland was attempting to overthrow the domination of the English and become a free nation.

THE RISING OF THE MOON

SCENE *Side of a wharf in a seaport town. Some posts and chains. A large barrel. Enter three* POLICEMEN. *Moonlight.*
SERGEANT, *who is older than the others, crosses the stage to right and looks down steps. The others put down a paste-pot and unroll a bundle of placards.*

POLICEMAN B I think this would be a good place to put up a notice.

He points to barrel.

POLICEMAN X   Better ask him. (*Calls to* SERGEANT.) Will this be a good place for a placard?

No answer.

POLICEMAN B   Will we put up a notice on the barrel?

No answer.

SERGEANT   There's a flight of steps here that leads to the water. This is a place that should be minded well. If he got down here, his friends might have a boat to meet him; they might send it in here from outside.

POLICEMAN B   Would the barrel be a good place to put up a notice?

SERGEANT   It might; you can put it there.

They paste the notice up.

SERGEANT   (*Reading it*) Dark hair—dark eyes, smooth face, height, five feet five—there's not much to take hold of in that—It's a pity I had no chance of seeing him before he broke out of jail. They say he's a wonder, that it's he makes all the plans for the whole organization. There isn't another man in Ireland would have broken jail the way he did. He must have some friends among the jailers.

POLICEMAN B   A hundred pounds is little enough for the Government to offer for him. You may be sure any man in the force that takes him will get promotion.

SERGEANT   I'll mind this place myself. I wouldn't wonder at all if he came this way. He might come slipping along there (*points to side of wharf*), and his friends might be waiting for him there (*points down steps*), and once he got away it's little chance we'd have of finding him; it's maybe under a load of kelp he'd be in a fishing boat, and not one to help a married man that wants it to the reward.

POLICEMAN X   And if we get him itself, nothing but abuse on our heads for it from the people, and maybe from our own relations.

SERGEANT   Well, we have to do our duty in the force. Haven't we the whole country depending on us to keep law and order? It's those that are down would be up and those that are up would be down, if it wasn't for us. Well, hurry on, you have plenty of other places to placard yet, and come back here then to me. You can take the lantern. Don't be too long now. It's very lonesome here with nothing but the moon.

POLICEMAN B It's a pity we can't stop with you. The Government should have brought more police into the town, with *him* in jail, and at assize time too. Well, good luck to your watch.

> *They go out.*

SERGEANT (*Walks up and down once or twice and looks at placard.*) A hundred pounds and promotion sure. There must be a great deal of spending in a hundred pounds. It's a pity some honest man not to be the better of that.

> *A ragged man appears at left and tries to slip past,* SERGEANT *suddenly turns.*

SERGEANT Where are you going?

MAN I'm a poor ballad-singer, your honor. I thought to sell some of these (*holds out bundle of ballads*) to the sailors.

> *He goes on.*

SERGEANT Stop! Didn't I tell you to stop? You can't go on there.

MAN Oh, very well. It's a hard thing to be poor. All the world's against the poor.

SERGEANT Who are you?

MAN You'd be as wise as myself if I told you, but I don't mind. I'm one Jimmy Walsh, a ballad-singer.

SERGEANT Jimmy Walsh? I don't know that name.

MAN Ah, sure, they know it well enough in Ennis. Were you ever in Ennis, sergeant?

SERGEANT What brought you here?

MAN Sure, it's to the assizes I came, thinking I might make a few shillings here or there. It's in the one train with the judges I came.

SERGEANT Well, if you came so far, you may as well go farther, for you'll walk out of this.

MAN   I will, I will; I'll just go on where I was going.

Goes toward steps.

SERGEANT   Come back from those steps; no one has leave to pass down them tonight.

MAN   I'll just sit on the top of the steps till I see will some sailor buy a ballad off me that would give me my supper. They do be late going back to the ship. It's often I saw them in Cork carried down the wharf in a hand-cart.

SERGEANT   Move on, I tell you. I won't have anyone lingering about the wharf tonight.

MAN   Well, I'll go. It's the poor have the hard life! Maybe yourself might like one, sergeant. Here's a good sheet now. (*Turns one over.*) "Content and a pipe"—that's not much. "The Peeler and the Goat"—you wouldn't like that. "Johnny Hart"—that's a lovely song.

SERGEANT   Move on.

MAN   Ah, wait till you hear it. (*Sings.*)

There was a rich farmer's daughter lived near the town of Ross;
She courted a Highland soldier, his name was Johnny Hart;
Says the mother to her daughter, "I'll go distracted mad
If you marry that Highland soldier dressed up in Highland plaid.

SERGEANT   Where are you going?

MAN   Sure you told me to be going, and I am going.

SERGEANT   Don't be a fool. I didn't tell you to go that way; I told you to go back to the town..

MAN   Back to the town, is it?

SERGEANT   (*Taking him by the shoulder and shoving him before him.*) Here, I'll show you the way. Be off with you. What are you stopping for?

MAN   (*Who has been keeping his eye on the notice, points to it.*) I think I know what you're waiting for, sergeant.

SERGEANT   What's that to you?

MAN   And I knew well the man you're waiting for—I know him well—I'll be going.

He shuffles on.

SERGEANT   You know him? Come back here. What sort is he?

MAN   Come back is it, sergeant? Do you want to have me killed?

SERGEANT   Why do you say that?

MAN   Never mind. I'm going. I wouldn't be in your shoes if the reward was ten times as much. (*Goes off stage to left.*) Not if it was ten times as much.

SERGEANT   (*Rushing after him.*)   Come back here, come back. (*Drags him back.*) What sort is he? Where did you see him?

MAN   I saw him in my own place, in the County Clare. I tell you you wouldn't like to be looking at him. You'd be afraid to be in the one place with him. There isn't a weapon he doesn't know the use of, and as to strength, his muscles are as hard as that board.

   Slaps barrel.

SERGEANT   Is he as bad as that?

MAN   He is then.

SERGEANT   Do you tell me so?

MAN   There was a poor man in our place, a sergeant from Bally-vaughan.—It was with a lump of stone he did it

SERGEANT   I never heard of that.

MAN   And you wouldn't, sergeant. It's not everything that happens gets into the papers. And there was a policeman in plain clothes, too. . . . It is in Limerick he was. . . . It was after the time of the attack on the police barrack at Kilmallock. . . . Moonlight . . . just like this . . . waterside. . . . Nothing was known for certain.

SERGEANT   Do you say so? It's a terrible country to belong to.

MAN   That's so, indeed! You might be standing there, looking out that way, thinking you saw him coming up this side of the wharf (*points*), and he might be coming up this other side (*points*), and he'd be on you before you know where you were.

SERGEANT   It's a whole troop of police they ought to put here to stop a man like that.

MAN   But if you'd like me to stop with you, I could be looking down this side. I could be sitting up here on this barrel.

SERGEANT   And you know him well, too?

MAN   I'd know him a mile off, sergeant.

SERGEANT   But you wouldn't want to share the reward?

MAN   Is it a poor man like me, that has to be going the roads and and singing in fairs, to have the name on him that he took a reward? But you don't want me. I'll be safer in the town.

SERGEANT   Well, you can stop.

MAN (*Getting up on barrel.*) All right, sergeant. I wonder, now, you're not tired out, sergeant, walking up and down the way you are.

SERGEANT If I'm tired I'm used to it.

MAN You might have hard work before you tonight yet. Take it easy while you can. There's plenty of room up here on the barrel, and you can see farther when you're higher up.

SERGEANT May be so. (*Gets up beside him on barrel, facing right. They sit back to back, looking different ways.*) You made me feel a bit queer with the way you talked.

MAN Give me a match, sergeant (*He gives it, and* MAN *lights pipe*); take a draw yourself? It'll quiet you. Wait now till I give you a light, but you needn't turn round. Don't take your eye off the wharf for the life of you.

SERGEANT Never fear, I won't. (*Lights pipe. They both smoke.*) Indeed, it's a hard thing to be in the force, out at night and no thanks for it, for all the danger we're in. And it's little we get but abuse from the people, and no choice but to obey our orders, and never asked when a man is sent into danger, if you are a married man with a family.

MAN (*Sings*)

As through the hills I walked to view the hills and shamrock plain,
I stood awhile where nature smiles to view the rocks and streams,
On a matron fair I fixed my eyes beneath a fertile vale,
As she sang her song it was on the wrong of poor old Granuaile.

SERGEANT Stop that; that's no song to be singing in these times.

MAN Ah, sergeant, I was only singing to keep my heart up. It sinks when I think of him. To think of us two sitting here, and he creeping up the wharf, maybe, to get to us.

SERGEANT Are you keeping a good lookout?

MAN I am; and for no reward too. Amn't I the foolish man? But when I saw a man in trouble, I never could help trying to get him out of it. What's that? Did something hit me?

SERGEANT (*patting him on the shoulder*). You will get your reward in heaven.

MAN I know that, I know that, sergeant, but life is precious.

SERGEANT Well, you can sing if it gives you more courage.

MAN (*Sings*)

Her head was bare, her hands and feet with iron bands were
bound,
Her pensive strain and plaintive wail mingled with the eve-
ning gale,
And the song she sang with mournful air, I am old Granuaile.
Her lips so sweet that monarchs kissed . . .

SERGEANT That's not it . . . "Her gown she wore was stained
with gore." . . . That's it—you missed that.

MAN You're right, sergeant, so it is; I missed it. (*Repeats the
line.*) But to think a man like you knowing a song like that.

SERGEANT There's many a thing a man might know and might not
have any wish for.

MAN Now, I daresay, sergeant, in your youth, you used to be
sitting up on a wall, the way you are sitting up on this barrel now, and
the other lads beside you, and you singing "Granuaile"?

SERGEANT I did then.

MAN And the "Shan Bhean Bhocht"?

SERGEANT I did then.

MAN And the "Green on the Cape"?

SERGEANT That was one of them.

MAN And maybe the man you are watching for tonight used to
be sitting on the wall, when he was young, and singing those same
songs. . . . It's a queer world. . . .

SERGEANT Whisht! . . . I think I see something coming. . . . It's
only a dog.

MAN And isn't it a queer world? . . . Maybe it's one of the boys
you used to be singing with that time you will be arresting today or
tomorrow, and sending into the dock. . . .

SERGEANT That's true indeed.

MAN And maybe one night, after you had been singing, if the
other boys had told you some plan they had, some plan to free the
country, you might have joined them . . . and maybe it is you might
be in trouble now.

SERGEANT Well, who knows but I might? I had great spirit in
those days.

MAN It's a queer world, sergeant, and it's a little any mother
knows when she sees her child creeping on the floor what might
happen to it before it has gone through its life, or who will be who
in the end.

SERGEANT That's a queer thought now, and a true thought. Wait now till I think it out. . . . If it wasn't for the sense I have, and for my wife and family, and for me joining the force the time I did, it might be myself now would be after breaking jail and hiding in the dark, and it might be him that's hiding in the dark and that got out of jail would be sitting up where I am on this barrel. . . . And it might be myself would be creeping up trying to make my escape from himself, and it might be himself would be keeping the law, and myself would be breaking it, and myself would be trying maybe to put a bullet in his head, or to take up a lump of stone the way you said he did . . . no, that myself did. . . . Oh! (*Gasps. After a pause.*) What's that?

> *Grasps man's arm.*

MAN (*Jumps off barrel and listens, looking out over water.*) It's nothing, sergeant.

SERGEANT I thought it might be a boat. I had a notion there might be friends of his coming about the wharfs with a boat.

MAN Sergeant, I am thinking it was with the people you were, and not with the law you were when you were a young man.

SERGEANT Well, if I was foolish then, that time's gone.

MAN Maybe, sergeant, it comes into your head sometimes, in spite of your belt and your tunic, that it might have been as well for you to have followed Granuaile.

SERGEANT It's no business of yours what I think.

MAN Maybe, sergeant, you'll be on the side of the country yet.

SERGEANT (*Gets off barrel.*) Don't talk to me like that. I have my duties and I know them. (*Looks round.*) That was a boat; I hear the oars.

> *Goes to the steps and looks down.*

MAN (*Sings*)

> O, then, tell me, Shawn O'Farrell,
> Where the gathering is to be.
> In the old spot by the river
> Right well known to you and me!

SERGEANT Stop that! Stop that, I tell you!

MAN (*Sings louder*)

> One word more, for signal token,
>> Whistle up the marching tune,
> With your pike upon your shoulder,
>> At the Rising of the Moon.

SERGEANT   If you don't stop that, I'll arrest you.

A whistle from below answers, repeating the air.

SERGEANT   That's a signal. (*Stands between him and steps.*) You must not pass this way. . . . Step farther back. . . . Who are you? You are no ballad-singer.

MAN   You needn't ask who I am; that placard will tell you.

Points to placard.

SERGEANT   You are the man I am looking for.

MAN   (*Takes off hat and wig.* SERGEANT *seizes them.*) I am. There's a hundred pounds on my head. There is a friend of mine below in a boat. He knows a safe place to bring me to.

SERGEANT   (*Looking still at hat and wig.*) It's a pity! It's a pity. You deceived me. You deceived me well.

MAN   I am a friend of Granuaile. There is a hundred pounds on my head.

SERGEANT   It's a pity, it's a pity!

MAN   Will you let me pass, or must I make you let me?

SERGEANT   I am in the force. I will not let you pass.

MAN   I thought to do it with my tongue. (*Puts hand in breast.*) What is that?

(*Voice of* POLICEMAN X *outside.*)   Here, this is where we left him.

SERGEANT   It's my comrades coming.

MAN   You won't betray me . . . the friend of Granuaile.

Slips behind barrel.

(*Voice of* POLICEMAN B.)   That was the last of the placards.

POLICEMAN X (*As they come in.*)   If he makes his escape it won't be unknown he'll make it.

SERGEANT *puts hat and wig behind his back.*

POLICEMAN B   Did any one come this way?

SERGEANT (*After a pause.*)   No one.

POLICEMAN B   No one at all?

SERGEANT   No one at all.

POLICEMAN B   We had no orders to go back to the station; we can stop along with you.

SERGEANT   I don't want you. There is nothing for you to do here.

POLICEMAN B   You bade us to come back here and keep watch with you.

SERGEANT   I'd sooner be alone. Would any man come this way and you making all that talk? It is better the place be quiet.

POLICEMAN B   Well, we'll leave you the lantern anyhow.

Hands it to him.

SERGEANT   I don't want it. Bring it with you.

POLICEMAN B   You might want it. There are clouds coming up and you have the darkness of the night before you yet. I'll leave it over here on the barrel.

Goes to barrel.

SERGEANT   Bring it with you, I tell you. No more talk.

POLICEMAN B   Well, I thought it might be a comfort to you. I often think when I have it in my hand and can be flashing it about into every dark corner (*doing so*) that it's the same as being beside the fire at home, and the bits of bogwood blazing up now and again.

Flashes it about, now on the barrel, now on SERGEANT.

SERGEANT (*furious*).   Be off the two of you, yourselves and your lantern!

They go out. MAN *comes from behind barrel. He and* SERGEANT *stand looking at one another.*

SERGEANT   What are you waiting for?

MAN   For my hat, of course, and my wig. You wouldn't wish me to get my death of cold?

SERGEANT *gives them.*

MAN (*Going toward steps.*) Well, good-night comrade, and thank you. You did me a good turn tonight, and I'm obliged to you. Maybe I'll be able to do as much for you when the small rise up and the big fall down . . . when we all change places at the Rising (*waves his hand and disappears*) of the Moon.

SERGEANT (*Turning his back to audience and reading placard.*) A hundred pounds reward! A hundred pounds! (*Turns toward audience.*) I wonder now, am I as great a fool as I think I am?

CURTAIN

DISCUSSION

1. Find passages from the play that provide essential background information. What is brought out? How?
2. Why does Lady Gregory arrange for the departure of Policeman X and Policeman B to precede the arrival of the "ballad singer?"
3. The sergeant has to decide between loyalty to his country and the law, and sympathy for a hunted man. How does the playwright intensify this conflict? How does she keep you in suspense as to what the outcome will be?
4. Four times during their meeting, the hunted man interrupts his conversation with the sergeant to sing excerpts from popular Irish ballads. Explain his motives for singing, and the effect of each song upon the sergeant.
5. Note particularly the passage that begins, "That's a queer thought now . . ." Why is this passage a crucial one? By what method might a short story writer or a novelist have put across the same point?
6. When do you get the first inkling that the ballad singer may really be "the man (they are) looking for"?
7. Explain the manner in which the conflict is finally resolved. Is the solution understandable? Given a similar set of circumstances, would the sergeant behave the same way again? Justify your reasoning.
8. What does the playwright accomplish by having the sergeant deliver his last speaking line directly to the audience?

9. Why does Lady Gregory deliberately avoid any mention of proper names, in *The Rising of the Moon*, referring to the wanted man simply as "he," and to the policemen as "sergeant," "X," and "B"?

TOPICS FOR WRITING

The playwright's dramatic use of timing
The function of the *setting*
A discussion of the theme

NOTES

p. 335   placard: a notice in a public place; a poster
p. 336   pound: an English banknote
p. 336   kelp: seaweed
p. 337   assize: trial sessions, civil or criminal, held periodically in specified locations in England
p. 337   Ennis: a town in Ireland
p. 337   shilling: an English coin
p. 338   Cork: a county in Ireland
p. 340   Granuaile: a symbol of Ireland
p. 341   dock: a place in court where the prisoner stands

THE MAN WITH THE HEART IN THE HIGHLANDS

William Saroyan

CHARACTERS

Jasper MacGregor
Johnny
Boy
Ben Alexander
Mr. Kosak
Johnny's Grandmother
Rufe Apley
Philip Carmichael
Friends and Neighbors

William Saroyan (1908-   )

A play about people who live as they please may seem puzzling to anyone who has long been a part of the conventional, workaday world. What kind of man allows his family to subsist for four days on a popcorn diet? What kind of father sends his son to the store to buy groceries on credit, so that he can remain at home composing poetry instead of securing a steady job? William Saroyan provides the answers in his sentimental drama, The Man With the Heart in the Highlands.

Since 1934, when he first attracted critical attention for a story called The Daring Young Man on a Flying Trapeze, *Saroyan has written a number of successful stories and plays. In 1940 he received both the Pulitzer Prize and the New York Drama Critics Award for the play* The Time of Your Life. *His novel,* The Human Comedy, *has become a modern classic.*

THE MAN WITH THE HEART IN THE HIGHLANDS

SCENE 1 *An old white broken-down frame house with a front porch on San Benito Avenue in Fresno, California. There are no other houses near by, only a desolation of bleak land and red sky. It is late afternoon of a day in August, 1914. The evening sun is going down.*

JOHNNY, *aged six, but essentially ageless, is sitting, dynamic and acrobatic, on the steps of the porch, dead to the world and deep in thought of a high and holy order. Far away a train whistle cries mournfully. He listens eagerly, cocking his head on one side like a chicken, trying to understand the meaning of the cry and at the same time to figure out everything. He doesn't quite make it, and when the cry ends he stops being eager. A fourteen-year-old boy on a bicycle, eating an ice-cream cone and carrying newspaper bags, goes by on the sidewalk in silence, oblivious of the weight on his shoulders and of the contraption on which he is seated because of the delight and glory of ice cream in the world.* JOHNNY *leaps to his feet and waves to the boy, smiling in a big humanitarian way, but is ignored. He sits down again and listens to a small over-joyed but angry bird. The bird flies away, after making a brief forceful speech of no meaning.*

From inside the house is heard the sombre voice of JOHNNY'S FATHER *reciting poetry of his own composition.*

JOHNNY'S FATHER   The long silent day journeys through the sore solemn heart, and (*Bitter pause.*) and (*Quickly.*) the long silent day journeys through the sore solemn heart, and (*Pause.*) no. (*He roars and begins again.*) Crippled, and sweeping, time stumbles through the lone lorn heart.

(A table or chair is pushed over in anger. A groan. Silence. The boy listens. He gets up and tries to stand on his head, fails, tries again, fails, tries again, and succeeds. While he is standing on his head he hears the loveliest and most amazing music in the world: a solo on a bugle. The music is so magnificent he doesn't dare get to his feet or move a muscle. The song is My Heart's in the Highlands. *The bugler,* MACGREGOR, *finishes the solo in front of the house. The boy leaps to his feet and runs up to the old man, amazed, delighted and bewildered.)*

JOHNNY   I sure would like to hear you play another song.

MACGREGOR   Young man, could you get a glass of water for an old man whose heart is not here, but in the highlands?

JOHNNY   What highlands?

MACGREGOR   The Scotch Highlands. Could you?

JOHNNY   What's your heart doing in the Scotch Highlands?

MACGREGOR   My heart's grieving there. Could you get me a glass of cool water?

JOHNNY   Where's your mother?

MACGREGOR   My mother's in Tulsa, Oklahoma, but her heart isn't.

JOHNNY   Where is her heart?

MACGREGOR   In the Scotch Highlands. I'm very thirsty, young man.

JOHNNY   How come the members of your family are always leaving their hearts in the highlands?

MACGREGOR   That's the way we are. Here today and gone tomorrow.

JOHNNY   Here today and gone tomorrow? (*To* MACGREGOR.) How do you figure?

MACGREGOR   Alive one minute and dead the next.

JOHNNY   Where's your mother's mother?

MACGREGOR   She's up in Vermont, in a little town called White River, but her heart isn't.

JOHNNY   Is her poor old withered heart in the highlands, too?

MACGREGOR   Right smack in the highlands. Son, I'm dying of thirst.

(JOHNNY'S FATHER *comes out of the house in a fury, as if he has just broken out of a cage, and roars at the boy like a tiger that has just awakened from evil dreams.*)

JOHNNY'S FATHER   Johnny, get the hell away from that poor old man. Get him a pitcher of water before he falls down and dies. Where in hell are your manners?

JOHNNY   Can't a fellow try to find out something from a traveler once in a while?

JOHNNY'S FATHER   Get the old man some water, damn it; don't stand there like a dummy. Get him a drink before he falls down and dies.

JOHNNY   *You* get him a drink! You ain't doing nothing.

JOHNNY'S FATHER   Ain't doing nothing? Why, Johnny, you know damn well I'm getting a new poem arranged in my mind.

JOHNNY   How do you figure I know?

JOHNNY'S FATHER (*Unable to find an answer.*)   Well, you ought to know. You're my son. If you shouldn't know, who should?

MACGREGOR   Good afternoon. Your son has been telling me how clear and cool the climate is in these parts.

JOHNNY   I didn't say anything about the climate. Where's he getting that stuff from?

JOHNNY'S FATHER   How do you do? Won't you come in for a little rest? We should be honored to have you at our table for a bite of supper.

MACGREGOR   Sir, I am starving. I shall come right in.

(*He moves to enter the house.* JOHNNY *gets in his way, looking up at him.*)

JOHNNY   Can you play *Drink to Me Only with Thine Eyes?* I sure would like to hear you play that song on the bugle. That song is my favorite. I guess I like that song better than any song in the world.

MACGREGOR   Son, when you get to be my age, you'll know songs aren't important; bread's the thing.

JOHNNY   Anyway, I sure would like to hear you play that song.

(MACGREGOR *goes up on the porch and shakes hands with* JOHNNY'S FATHER.)

MACGREGOR   My name is Jasper MacGregor. I am an actor.

JOHNNY'S FATHER   I'm mighty glad to make your acquaintance. Johnny, get Mr. MacGregor a pitcher of water.

(JOHNNY *runs around the house.*)

MACGREGOR   Charming boy.

JOHNNY'S FATHER   Like myself, he's a genius.

MACGREGOR   I suppose you're very fond of him?

JOHNNY'S FATHER   We are the same person—he is the heart of my youth—have you noticed his eagerness?

MACGREGOR   I should say I have.

JOHNNY'S FATHER   I am the same way myself, though older and less brilliant.

(JOHNNY, *running, returns with a pitcher of water which he hands to the old man. The old man throws back his shoulders, lifts his head, his nostrils expand, he snorts, his eyes widen, he lifts the pitcher of water to his lips and drinks all the water in one long swig, while* JOHNNY *and his* FATHER *watch with amazement and admiration. The old man breathes deeply, looks around at the landscape and up at the sky and to the end of San Benito Avenue where the evening sun is going down.*)

MACGREGOR   I recken I'm five thousand miles from home. Do you think we could eat a little bread and cheese to keep my body and spirit together?

JOHNNY'S FATHER   Johnny, run down to the grocer's and get a loaf of French bread and a pound of cheese.

JOHNNY   Give me the money.

JOHNNY'S FATHER   You know I ain't got a penny, Johnny. Tell Mr. Kosak to give us credit.

JOHNNY   He won't do it. He's tired of giving us credit. He says we don't work and never pay our bills. We owe him forty cents.

JOHNNY'S FATHER   Go on down there and argue it out with him. You know that's your job.

JOHNNY   He says he doesn't know anything about anything, all he wants is the forty cents.

JOHNNY'S FATHER   Go on down there and make him give you a loaf of bread and a pound of cheese. You can do it, Johnny.

MACGREGOR   Go on down there and tell Mr. Kosak to give you a loaf of bread and a pound of cheese, son.

JOHNNY'S FATHER   Go ahead, Johnny! You haven't yet failed to leave that store with provender. You'll be back here in ten minutes with food fit for a king.

JOHNNY   I don't know. Mr. Kosak says we are trying to give him the merry run-around. He wants to know what kind of work you do.

JOHNNY'S FATHER   (*Furiously.*)   Well, go ahead and tell him. I have nothing to conceal. I write poetry, night and day.

JOHNNY   Well, all right, but I don't think he'll be impressed. He says you never go out and look for work. He says you're lazy and no good.

JOHNNY'S FATHER   (*Roaring.*)   You go on down there and tell him he's crazy, Johnny! You go down there and tell that fellow your father is one of the greatest unknown poets living.

JOHNNY   He won't care, but I'll go. I'll do my best. Ain't we got nothing in the house?

JOHNNY'S FATHER   Only popcorn. We've been eating popcorn four days in a row now, Johnny. You got to get bread and cheese if you expect me to finish that long poem.

JOHNNY   I'll do my best.

MACGREGOR   Don't take too long, Johnny. I'm five thousand miles from home.

JOHNNY   I'll run all the way.

JOHNNY'S FATHER   If you find any money on the way, remember we go fifty-fifty.

JOHNNY   All right.

(JOHNNY *runs down the street.*)

SCENE 2   *The inside of* MR. KOSAK'S *grocery store.* MR. KOSAK *is sleeping on his folded arms when* JOHNNY *runs into the store.* MR. KOSAK *lifts his head. He is a fine, gentle, serious man with a big blonde old-fashioned moustache. He shakes his head trying to waken.*

JOHNNY   Mr. Kosak, if you were in China and didn't have a friend in the world and no money, you'd expect some Christian over there to give you a pound of rice, wouldn't you?

MR. KOSAK   What do you want?

JOHNNY   I just want to talk a little. You'd expect someone to help you out a little, wouldn't you, Mr. Kosak?

MR. KOSAK   How much money you got?

JOHNNY   It ain't a question of money, Mr. Kosak. I'm talking about being in China.

MR. KOSAK   I don't know nothing about nothing.

JOHNNY   How would you feel in China that way?

MR. KOSAK   I don't know. What would I be doing in China?

JOHNNY   Well, you'd be visiting there, and you'd be hungry and five thousand miles from home, and not a friend in the world. You wouldn't expect a good neighbor to turn you away without even a pound of rice, would you, Mr. Kosak?

MR. KOSAK   I guess not, but you ain't in China, Johnny, and neither is your Pa. You and your Pa's got to go out and work sometime in your lives, so you might as well start now. I ain't going to give you no more groceries on credit because I know you won't pay me.

JOHNNY   Mr. Kosak, you misunderstand me. I'm not talking about a few groceries. I'm talking about all them heathen people around you in China, and you hungry and dying.

MR. KOSAK   This ain't China. You got to go out and make your living in this country. Everybody's got to work in America.

JOHNNY   Mr. Kosak, suppose it was a loaf of bread and a pound of cheese you needed to keep you alive in the world, would you hesitate to ask a Christian missionary for these things?

MR. KOSAK   Yes, I would. I would be ashamed to ask.

JOHNNY   Even if you knew you would give him back two loaves of bread and two pounds of cheese instead of one loaf and one pound? Even then, Mr. Kosak?

MR. KOSAK   Even then.

JOHNNY   Don't be that way, Mr. Kosak. That's defeatist talk, and you know it. Why the only thing that would happen to you would be death. You would die out there in China, Mr. Kosak.

MR. KOSAK   I wouldn't care if I would. You and your Pa have got to pay for bread and cheese. Why don't your Pa go out and get a job?

JOHNNY   Mr. Kosak,—how are you, anyway?

MR. KOSAK   I'm fine, Johnny. How are you?

JOHNNY   Couldn't be better, Mr. Kosak. How are the children?

MR. KOSAK   They're all fine, Johnny. Stepan is beginning to walk now.

JOHNNY   That's great. How's Angela?

MR. KOSAK   Angela's beginning to sing. How's your grandmother?

JOHNNY   She's fine. She's beginning to sing too. She says she'd rather be an opera singer than Queen of England. How's your wife, Martha, Mr. Kosak?

MR. KOSAK   Oh, swell.

JOHNNY   I can't tell you how glad I am to hear that everything is well at your house. I know Stepan is going to be a great man some day.

MR. KOSAK   I hope so. I'm going to send him to high school and see that he gets every chance I didn't get. I don't want him to open a grocery store.

JOHNNY   I have great faith in Stepan, Mr. Kosak.

MR. KOSAK   What do you want, Johnny, and how much money you got?

JOHNNY   Mr. Kosak, you know I didn't come here to buy anything. You know I enjoy a quiet philosophical chat with you every now and then. (*Quickly.*) Let me have a loaf of French bread and a pound of cheese.

MR. KOSAK   You got to pay cash, Johnny.

JOHNNY   And Esther? How is your beautiful daughter, Esther?

MR. KOSAK   She's all right, Johnny, but you got to pay cash. You and your Pa are the worst citizens in this county.

JOHNNY   I'm glad Esther's all right, Mr. Kosak. Jasper MacGregor is visiting our house. He's a great actor.

MR. KOSAK   Never heard of him.

JOHNNY   And a bottle of beer for Mr. MacGregor.

MR. KOSAK   I can't give you a bottle of beer.

JOHNNY   Sure, you can.

MR. KOSAK   I can't. I'll let you have one loaf of French bread and a pound of cheese, but that's all. What kind of work does your Pa do when he works, Johnny?

JOHNNY   My father writes poetry, Mr. Kosak. That's the only work my father does. He's one of the greatest writers of poetry in the world.

MR. KOSAK   When does he get any money?

JOHNNY   He never gets any money. You can't have your cake and eat it too.

MR. KOSAK   I don't like that kind of work. Why doesn't your Pa work like everybody else, Johnny?

JOHNNY   He works harder than everybody else. My father works twice as hard as the average man.

> (MR. KOSAK *hands* JOHNNY *a loaf of French bread and a pound of cheese.*)

MR. KOSAK   Well, that's fifty-five cents you owe me, Johnny. I'll let you have some stuff this time, but never again.

JOHNNY   (*At the door.*)   Tell Esther I love her.

MR. KOSAK   All right.

JOHNNY   Good-bye, Mr. Kosak.

MR. KOSAK   Good-bye, Johnny.

(JOHNNY *runs out of the store.* MR. KOSAK *swings at a fly, misses, swings again, misses, and, objecting to the world in this manner, he chases the fly all around the store, swinging with all his might.*)

SCENE 3 *The same as* SCENE 1. JOHNNY'S FATHER *and* MAC-GREGOR *are looking down the street to see if* JOHNNY *is coming back with food. His* GRANDMOTHER *is standing on the porch also, eager to know if there is to be food.*

MACGREGOR I think he's got some food with him.

JOHNNY'S FATHER (*With pride.*) Of course he has. (*He waves at the* GRANDMOTHER *on the porch, who runs into the house to set the table.* JOHNNY *runs to his* FATHER *and* MACGREGOR.) I knew you'd do it.

MACGREGOR So did I.

JOHNNY He says we got to pay him fifty-five cents. He says he ain't going to give us no more stuff on credit.

JOHNNY'S FATHER That's his opinion. What did you talk about?

JOHNNY First I talked about being hungry and at death's door in China. Then I inquired about the family.

JOHNNY'S FATHER How is every one?

JOHNNY Fine. I didn't find any money, though, not even a penny.

JOHNNY'S FATHER That's all right.

(*They go into the house.*)

SCENE 4 *The living room. They are all at the table after supper.* MACGREGOR *finds crumbs here and there, which he places delicately in his mouth. He looks around the room to see if there isn't something more to eat.*

MACGREGOR That green can up there, Johnny! What's in there?

JOHNNY Marbles.

MACGREGOR That cupboard. Anything edible in there, Johnny?

JOHNNY Crickets.

MACGREGOR That big jar in the corner there, Johnny. What's good in there?

JOHNNY I got a gopher snake in that jar.

MACGREGOR Well, I could go for a bit of boiled gopher snake in a big way, Johnny.

JOHNNY   You can't have that snake.

MACGREGOR   Why not, Johnny? Why the hell not, son? I hear of fine Borneo natives eating snakes and grasshoppers. You ain't got a half dozen fat grasshoppers around, have you, Johnny?

JOHNNY   Only four.

MACGREGOR   Well, trot them out, son, and after we've had our fill, I'll play *Drink to Me Only with Thine Eyes* for you. I'm mighty hungry, Johnny.

JOHNNY   So am I, but I don't want anybody killing them poor things.

JOHNNY'S FATHER   (*To* MACGREGOR.)   How about a little music? I think the boy would be delighted.

JOHNNY   I sure would, Mr. MacGregor.

MACGREGOR   All right, Johnny.

(MACGREGOR *gets up and begins to blow into the bugle. He blows louder and more beautifully and mournfully than anybody ever blew into a bugle. Eighteen* NEIGHBORS *gather in front of the house and cheer when he finishes the solo.*)

JOHNNY'S FATHER   I want you to meet your public.

(*They go out on the porch.*)

SCENE 5   *The same as* SCENE 1. *The crowd is looking up at* JOHNNY'S FATHER, MACGREGOR, *and* JOHNNY.

JOHNNY'S FATHER   Good neighbors and friends, I want you to meet Jasper MacGregor, the greatest Shakespearean actor of our day.

MACGREGOR   I remember my first appearance in London in 1867 as if it was yesterday. I was a boy of fourteen from the slums of Glasgow. My first part was a courier in a play, the title of which I have unfortunately forgotten. I had no lines to speak, but moved about a good deal, running from officer to officer, and from lover to his beloved, and back again, over and over again.

RUFE APLEY   How about another song, Mr. MacGregor?

MACGREGOR   Have you got an egg at your house?

RUFE APLEY   I sure have. I've got a dozen eggs at my house.

MACGREGOR   Would it be convenient for you to go and get one of them dozen eggs? When you return, I'll play a song that will make your heart leap with joy and grief.

RUFE   I'm on my way already.

(*He goes.*)

MACGREGOR (*To the crowd.*)   My friends, I should be delighted to play another song for you on this golden-throated bugle, but time and distance from home finds me weary. If you will be so good as to go, each of you to his home, and return in a moment with some morsel of food, I shall be delighted to gather my spirit together and play a song I know will change the course of each of your lives, and change it, mind you, for the better. (*The* NEIGHBORS *go.* MACGREGOR, JOHNNY'S FATHER, *and* JOHNNY *sit on the steps and remain in silence, and one by one the people return, bringing food to* MACGREGOR: *an egg, a sausage, a dozen green onions, two kinds of cheese, butter, two kinds of bread, boiled potatoes, fresh tomatoes, a melon, tea, and many other good things to eat.*) Thank you, my friends, thank you. (*He stands solemnly, waiting for absolute silence, straightens himself, looks about him furiously, lifts the bugle to his lips and plays* My Heart's in the Highlands, My Heart Is Not Here. *The* NEIGHBORS *weep and go away.* MACGREGOR *turns.*) Sir, if it is all the same to you, I should like to dwell in your house for some time to come.

JOHNNY'S FATHER   Sir, my house is your house.

(*They go into the house.*)

SCENE 6   *The same as* SCENE 4. *Eighteen days later.* MAC-GREGOR *is lying on the floor, face up, asleep.* JOHNNY *is walking about quietly in the room, looking at everybody. His* FATHER *is at the table, writing poetry. His* GRANDMOTHER *is sitting in the rocking chair, rocking. There is a knock on the door. Everybody but* MACGREGOR *jumps up and runs to it.*

JOHNNY'S FATHER (*At the door.*)   Yes?
CARMICHAEL   I am looking for Jasper MacGregor, the actor.
JOHNNY'S FATHER   What do you want?
JOHNNY   Well, ask him in anyway, Pa.

JOHNNY'S FATHER   Yes, of course. Excuse me. Won't you please come in?

CARMICHAEL   (*Entering.*)   My name is Philip Carmichael. I am from the Old People's Home. I have been sent to bring Mr. MacGregor home.

MACGREGOR   (*Awakening and sitting up.*)   Home? Did some one mention home? I'm five thousand miles from home, always have been, and always will be. Who is this young man?

CARMICHAEL   Mr. MacGregor, I'm Philip Carmichael, from the Old People's Home. They've sent me to bring you back. We are putting on our annual show in two weeks and need you for the leading role.

MACGREGOR   (*Getting up with the help of* JOHNNY'S FATHER *and* JOHNNY)   What kind of a part is it? I can't be playing young adventurers any longer.

CARMICHAEL   The part is King Lear, Mr. MacGregor. It is perfect for you.

MACGREGOR   (*To* JOHNNY'S FATHER, JOHNNY, *and the* GRANDMOTHER)   Good-bye, my beloved friends. Good-bye. In all the hours of my life, in all the places I have visited, never and nowhere have I had the honor and pleasure to commune with souls loftier, purer, or more delightful than yours. Good-bye.

> (*They say "good-bye," and leave the house. There is a long silence, full of melancholy and loneliness.*)

JOHNNY'S FATHER   Johnny, go on down to Mr. Kosak's store and get a little something to eat. I know you can do it, Johnny. Get *anything*.

JOHNNY   Mr. Kosak wants eighty-five cents. He won't give us anything more without money.

JOHNNY'S FATHER   Go on down there, Johnny. You know you can get that fine Slovak gentleman to give you a bit of something to eat.

JOHNNY   (*With despair.*)   Aw, Pa.

JOHNNY'S FATHER   (*Amazed.*)   What? You, my son, in a mood like that? Come on. I've fought the world this way before you were born, and after you were born we've fought it together, and we're going to keep on fighting on it. The people love poetry but don't know it. Nothing is going to stop us, Johnny. Go on down there now and get something to eat. You didn't do so well last time. Remember? I can't

write great poetry on the bird seed and maple syrup you brought back.
Go on now!

JOHNNY   All right, Pa. I'll do my best.

(*He runs to the door.*)

JOHNNY'S FATHER   Remember, if you find any money on the way,
we go fifty-fifty.

CURTAIN

DISCUSSION

1. Describe some of the things that Johnny sees and hears as he
   sits outside the house at the beginning of scene one. Comment
   on his reactions.
2. Why does Saroyan state that Johnny is "aged six, but essentially
   ageless"? What might you find unconvincing, were it not for this
   explanation?
3. Do you attach any special significance to the fact that there are
   no other houses in the vicinity of Ben Alexander's, "only a desolation of bleak land and red sky"? Explain.
4. Why is MacGregor's arrival timed to coincide with the moment
   when (a) Ben fails in his attempt to write poetry, and (b)
   Johnny succeeds in his attempt to stand on his head?
5. What is unusual about the relationship between Johnny and
   Ben? As a father, what does Ben expect of his son? Why? How
   does Johnny respond to these expectations?
6. Ben states that he and Johnny "are the same person—he is the
   heart of my youth." Do you think Ben believes this? Are he and
   Johnny really the same person?
7. Although Ben and Johnny seldom refer directly to their feelings
   for one another, how are these feelings made apparent by the end
   of the play?
8. Contrast the first on-stage appearance of MacGregor to that of
   Ben. What spirit in human nature does MacGregor represent?
   How does the song, "My Heart's in the Highlands," symbolize this
   spirit?
9. Do any other characters share MacGregor's spirit, or is he the
   only man with his "heart in the Highlands"?

10. Why does Mr. Kosak say to Johnny, "You and your Pa are the worst citizens in this county"? What does Mr. Kosak consider real work? How does his interpretation differ from Ben's? Can you say with certainty which interpretation is correct? Why?

11. Why does Johnny sum up his conversation with Kosak in four brief sentences, when questioned by Ben, instead of accounting for himself in detail? Does Johnny enjoy his role as "bread-winner"? How do you know?

12. Is your attitude toward MacGregor in any way affected by the facts that you eventually learn about him? Why does Saroyan withhold this information until the final scene?

13. Scenes one to five take place on the same day, but there is a lapse of eighteen days between scenes five and six. What is Saroyan's purpose? Does the division of the play into scenes weaken its "singleness of effect"?

14. The ending of the play repeats story elements that have appeared earlier. What is repeated, and why?

15. Considering Saroyan's theme, how is it ironic that the story takes place during the month of August, 1914? Do you think the irony was consciously intended?

TOPICS FOR WRITING

Write a character study of Johnny, Ben Alexander, or Jasper Mac-Gregor.

Discuss the playwright's viewpoint on (a) courage, (b) loyalty, (c) determination, or (d) failure and success, as clarified by the events of the play.

THE BROWNING VERSION

Terence Rattigan

CHARACTERS

John Taplow
Frank Hunter
Millie Crocker-Harris
Andrew Crocker-Harris
Dr. Frobisher
Peter Gilbert
Mrs. Gilbert

Terence Rattigan (*1911-*   )

*One of England's leading playwrights, Terence Rattigan was born in
London in 1911, and educated at Harrow and Trinity College, Oxford.
Although his father encouraged him to enter the diplomatic service,
Rattigan was determined to become a playwright. His best-known
plays are* The Winslow Boy, Separate Tables, *and* The Browning
Version. *Critics have praised Rattigan both for his unerring sense of
craftsmanship and for his insight into the circumstances that cause
people to behave as they do.*

Rattigan's skill as a dramatist is nowhere more apparent than in
The Browning Version, *a play about a school teacher who has lost his
capacity to communicate effectively with others. If you are a percep-
tive reader, you will note how subtly Rattigan introduces the conflict,
and how deftly he resolves it.*

THE BROWNING VERSION

SCENE   *The sitting-room in the Crocker-Harris's flat in a
public school in the south of England. About 6:30 P.M. of a
day in July.*

*The building in which the flat is situated is large and
Victorian, and at some fairly recent time has been converted
into flats of varying size for masters, married and unmarried.
The Crocker-Harris's have the ground floor and their sitting-*

room is probably the biggest—and gloomiest—room in the house. It boasts, however, access (through a stained glass door L.*) to a small garden, and is furnished with chintzy and genteel cheerfulness. Another door, up* R.*, leads into the hall and a third, up* C.*, to the rest of the flat. The hall door is partially concealed by a screen. There is a large bay-window in the* L. *wall below the garden door. Near the window is a flat-topped desk with a swivel chair behind it and an upright chair on the other side. The fireplace is down* R. *Below it is an easy chair and a small table with a telephone. A settee stands in front of the fireplace at* R.C. *There is an oval dining-table with two chairs up* C. R. *of the door up* C. *is a sideboard; and against the wall* L. *of the door up* R. *is a hall-stand, in which some walking-sticks are kept. A small cupboard stands against the wall down* R.

When the CURTAIN *rises the room is empty. There are copies of "The Times" and the "Tatler" on the settee. We hear the front door opening and closing and immediately after there is a timorous knock on the door up* R. *After a pause the knock is repeated. The door opens and* JOHN TAPLOW *makes his appearance. He is a plain moon-faced boy of about sixteen, with glasses. He carries a book and an exercise-book. He is dressed in grey flannels, a dark blue coat and white scarf. He stands in doubt at the door for a moment, then goes back into the hall.*

TAPLOW (*off; calling*) Sir! Sir! (*After a pause he comes back into the room, crosses to the garden door up* L. *and opens it. He calls*). Sir! (*There is no reply.* TAPLOW, *standing in the bright sunshine at the door, emits a plaintive sigh, then closes it firmly and comes down* R. *of the desk on which he places the book, the notebook and a pen. He sits in the chair* R. *of the desk. He looks round the room. On a table* C. *is a small box of chocolates, probably the Crocker-Harris's ration for the month.* TAPLOW *rises, moves above the table and opens the box. He counts the number inside, and removes two. One of these he eats and the other, after a second's struggle, either with his conscience or his judgment of what he might be able to get away with, virtuously re-places in the box. He puts back the box on the table, and moves up* R. *to the hall-stand. He selects a walking-stick with a crooked handle, comes down* C.*, and makes a couple of golf-swings, with an air of great* concentration. FRANK HUNTER *enters up* R. *and appears from behind the screen covering the door. He is a rugged young man—not perhaps quite as rugged as his deliberately-cultivated manner of ruthless honesty makes him appear, but wrapped in all the self-confidence of the popular master. He watches* TAPLOW, *whose back is to the door, making his swing.*)

FRANK (*coming down behind* TAPLOW) Roll the wrists away from the ball. Don't break them like that. (*He puts his large hands over the abashed* TAPLOW's). Now swing. (TAPLOW, *guided by* FRANK's *evidently expert hands, succeeds in hitting the carpet with more effect than before. He breaks away* R. *of* TAPLOW). Too quick. Slow back and stiff left arm. It's no good just whacking the ball as if you were the headmaster and the ball was you. It'll never go more than fifty yards if you do. Get a rhythm. A good golf swing is a matter of aesthetics, not of brute strength. (TAPLOW, *only half listening, is gazing at the carpet.*)

FRANK What's the matter?

TAPLOW I think we've made a tear in the carpet, sir.

(FRANK *examines the spot perfunctorily.*)

FRANK (*taking the stick from* TAPLOW) Nonsense. That was there already. (*He crosses up* R. *and puts the stick in the hall-stand*). Do I know you? (*He comes down* L. *of the settee to* R. *of* TAPLOW.)

TAPLOW No, sir.

FRANK What's your name?

TAPLOW Taplow.

FRANK Taplow? No, I don't. You're not a scientist, I gather.

TAPLOW No, sir. I'm still in the lower fifth. I can't specialize until next term—that's to say if I've got my remove all right.

FRANK Don't you know yet if you've got your remove?

TAPLOW No, sir. Mr. Crocker-Harris doesn't tell us the results like the other masters.

FRANK Why not?

TAPLOW Well, you know what he's like, sir.

FRANK (*moving away to the fireplace*) I believe there *is* a rule that form results should only be announced by the headmaster on the last day of term.

TAPLOW Yes; but who else pays any attention to it—except Mr. Crocker-Harris?

FRANK   I don't, I admit—but that's no criterion. So you've got to wait until tomorrow to know your fate, have you?

TAPLOW   Yes, sir.

FRANK   Supposing the answer is favourable—what then?

TAPLOW   Oh—science sir, of course.

FRANK (*sadly*)   Yes. We get all the slackers.

TAPLOW (*protestingly*)   I'm extremely interested in science, sir.

FRANK   Are you? I'm not. Not at least in the science I have to teach.

TAPLOW (*moving above the desk*)   Well, anyway, sir, it's a good deal more exciting than this muck. (*He indicates the book he put on the desk.*)

FRANK   What is this muck?

TAPLOW   Aeschylus, sir. *The Agamemnon.*

FRANK (*moving to the L. end of the couch*).   And your considered view is that *The Agamemnon* of Aeschylus is muck, is it?

TAPLOW   Well, no, sir. I don't think the play is muck—exactly. I suppose, in a way, it's rather a good plot, really; a wife murdering her husband and having a lover and all that. I only meant the way it's taught to us—just a lot of Greek words strung together and fifty lines if you get them wrong.

FRANK   You sound a little bitter, Taplow.

TAPLOW   I am rather, sir.

FRANK   Kept in, eh?

Taplow   No, sir. Extra work.

FRANK   Extra work—on the last day of school?

TAPLOW   Yes, sir—and I might be playing golf. (*He moves into the window, upstage end*). You'd think *he'd* have enough to do anyway himself, considering he's leaving tomorrow for good—but oh no. I missed a day last week when I had 'flu—so here I am—and look at the weather, sir.

FRANK   Bad luck. Still there's one consolation. You're pretty well bound to get your remove tomorrow for being a good boy in taking extra work.

TAPLOW (*crossing to* c.)   Well, I'm not so sure, sir. That would be true of the ordinary masters all right. They just wouldn't dare not give a chap a remove after his taking extra work—it would be such a bad advertisement for them. But those sort of rules don't apply to the Crock—Mr. Crocker-Harris. I asked him yesterday outright if he'd given me a remove and do you know what he said, sir?

FRANK   No. What?

TAPLOW   (*mimicking a very gentle, rather throaty voice*) "My dear Taplow, I have given you exactly what you deserve. No less; and certainly no more." Do you know, sir, I think he may have marked me down, rather than up, for taking extra work. I mean, the man's barely human. (*He breaks off quickly.*) Sorry, sir. Have I gone too far?

FRANK   (*sitting on the settee, L. end, and picking up "The Times"*) Yes. Much too far.

TAPLOW   Sorry, sir. I got sort of carried away.

FRANK   Evidently. (*He opens "The Times" and reads.* TAPLOW *moves to the chair R. of the desk and sits*). Er—Taplow.

TAPLOW   Yes, sir?

FRANK   What was that Mr. Crocker-Harris said to you? Just—er—repeat it, would you?

TAPLOW   (*mimicking*)   "My dear Taplow, I have given you exactly what you deserve. No less; and certainly no more." (FRANK *snorts, then looks stern.*)

FRANK   Not in the least like him. Read your nice Aeschylus and be quiet.

TAPLOW   (*with weary disgust*)   Aeschylus.

FRANK   Look, what time did Mr. Crocker-Harris tell you to be here?

TAPLOW   Six-thirty, sir.

FRANK   Well, he's ten minutes late. Why don't you cut? You could still get nine holes in before lock-up.

TAPLOW   (*genuinely shocked*)   Oh, no, I couldn't cut. Cut the Crock—Mr. Crocker-Harris? I shouldn't think it's ever been done in the whole time he's been here. God knows what would happen if I did. He'd probably follow me home, or something.

FRANK   I must admit I envy him the effect he seems to have on you boys in his form. You all seem scared to death of him. What does he do—beat you all, or something?

TAPLOW   (*rising and moving to the L. end of the settee*)   Good Lord, no. He's not a sadist, like one or two of the others.

FRANK   I beg your pardon?

TAPLOW   A sadist, sir, is someone who gets pleasure out of giving pain.

FRANK   Indeed? But I think you went on to say that some other masters . . .

TAPLOW   Well, of course they are, sir. I won't mention names, but

you know them as well as I do. Of course I know most masters think
we boys don't understand a thing—but dash it, sir, you're different.
You're young—well comparatively anyway—and you're science and
you canvassed for Labour in the last election. You must know what
sadism is. (FRANK *stares for a moment at* TAPLOW, *then turns away.*)

FRANK   Good Lord! What are public schools coming to?

TAPLOW (*crossing to* R. *of the desk, below the chair, and leaning
against it*)   Anyway, the Crock isn't a sadist. That's what I'm saying.
He wouldn't be so frightening if he were—because at least it would
show he had some feelings. But he hasn't. He's all shrivelled up inside
like a nut and he seems to hate people to like him. It's funny, that. I
don't know any other master who doesn't like being liked.

FRANK   And I don't know any boy who doesn't trade on that very
foible.

TAPLOW   Well, it's natural, sir. But not with the Crock.

FRANK (*making a feeble attempt at re-establishing the correct
relationship*)   Mr. Crocker-Harris.

TAPLOW   Mr. Crocker-Harris. The funny thing is that in spite of
everything, I do rather like him. I can't help it. And sometimes I think
he sees it and that seems to shrivel him up even more.

FRANK   I'm sure you're exaggerating.

TAPLOW   No, sir. I'm not. In form the other day he made one of
his little classical jokes. Of course nobody laughed because nobody
understood it, myself included. Still, I knew he'd meant it as funny,
so I laughed. Not out of sucking-up, sir, I swear, but ordinary common
politeness, and feeling a bit sorry for him having made a dud joke.
(*He moves round below the desk to* L. *of it*). Now I can't remember
what the joke was—but let's say it was—(*mimicking*) Benedictus,
benedicatur, benedictine . . . Now, you laugh, sir. (FRANK *laughs
formally.* TAPLOW *looks at him over an imaginary pair of spectacles,
and then, very gently crooks his fore-finger to him in indication to
approach the table.* FRANK *rises. He is genuinely interested in the incident. In a gentle, throaty voice*). Taplow—you laughed at my little
pun, I noticed. I must confess I am flattered at the evident advance
your Latinity has made that you should so readily have understood
what the rest of the form did not. Perhaps, now, you would be good
enough to explain it to them, so that they too can share your pleasure.
(*The door up* R. *is pushed open and* MILLIE CROCKER-HARRIS *enters. She
is a thin woman in the late thirties, rather more smartly dressed than*

the general run of school-masters' wives. She is wearing a cape and carries a shopping basket. She closes the door and then stands by the screen watching TAPLOW *and* FRANK. *It is a few seconds before they notice her*). Come along, Taplow. (FRANK *moves slowly above the desk*). Do not be so selfish as to keep a good joke to yourself. Tell the others . . . (*He breaks off suddenly, noticing* MILLIE). Oh Lord! (FRANK *turns quickly, and seems infinitely relieved at seeing* MILLIE.)

FRANK   Oh, hullo.

MILLIE (*without expression*). Hullo. (*She comes down to the sideboard and puts her basket on it.*)

TAPLOW (*moving up to* L. *of* FRANK; *whispering frantically*)   Do you think she heard? (FRANK *shakes his head comfortingly.* MILLIE *takes off her cape and hangs it on the hall-stand*). I think she did. She was standing there quite a time. If she did and she tells him, there goes my remove.

FRANK   Nonsense. (*He crosses to the fireplace.* MILLIE *takes the basket from the sideboard, moves above the table* C. *and puts the basket on it.*)

MILLIE (*to* TAPLOW)   Waiting for my husband?

TAPLOW (*moving down* L. *of the table* C.)   Er—yes.

MILLIE   He's at the Bursar's and might be there quite a time. If I were you I'd go.

TAPLOW (*doubtfully*)   He said most particularly I was to come.

MILLIE   Well, why don't you run away for a quarter of an hour and come back? (*She unpacks some things from the basket.*)

TAPLOW   Supposing he gets here before me?

MILLIE (*smiling*)   I'll take the blame. (*She takes a prescription out of the basket*). I tell you what—you can do a job for him. Take this prescription to the chemist and get it made up.

TAPLOW   All right, Mrs. Crocker-Harris. (*He crosses towards the door up* R).

MILLIE   And while you're there you might as well slip into Stewart's and have an ice. Here. Catch. (*She takes a shilling from her bag and throws it to him.*)

TAPLOW (*turning and catching it*)   Thanks awfully. (*He signals to* FRANK *not to tell, and moves to the door up* R.)

MILLIE   Oh, Taplow. (*She crosses to him.*)

TAPLOW (*turning on the step*)   Yes, Mrs. Crocker-Harris.

MILLIE   I had a letter from my father today in which he says he once had the pleasure of meeting your mother.

TAPLOW   (*uninterested but polite*)   Oh, really?

MILLIE   Yes. It was at some fête or other in Bradford. My uncle —that's Sir William Bartop, you know—made a speech and so did your mother. My father met her afterwards at tea.

TAPLOW   Oh really?

MILLIE   He said he found her quite charming.

TAPLOW   Yes, she's jolly good at those sort of functions. (*Becoming aware of his lack of tact*). I mean—I'm sure she found him charming, too. So long. (*He goes out up* R.)

MILLIE   (*coming down to the* L. *end of the settee*)   Thank you for coming round.

FRANK   That's all right.

MILLIE   You're staying for dinner?

FRANK   If I may.

MILLIE   If you may! (*She crosses below the settee to him*). Give me a cigarette. (FRANK *takes out his case and extends it to her.* MILLIE *takes a cigarette. Indicating the case*). You haven't given it away yet, I see.

FRANK   Do you think I would?

MILLIE   Frankly, yes. Luckily it's a man's case. I don't suppose any of your girl friends would want it.

FRANK   Don't be silly.

MILLIE   Where have you been all this week?

FRANK   (*sitting in the easy chair*)   Correcting exam papers— making reports. You know what end of term is like.

MILLIE   (*crossing below the settee and moving above the table* C.). I do know what end of term is like. But even Andrew has managed this last week to take a few hours off to say good-bye to people. (*She takes some packages out of the shopping basket.*)

FRANK   I really have been appallingly busy. Besides, I'm coming to stay with you in Bradford.

MILLIE   Not for over a month. Andrew doesn't start his new job until September first. That's one of the things I had to tell you.

FRANK   Oh. I had meant to be in Devonshire in September.

MILLIE   (*quickly*)   Who with?

FRANK   My family.

MILLIE   Surely you can go earlier, can't you? Go in August.

FRANK   It'll be difficult.

MILLIE Then you'd better come to me in August.

FRANK But Andrew will still be there. (*There is a pause.* MILLIE *crosses to* L. *of the desk, opens a drawer and takes out some scissors.*) I think I can manage September.

MILLIE (*shutting the drawer*) That'd be better—from every point of view. (*She moves below the table* C. *and puts down the scissors*). Except that it means I shan't see you for six weeks.

FRANK (*lightly*) You'll survive that, all right.

MILLIE Yes, I'll survive it—(*she moves to the* L. *end of the settee*) but not as easily as you will. (FRANK *says nothing*). I haven't much pride, have I? (*She crosses to* FRANK *and stands above the easy chair*). Frank, darling—(*she sits on the arm of the chair and kisses him*) I love you so much. (FRANK *kisses her on the mouth, but a trifle perfunctorily, and then rises and breaks quickly away, as if afraid someone had come into the room. He moves below the settee. She laughs*). You're very nervous.

FRANK I'm afraid of that screen arrangement. You can't see people coming in.

MILLIE Oh yes. (*She rises and stands by the fireplace*). That reminds me. What were you and Taplow up to when I came in just now? Making fun of my husband?

FRANK Afraid so. Yes.

MILLIE It sounded rather a good imitation. I must get him to do it for me sometime. It was very naughty of you to encourage him.

FRANK I know. It was.

MILLIE (*ironically*) Bad for discipline.

FRANK (*sitting on the settee*) Exactly. Currying favour with the boys, too. My God, how easy it is to be popular. I've only been a master three years, but I've already slipped into an act and a vernacular that I just can't get out of. Why can't anyone ever be natural with the little blighters?

MILLIE They probably wouldn't like it if you were. (*She crosses below the settee and moves above the table* C. *She picks up the scissors and a packet of luggage labels and cuts the latter one by one from the packet.*)

FRANK I don't see why not. No one seems to have tried it yet, anyway. I suppose the trouble is—we're all too scared of them. Either one gets forced into an attitude of false and hearty and jocular bonhomie like myself, or into the sort of petty, soulless tyranny which your husband uses to protect himself against the lower fifth.

MILLIE (*rather bored with this*) He'd never be popular—whatever he did.

FRANK Possibly not. He ought never to have become a schoolmaster really. Why did he?

MILLIE It was his vocation, he said. He was sure he'd make a big success of it, especially when he got his job here first go off. (*Bitterly*). Fine success he's made, hasn't he?

FRANK You should have stopped him.

MILLIE How was I to know? He talked about getting a house, then a headmastership.

FRANK (*rising*) The Crock a headmaster! That's a pretty thought.

MILLIE Yes, it's funny to think of now, all right. Still, he wasn't always the Crock, you know. He had a bit more gumption once. At least I thought he had. Don't let's talk any more about him—(*she comes R. round the table to C.*) it's too depressing. (*She starts to move L.*)

FRANK I'm sorry for him.

MILLIE (*stopping and turning; indifferently*) He's not sorry for himself, so why should you be? It's me you should be sorry for.

FRANK I am.

MILLIE (*moving in a few steps towards* FRANK; *smiling*) Then show me. (*She stretches out her arms to him.* FRANK *moves to her and kisses her again quickly and lightly. She holds him hungrily. He has to free himself almost roughly.*)

FRANK (*crossing to the fireplace*) What have you been doing all day?

MILLIE Calling on the other masters' wives—saying fond farewells. I've worked off twelve. I've another seven to do tomorrow.

FRANK You poor thing! I don't envy you.

MILLIE (*moving above the desk to L. of it with some labels*) It's the housemasters' wives that are the worst. (*She picks up a pen and writes on the labels*). They're all so damn patronizing. You should have heard Betty Carstairs. "My dear—it's such terrible bad luck on you both—that your husband should get this heart trouble just when, if only he'd stayed on, he'd have been bound to get a house. I mean, he's considerably senior to my Arthur as it is, and they simply couldn't have gone on passing him over, could they?"

FRANK There's a word for Betty Carstairs, my dear, that I would hesitate to employ before a lady.

MILLIE She's got her eye on you, anyway.

FRANK Betty Carstairs? What utter rot!

MILLIE Oh yes, she has. I saw you at that concert. Don't think I didn't notice.

FRANK Millie, darling! Really! I detest the woman.

MILLIE Then what were you doing in her box at Lord's?

FRANK Carstairs invited me. I went there because it was a good place to see the match from.

MILLIE Yes, I'm sure it was. Much better than the grandstand, anyway.

FRANK (*remembering something suddenly*) Oh, my God!

MILLIE (*coming below the desk*) It's all right, my dear. Don't bother to apologize. We gave the seat away, as it happens.

FRANK I'm most terribly sorry.

MILLIE It's all right. (*She moves to R. of the desk*). We couldn't afford a box, you see.

FRANK (*moving a few steps towards R. C.*) It wasn't that. You know it wasn't that. It's just that I—well, I clean forgot.

MILLIE Funny you didn't forget the Carstairs invitation.

FRANK Millie—don't be a fool.

MILLIE It's you who are the fool. (*Appealingly*). Frank—have you never been in love? I know you're not in love with me—but haven't you ever been in love with anyone? Don't you realize what torture you inflict on someone who loves you when you do a thing like that?

FRANK I've told you I'm sorry—I don't know what more I can say.

MILLIE Why not the truth?

FRANK The truth is—I clean forgot.

MILLIE The truth is—you had something better to do—and why not say it?

FRANK All right. Believe that if you like. It happens to be a lie, but believe it all the same. Only for God's sake stop this. (*He turns and moves down R.*)

MILLIE Then for God's sake show me some pity. Do you think it's any pleasanter for me to believe that you cut me because you forgot? Do you think that doesn't hurt either? (FRANK *turns away. She moves above the up R. corner of the desk and faces the door up L.*). Oh damn! I was so determined to be brave and not mention Lord's,

Why did I? Frank, just tell me one thing. Just tell me you're not running away from me—that's all I want to hear.

FRANK   I'm coming to Bradford.

MILLIE (*turning to* FRANK)   I think, if you don't, I'll kill myself.

FRANK (*turning and taking a few steps in towards* MILLIE)   I'm coming to Bradford. (*The door up* R. *opens.* FRANK *stops at the sound.* MILLIE *recovers herself and crosses above the table* C. *to the sideboard.* ANDREW CROCKER-HARRIS *enters and appears from behind the screen. Despite the summer sun he wears a serge suit and a stiffcollar. He carries a mackintosh and a rolled-up time-table and looks, as ever, neat, complacent and unruffled. He speaks in a very gentle voice which he rarely raises.*)

ANDREW (*hanging his mackintosh on the hall-stand*)   Is Taplow here? (FRANK *eases towards the fireplace.*)

MILLIE   I sent him to the chemist to get your prescription made up.

ANDREW   What prescription?

MILLIE   Your heart medicine. Don't you remember? You told me this morning it had run out.

ANDREW   Of course I remember, my dear, but there was no need to send Taplow for it. If you had telephoned the chemist he would have set it round in plenty of time. He knows the prescription. (*He comes down to the* L. *end of the settee*). Now Taplow will be late and I am so pressed for time I hardly know how to fit him in. (*He sees* FRANK). Ah, Hunter! How are you? (*He moves* R. *to* FRANK.)

FRANK   Very well, thanks. (*They shake hands.*)

ANDREW   Most kind of you to drop in, but, as Millie should have warned you, I am expecting a pupil for extra work and . . .

MILLIE   He's staying to dinner, Andrew.

ANDREW   Good. Then I shall see something of you. However, when Taplow returns I'm sure you won't mind . . .

FRANK (*making a move*)   No, of course not. I'll make myself scarce now, if you'd rather—I mean, if you're busy . . . (*He turns away and moves* C.)

ANDREW   Oh no. There is no need for that. Sit down, do. Will you smoke? I don't, as you know, but Millie does. (*He crosses below the desk and moves up* L. *of it*). Millie, give our guest a cigarette.

MILLIE (*moving down to the table* C.)   I haven't any. I'm afraid. I've had to cadge from him. (*She takes a copy of the "Tatler" from the basket.* ANDREW *opens the drawer that should contain the scissors.*

FRANK *takes out his cigarette case, crosses to* R. *of the table* C., *and offers it to* MILLIE. *She exchanges a glance with him as she takes a cigarette.*)

ANDREW (*looking for the scissors*) We expected you at Lord's, Hunter.

FRANK What? Oh yes. I'm most terribly sorry. I . . .

MILLIE (*crossing behind the settee*) He clean forgot, Andrew. Imagine.

ANDREW Forgot?

MILLIE Not everyone is blessed with your superhuman memory, you see.

FRANK I really can't apologize enough.

ANDREW Please don't bother to mention it. On the second day we managed to sell the seat to a certain Dr. Lambert, who wore, I regret to say, the colours of the opposing faction, but who otherwise seemed a passably agreeable person. (*He moves above the table* C.). You liked him, didn't you, Millie?

MILLIE (*looking at* FRANK) Very much indeed. I thought him quite charming.

ANDREW A charming old gentleman. (*To* FRANK). You have had tea? (*He picks up the scissors.*)

FRANK Yes—thank you.

ANDREW Is there any other refreshment I can offer you?

FRANK No, thank you.

ANDREW (*cutting the string round the time-table*) Would it interest you to see the new time-table I have drafted for next term?

FRANK Yes, very much. (*He moves up* R. *of* ANDREW. ANDREW *opens out a long roll of paper, made by pasting pieces of foolscap together, and which is entirely covered by his meticulous writing.*) I never knew you drafted our time-tables.

ANDREW Didn't you? I have done so for the last fifteen years. (MILLIE *wanders down* R. *of the settee*). Of course, they are always issued in mimeograph under the headmaster's signature. Now what form do you take? Upper fifth Science—there you are—that's the general picture; but on the back you will see each form specified under separate headings—there—that's a new idea of mine—Millie, this might interest you.

MILLIE (*sitting in the easy chair; suddenly harsh*) You know it bores me to death. (FRANK *looks up, surprised and uncomfortable.* ANDREW *does not remove his eyes from the time-table.*)

ANDREW   Millie has no head for this sort of work. There you see. Now here you can follow the upper fifth Science throughout every day of the week.

FRANK   (*indicating the time-table*)   I must say, I think this is a really wonderful job.

ANDREW   Thank you. It has the merit of clarity, I think. (*He starts to roll up the time-table.*)

FRANK   I don't know what they'll do without you.

ANDREW   (*without expression*)   They'll find somebody else, I expect. (*There is a pause.*)

FRANK   What sort of job is this you're going to?

ANDREW   (*looking at* MILLIE *for the first time*)   Hasn't Millie told you?

FRANK   She said it was a cr— a private school.

ANDREW   A crammer's—for backward boys. It is run by an old Oxford contemporary of mine who lives in Dorset. (*He moves round* L. *of the table* C. *and finishes rolling up the time-table*)   The work will not be so arduous as here and my doctor seems to think I will be able to undertake it without—er danger.

FRANK   (*with genuine sympathy*)   It's the most rotten bad luck for you. I'm awfully sorry.

ANDREW   (*raising his voice a little*)   My dear Hunter, there is nothing whatever to be sorry for. I am looking forward to the change. (*There is a knock at the door up* R.*).* Come in. (*He crosses below the table to* C. TAPLOW *enters up* R., *a trifle breathless and guilty-looking. He carries a medicine bottle wrapped and sealed*). Ah, Taplow. Good. You have been running, I see.

TAPLOW   Yes, sir. (*He crosses to the* L. *end of the settee.*)

ANDREW   There was a queue at the chemist's, I suppose?

TAPLOW   Yes, sir.

ANDREW   And doubtless an even longer one at Stewart's?

TAPLOW   Yes, sir—I mean—no, sir—I mean—(*he looks at* MILLIE*)* yes, sir. (*He crosses below the settee to* MILLIE *and hands her the medicine.*)

MILLIE   You were late yourself, Andrew.

ANDREW   Exactly. And for that I apologize, Taplow.

TAPLOW   That's all right, sir.

ANDREW   (*crossing below the desk and moving* L. *of it*)   Luckily we have still a good hour before lock-up, so nothing has been lost. (*He puts the time-table on the desk.*)

FRANK (*moving to the door up* L.; *to* MILLIE) May I use the short cut? I'm going back to my digs. (ANDREW *sits at his desk and opens a book.*)

MILLIE (*rising and moving up* R. *of the settee*) Yes. Go ahead. Come back soon. If Andrew hasn't finished we can sit in the garden. (*She crosses above the table* C. *and picks up the shopping basket. She puts the medicine on the sideboard*). I'd better go and see about dinner. (*She goes out up* C.)

ANDREW (*to* FRANK) Taplow is desirous of obtaining a remove from my form, Hunter, so that he can spend the rest of his career here playing happily with the crucibles, retorts and bunsen burners of your science fifth.

FRANK (*turning at the door*) Oh. Has he?

ANDREW Has he what?

FRANK Obtained his remove?

ANDREW (*after a pause*) He has obtained exactly what he deserves. No less; and certainly no more. (TAPLOW *mutters an explosion of mirth.* FRANK *nods, thoughtfully, and goes out.* ANDREW *has caught sight of* TAPLOW's *contorted face, but passes no remark on it. He beckons* TAPLOW *across and signs to him to sit in the chair* R. *of the desk.* TAPLOW *sits.* ANDREW *picks up a copy of "The Agamemnon" and* TAPLOW *does the same.*) Line thirteen hundred and ninety-nine. Begin. (*He leans back.*)

TAPLOW (*reading slowly*) Chorus. We—are surprised at . . .

ANDREW (*automatically*) We marvel at.

TAPLOW We marvel at—thy tongue—how bold thou art—that you . . .

ANDREW Thou. (*His interruptions are automatic. His thoughts are evidently far distant.*)

TAPLOW Thou—can . . .

ANDREW Canst.

TAPLOW Canst—boastfully speak . . .

ANDREW Utter such a boastful speech.

TAPLOW Utter such a boastful speech—over—(*in a sudden rush of inspiration*) the bloody corpse of the husband you have slain. (ANDREW *puts on his glasses and looks down at his text for the first time.* TAPLOW *looks apprehensive.*)

ANDREW (*after a pause*) Taplow—I presume you are using a different text from mine.

TAPLOW No, sir.

ANDREW   That is strange, for the line as I have it reads: "heetis toiond ep andri compadzise logon." However diligently I search I can discover no "bloody"—no "corpse"—no "you have slain." Simply "husband".

TAPLOW   Yes, sir. That's right.

ANDREW   Then why do you invent words that simply are not there?

TAPLOW   I thought they sounded better, sir. More exciting. After all, she did kill her husband, sir. (*With relish*). She's just been revealed with his dead body and Cassandra's weltering in gore.

ANDREW   I am delighted at this evidence, Taplow, of your interest in the rather more lurid aspects of dramaturgy, but I feel I must remind you that you are supposed to be construing Greek, not collaborating with Aeschylus. (*He leans back.*)

TAPLOW   (*greatly daring*)   Yes, but still, sir, translator's licence, sir—I didn't get anything wrong—and after all it *is* a play and not just a bit of Greek construe.

ANDREW   (*momentarily at a loss*)   I seem to detect a note of end of term in your remarks. I am not denying that *The Agamemnon* is a play. It is perhaps the greatest play ever written. (*He leans forward.*)

TAPLOW   (*quickly*)   I wonder how many people in the form think that? (*He pauses; instantly frightened of what he has said*). Sorry, sir. Shall I go on? (ANDREW *does not answer. He sits motionless, staring at his book*). Shall I go on, sir? (*There is another pause.* ANDREW *raises his head slowly from his book.*)

ANDREW   (*murmuring gently, not looking at* TAPLOW)   When I was a very young man, only two years older than you are now, Taplow, I wrote, for my own pleasure, a translation of *The Agamemnon*—a very free translation—I remember—in rhyming couplets.

TAPLOW   The whole *Agamemnon*—in verse? That must have been hard work, sir.

ANDREW   It was hard work; but I derived great joy from it. The play had so excited and moved me that I wished to communicate, however imperfectly, some of that emotion to others. When I had finished it, I remember, I thought it very beautiful—almost more beautiful than the original. (*He leans back.*)

TAPLOW   Was it ever published, sir?

ANDREW   No. Yesterday I looked for the manuscript while I was packing my papers. I was unable to find it. I fear it is lost—like so many other things. Lost for good.

TAPLOW Hard luck, sir. (ANDREW *is silent again.* TAPLOW *steals a timid glance at him*). Shall I go on, sir? (ANDREW, *with a slight effort, lowers his eyes again to his text.*)

ANDREW (*leaning forward; raising his voice slightly*) No. Go back and get that last line right. (TAPLOW, *out of* ANDREW's *vision, as he thinks, makes a disgusted grimace in his direction.*)

TAPLOW That—thou canst utter such a boastful speech over thy husband.

ANDREW Yes. And now, if you would be so kind, you will do the line again, without the facial contortion which you just found necessary to accompany it. (TAPLOW *is about to begin the line again.* MILLIE *enters up* C., *hurriedly. She is wearing an apron.* TAPLOW *rises.*)

MILLIE The headmaster's just coming up the drive. Don't tell him I'm in. The fish pie isn't in the oven yet. (*She exits up* C.)

TAPLOW (*turning hopefully to* ANDREW) I'd better go, hadn't I, sir? I mean—I don't want to be in the way.

ANDREW We do not yet know that it is I the headmaster wishes to see. Other people live in this building. (*There is a knock at the door up* R.). Come in. (DR. FROBISHER *enters up* R. *He looks more like a distinguished diplomat than a doctor of literature and a classical scholar. He is in the middle fifties and goes to a very good tailor.* ANDREW *rises.*)

FROBISHER Ah, Crocker-Harris, I've caught you in. I'm so glad. (*He crosses behind the settee and comes down* L. *of it*). I hope I'm not disturbing you?

ANDREW I have been taking a pupil in extra work. (TAPLOW *eases below the table* C.)

FROBISHER On the penultimate day of term? That argues either great conscientiousness on your part or considerable backwardness on his.

ANDREW Perhaps a combination of both.

FROBISHER Quite so, but as this is my only chance of speaking to you before tomorrow, I think that perhaps your pupil will be good enough to excuse. (*He turns politely to* TAPLOW.)

TAPLOW Oh yes, sir. That's really quite all right. (*He grabs his books off* ANDREW's *desk.*)

ANDREW (*crossing to* TAPLOW) I'm extremely sorry, Taplow. You will please explain to your father exactly what occurred over this lost hour and tell him that I shall in due course be writing to him to return the money involved. (FROBISHER *moves below the settee to the fireplace.*)

TAPLOW (*hurriedly*) Yes, sir. But please don't bother, sir. (*He dashes to the door up* R.). I know it's all right, sir. Thank you, sir. (*He darts out.*)

FROBISHER (*idly picking up an ornament on the mantel-piece*) Have the Gilberts called on you yet? (*He turns to* ANDREW.)

ANDREW (*moving* C.) The Gilberts, sir? Who are they?

FROBISHER Gilbert is your successor with the lower fifth. He is down here today with his wife, and as they will be taking over this flat I thought perhaps you wouldn't mind if they came in to look it over.

ANDREW Of course not.

FROBISHER I've told you about him, I think. He is a very brilliant young man and won exceptionally high honours at Oxford.

ANDREW So I understand, sir.

FROBISHER Not, of course, as high as the honours you yourself won there. He didn't, for instance, win the Chancellor's prize for Latin verse or the Gainsford.

ANDREW He won the Hertford Latin, then?

FROBISHER (*replacing the ornament*) No. (*Mildly surprised*). Did you win that, too? (ANDREW *nods*). It's sometimes rather hard to remember that you are perhaps the most brilliant classical scholar we have ever had at the school.

ANDREW You are very kind.

FROBISHER (*urbanely correcting his gaffe*) Hard to remember, I mean—because of your other activities—your brilliant work on the school time-table, for instance, and also for your heroic battle for so long and against such odds with the soul-destroying lower fifth.

ANDREW I have not found that my soul has been destroyed by the lower fifth, Headmaster.

FROBISHER I was joking, of course.

ANDREW Oh. I see.

FROBISHER Is your wife in?

ANDREW Er—no. Not at the moment.

FROBISHER I shall have a chance of saying good-bye to her tomorrow. (*He moves in a few steps below the settee*). I am rather glad I have got you to myself. I have a delicate matter—two rather delicate matters—to broach.

ANDREW (*moving in slightly; indicating the settee*) Please sit down. (*He stands at the* L. *end of the settee.*)

FROBISHER Thank you. (*He sits*). Now you have been with us, in all, eighteen years, haven't you? (ANDREW *nods*). It is extremely unlucky that you should have had to retire at so comparatively early an age and so short a time before you would have been eligible for a pension. (*He is regarding his nails, as he speaks, studiously avoiding meeting* ANDREW'S *gaze.* ANDREW *crosses below the settee to the fireplace and stands facing it.*)

ANDREW (*after a pause*) You have decided, then, not to award me a pension?

FROBISHER Not I, my dear fellow. It has nothing at all to do with me. It's the governors who, I'm afraid, have been forced to turn down your application. I put your case to them as well as I could— (ANDREW *turns and faces* FROBISHER.)—but they decided with great regret, that they couldn't make an exception to the rule.

ANDREW But I thought—my wife thought, that an exception was made some five years ago . . .

FROBISHER Ah! In the case of Buller, you mean? True. But the circumstances with Buller were quite remarkable. It was, after all, in playing rugger against the school that he received that injury.

ANDREW Yes. I remember.

FROBISHER And then the governors received a petition from boys, old boys and parents, with over five hundred signatures.

ANDREW I would have signed that petition myself, but through some oversight I was not asked.

FROBISHER He was a splendid fellow, Buller. Splendid. Doing very well, too, now, I gather.

ANDREW I'm delighted to hear it.

FROBISHER Your own case, of course, is equally deserving. If not more so—for Buller was a younger man. Unfortunately—rules are rules—and are not made to be broken every few years; at any rate that is the governors' view.

ANDREW I quite understand.

FROBISHER I knew you would. Now might I ask you a rather impertinent question?

ANDREW Certainly.

FROBISHER You have, I take it, private means?

ANDREW My wife has some.

FROBISHER Ah, yes. Your wife has often told me of her family

connexions. I understand her father has a business in—Bradford—
isn't it?

ANDREW   Yes. He runs a men's clothing shop in the Arcade.

FROBISHER   Indeed? Your wife's remarks had led me to imagine
something a little more—extensive.

ANDREW   My father-in-law made a settlement on my wife at the
time of our marriage. She has about three hundred a year of her own.
I have nothing. Is that the answer to your question, Headmaster?

FROBISHER   Yes. Thank you for your frankness. Now, this private
school you are going to . . .

ANDREW   My salary at the crammer's is to be two hundred
pounds a year.

FROBISHER   Quite so. With board and lodging, of course?

ANDREW   For eight months of the year.

FROBISHER   Yes, I see. (*He ponders a second*). Of course, you
know, there is the School Benevolent Fund that deals with cases of
actual hardship.

ANDREW   There will be no actual hardship, Headmaster.

FROBISHER   No. I am glad you take that view. I must admit,
though, I had hoped that your own means had proved a little more
ample. Your wife had certainly led me to suppose . . .

ANDREW   I am not denying that a pension would have been very
welcome, Headmaster, but I see no reason to quarrel with the
governors' decision. What is the other delicate matter you have to
discuss?

FROBISHER   Well, it concerns the arrangements at prize-giving
tomorrow. You are, of course, prepared to say a few words?

ANDREW   I had assumed you would call on me to do so.

FROBISHER   Of course. It is always done, and I know the boys
appreciate the custom.

ANDREW   (*crossing to the upstage end of the desk*) I have
already made a few notes of what I am going to say. Perhaps you
would care . . .

FROBISHER   No, no. That isn't necessary at all. I know I can
trust your discretion—not to say your wit. It will be, I know, a very
moving moment for you—indeed for us all—but, as I'm sure you
realize, it is far better to keep these occasions from becoming too
heavy and distressing. You know how little the boys appreciate sentiment.

ANDREW   I do.

FROBISHER   That is why I've planned my own reference to you at the end of my speech to be rather more light and jocular than I would otherwise have made it.

ANDREW   I quite understand. (*He moves to* L. *of the desk, puts on his glasses and picks up his speech*). I too have prepared a few little jokes and puns for my speech. One—a play of words on *vale*, farewell and Wally, the Christian name of a backward boy in my class, is, I think, rather happy.

FROBISHER   Yes. (*He laughs belatedly*). Very neat. That should go down extremely well.

ANDREW   I'm glad you like it.

FROBISHER   (*rising and crossing to* R. *of the desk*). Well, now—there is a particular favour I have to ask of you in connexion with the ceremony, and I know I shall not have to ask in vain. Fletcher, as you know, is leaving too.

ANDREW   Yes. He is going into the city, they tell me.

FROBISHER   Yes. Now he is, of course, considerably junior to you. He has only been here—let me see—five years. But, as you know, he has done great things for our cricket—positive wonders, when you remember what doldrums we were in before he came.

ANDREW   Our win at Lord's this year was certainly most inspiriting.

FROBISHER   Exactly. (*He moves above the desk*). Now I'm sure that tomorrow the boys will make the occasion of his farewell speech a tremendous demonstration of gratitude. The applause might go on for minutes—you know what the boys feel about Lord's—and I seriously doubt my ability to cut it short or even, I admit, the propriety of trying to do so. Now, you see the quandary in which I am placed?

ANDREW   Perfectly. You wish to refer to me and for me to make my speech before you come to Fletcher?

FROBISHER   It's extremely awkward, and I feel wretched about asking it of you—but it's more for your own sake than for mine or Fletcher's that I do. After all, a climax is what one must try to work up to on these occasions.

ANDREW   Naturally, Headmaster, I wouldn't wish to provide an anti-climax.

FROBISHER   You really mustn't take it amiss, my dear fellow. The

boys, in applauding Fletcher for several minutes and yourself say—
for—well, for not quite so long—won't be making any personal
demonstration between you. It will be quite impersonal—I assure
you—quite impersonal.

ANDREW   I understand.

FROBISHER   (*patting* ANDREW's *shoulder; warmly*) I knew you
would (*he looks at his watch*) and I can hardly tell you how wisely
I think you have chosen. Well now—as that is all my business, I
think perhaps I had better be getting along. (*He crosses to* R. *of the
table* C.). This has been a terribly busy day for me—for you too, I
imagine.

ANDREW   Yes. (MILLIE *enters up* C. *She has taken off her apron,
and tidied herself up. She comes to* L. *of* FROBISHER.)

MILLIE   (*in her social manner*) Ah, Headmaster. How good of
you to drop in.

FROBISHER   (*more at home with her than with* ANDREW) Mrs.
Crocker-Harris. How are you? (*They shake hands*). You're looking
extremely well, I must say. (*To* ANDREW). Has anyone ever told you,
Crocker-Harris, that you have a very attractive wife?

ANDREW   Many people, sir. But then I hardly need to be told.

MILLIE   Can I persuade you to stay a few moments and have a
drink, Headmaster? It's so rarely we have the pleasure of seeing you.

FROBISHER   Unfortunately, dear lady, I was just on the point
of leaving. I have two frantic parents waiting for me at home. You
are dining with us tomorrow—both of you, aren't you?

MILLIE   Yes, indeed—and so looking forward to it. (FROBISHER
and MILLIE *move to the door up* R.)

FROBISHER   I'm so glad. We can say our sad farewells then. (*To*
ANDREW). Au revoir, Crocker-Harris, and thank you very much. (*He
opens the door.* ANDREW *gives a slight bow.* MILLIE *holds the door
open.* FROBISHER *goes out.*)

MILLIE   (*to* ANDREW) Don't forget to take your medicine, dear,
will you? (*She goes out.*)

ANDREW   No.

FROBISHER   (*off*) Lucky invalid! To have such a very charming
nurse.

MILLIE   (*off*) I really don't know what to say to all these compli-
ments, Headmaster. I don't believe you mean a word of them.
(ANDREW *turns and looks out of the window.*)

FROBISHER (*off*) Every word. Till tomorrow, then? Good-bye. (*The outer door is heard to slam.* ANDREW *is staring out of the window.* MILLIE *enters up* R.)

MILLIE Well? Do we get it? (*She stands on the step.*)

ANDREW (*turning and moving below the chair* L. *of his desk; absently*) Get what?

MILLIE The pension, of course. Do we get it?

ANDREW No.

MILLIE (*crossing above the settee to* C.) My God! Why not?

ANDREW (*sitting at his desk*) It's against the rules.

MILLIE Buller got it, didn't he? Buller got it? What's the idea of giving it to him and not to us?

ANDREW The governors are afraid of establishing a precedent.

MILLIE The mean old brutes! My God, what I wouldn't like to say to them! (*She moves above the desk and rounds on* ANDREW). And what did you say? Just sat there and made a joke in Latin, I suppose?

ANDREW There wasn't very much I could say, in Latin or any other language.

MILLIE Oh, wasn't there? I'd have said it all right. I wouldn't just have sat there twiddling my thumbs and taking it from that old phoney of a headmaster. But, then, of course, I'm not a man. (ANDREW *is turning the pages of "The Agamemnon," not looking at her*). What do they expect you to do? Live on my money, I suppose.

ANDREW There has never been any question of that. I shall be perfectly able to support myself.

MILLIE Yourself? Doesn't the marriage service say something about the husband supporting his wife? (*She leans on the desk*). Doesn't it? You ought to know.

ANDREW Yes, it does.

MILLIE And how do you think you're going to do that on two hundred a year?

ANDREW I shall do my utmost to save some of it. You're welcome to it, if I can.

MILLIE Thank you for precisely nothing. (ANDREW *underlines a word in the text he is reading*). What else did the old fool have to say? (*She moves to* R. *of the chair,* R. *of the desk.*)

ANDREW The headmaster? He wants me to make my speech tomorrow before instead of after Fletcher.

MILLIE (*sitting* R. *of the desk*)   Yes. I knew he was going to ask that.

ANDREW (*without surprise*)   You knew?

MILLIE   Yes. He asked my advice about it a week ago. I told him to go ahead. I knew you wouldn't mind, and as there isn't a Mrs. Fletcher to make *me* look a fool, I didn't give two hoots. (*There is a knock on the door up* R.). Come in. (MR. *and* MRS. GILBERT *enter up* R. *He is about twenty-two, and his wife a year or so younger.* MILLIE *rises and stands at the downstage corner of the desk.*)

GILBERT   Mr. Crocker-Harris?

ANDREW   Yes. (*He rises*).   Is it Mr. and Mrs. Gilbert? The headmaster told me you might look in.

MRS. GILBERT (*crossing above the settee to* C.)   I do hope we're not disturbing you. (GILBERT *follows* MRS. GILBERT *and stands down stage of, and slightly behind, her.*)

ANDREW   Not at all. This is my wife.

MRS. GILBERT   How do you do?

ANDREW   Mr. and Mrs. Gilbert are our successors to this flat, my dear.

MILLIE   Oh yes. (*She moves to* L. *of* MRS. GILBERT).   How nice to meet you both.

GILBERT   How do you do? We really won't keep you more than a second—my wife thought as we were here you wouldn't mind us taking a squint at our future home.

MRS. GILBERT (*unnecessarily*)   This is the drawing-room, I suppose? (GILBERT *crosses to the fireplace. He looks for a moment at the picture above the mantelpiece, then turns and watches the others.*)

MILLIE   Well, it's really a living-room. Andrew uses it as a study.

MRS. GILBERT   How charmingly you've done it!

MILLIE   Oh, do you think so? I'm afraid it isn't nearly as nice as I'd like to make it—but a schoolmaster's wife has to think of so many other things besides curtains and covers. Boys with dirty books and a husband with leaky fountain pens, for instance.

MRS. GILBERT   Yes, I suppose so. Of course, I haven't been a schoolmaster's wife for very long, you know.

GILBERT   Don't swank, darling. You haven't been a schoolmaster's wife at all yet.

MRS. GILBERT   Oh yes, I have—for two months. You were a schoolmaster when I married you.

GILBERT   Prep school doesn't count.

MILLIE   Have you only been married two months?

MRS. GILBERT   Two months and sixteen days.

GILBERT   Seventeen.

MILLIE   (*sentimentally*)   Andrew, did you hear? They've only been married two months.

ANDREW   Indeed? Is that all?

MRS. GILBERT   (*crossing above* MILLIE *to the window*)   Oh, look, darling. They've got a garden. It is yours, isn't it?

MILLIE   Oh, yes. It's only a pocket handkerchief, I'm afraid, but it's very useful to Andrew. He often works out there, don't you, dear?

ANDREW   Yes, indeed. I find it very agreeable.

MILLIE   (*moving to the door up* C.)   Shall I show you the rest of the flat? It's a bit untidy, I'm afraid, but you must forgive that. (*She opens the door.*)

MRS. GILBERT   (*moving up to* L. *of* MILLIE)   Oh, of course.

MILLIE   And the kitchen is in a terrible mess. I'm in the middle of cooking dinner.

MRS. GILBERT   (*breathlessly*)   Oh, do you cook?

MILLIE   Oh, yes. I have to. We haven't had a maid for five years.

MRS. GILBERT   Oh! I do think that's wonderful of you. I'm scared stiff of having to do it for Peter—I know the first dinner I have to cook for him will wreck our married life.

GILBERT   Highly probable. (MRS. GILBERT *exits up* C.)

MILLIE   (*following* MRS. GILBERT)   Well, these days we've all got to try and do things we weren't really brought up to do. (*She goes out, closing the door.*)

ANDREW   (*to* GILBERT)   Don't you want to see the rest of the flat?

GILBERT   (*crossing to* C.)   No. I leave all that sort of thing to my wife. She's the boss. I thought perhaps you could tell me something about the lower fifth.

ANDREW   What would you like to know?

GILBERT   Well, sir, quite frankly, I'm petrified.

ANDREW   I don't think you need to be. May I give you some sherry? (*He comes down* L. *to the cupboard.*)

GILBERT   Thank you.

ANDREW   They are mostly boys of about fifteen or sixteen. They are not very difficult to handle. (*He takes out a bottle and a glass.*)

GILBERT   The headmaster said you ruled them with a rod of iron. He called you "the Himmler of the lower fifth."

ANDREW   (*turning, bottle and glass in hand*)   Did he? "The

Himmler of the lower fifth." I think he exaggerated. I hope he exaggerated. "The Himmler of the lower fifth." (*He puts the bottle on the desk, then fills the glass.*)

GILBERT (*puzzled*) He only meant that you kept the most wonderful discipline. I must say I do admire you for that. I couldn't even manage that with eleven-year-olds, so what I'll be like with fifteens and sixteens I shudder to think. (*He moves below the chair* R. *of the desk.*)

ANDREW It is not so difficult. (*He hands* GILBERT *the glass*). They aren't bad boys. Sometimes a little wild and unfeeling, perhaps —but not bad. "The Himmler of the lower fifth." Dear me! (*He turns to the cabinet with the bottle.*)

GILBERT Perhaps I shouldn't have said that. I've been tactless, I'm afraid.

ANDREW Oh no. (*He puts the bottle in the cupboard*). Please sit down. (*He stands by the downstage end of the desk.*)

GILBERT Thank you, sir. (*He sits* R. *of the desk*).

ANDREW From the very beginning I realized that I didn't possess the knack of making myself liked—a knack that you will find you do possess.

GILBERT Do you think so?

ANDREW Oh yes. I am quite sure of it. (*He moves up* L. *of the desk*). It is not a quality of great importance to a schoolmaster though, for too much of it, as you may also find, is as great a danger as the total lack of it. Forgive me lecturing, won't you?

GILBERT I want to learn.

ANDREW I can only teach you from my own experience. For two or three years I tried very hard to communicate to the boys some of my own joy in the great literature of the past. Of course I failed, as you will fail, nine hundred and ninety-nine times out of a thousand. But a single success can atone, and more than atone, for all the failure in the world. And sometimes—very rarely, it is true—but sometimes I had that success. That was in the early years.

GILBERT (*eagerly listening*) Please go on, sir.

ANDREW In early years too, I discovered an easy substitute for popularity. (*He picks up his speech*). I had of course acquired—we all do—many little mannerisms and tricks of speech, and I found that the boys were beginning to laugh at me. I was very happy at that, and encouraged the boys' laughter by playing up to it. It made our relationship so very much easier. They didn't like me as a man, but they found me funny as a character, and you can teach more things by laughter than by earnestness—for I never did have much sense of humour. So, for a time, you see, I was quite a success as a schoolmaster . . . (*He stops*). I fear this is all very personal and embarrassing to you. Forgive me. You need have no fears about the lower fifth. (*He puts the speech into his pocket and turns to the window.* GILBERT *rises and moves above the desk.*)

GILBERT (*after a pause*) I'm afraid I said something that hurt you very much. It's myself you must forgive, sir. Believe me, I'm desperately sorry.

ANDREW (*turning down stage and leaning slightly on the back of the swivel chair*) There's no need. You were merely telling me what I should have known for myself. Perhaps I did in my heart, and hadn't the courage to acknowledge it. I knew, of course, that I was not only not liked, but now positively disliked. I had realized too that the boys—for many long years now—had ceased to laugh at me. I don't know why they no longer found me a joke. Perhaps it was my illness. No, I don't think it was that. Something deeper than that. Not a sickness of the body, but a sickness of the soul. At all events it didn't take much discernment on my part to realize I had become an utter failure as a schoolmaster. Still, stupidly enough, I hadn't realized that I was also feared. "The Himmler of the lower fifth." I suppose that will become my epitaph. (GILBERT *is now deeply embarrassed and rather upset, but he remains silent. He sits on the upstage end of the window seat. With a mild laugh*). I cannot for the life of me imagine why I should choose to unburden myself to you—a total stranger— when I have been silent to others for so long. Perhaps it is because my very unworthy mantle is about to fall on your shoulders. If that is so I shall take a prophet's privilege and foretell that you will have a very great success with the lower fifth.

GILBERT Thank you, sir. I shall do my best.

ANDREW I can't offer you a cigarette, I'm afraid. I don't smoke.

GILBERT That's all right, sir. Nor do I.

MRS. GILBERT (*off*) Thank you so much for showing me round. (MILLIE *and* MRS. GILBERT *enter up* C. ANDREW *rises.* MILLIE *comes down* R. *of the table* C., *picks up the papers on the settee and puts them on the fender down* R. MRS. GILBERT *comes down* L. *of the table* C. *to* R. *of* GILBERT.)

ANDREW   I trust your wife has found no major snags in your new flat.

MR. GILBERT   No. None at all.

MRS. GILBERT   Just imagine, Peter, Mr. and Mrs. Crocker-Harris first met each other on a holiday in the Lake District. Isn't that a coincidence?

GILBERT   (*a little distrait*)   Yes. Yes, it certainly is. On a walking tour, too? (ANDREW *turns and looks out of the window.*)

MILLIE   Andrew was on a walking tour. No walking for me. I can't abide it. I was staying with my uncle—that's Sir William Bartop, you know—you may have heard of him. (GILBERT *and* MRS. GILBERT *try to look as though they had heard of him constantly. She moves below the settee*). He'd taken a house near Windermere—quite a mansion it was really—rather silly for an old gentleman living alone— and Andrew knocked on our front door one day and asked the foot-man for a glass of water. So my uncle invited him in to tea.

MRS. GILBERT   (*moving* C.)   Our meeting wasn't quite as romantic as that.

GILBERT   I knocked her flat on her face. (*He moves behind* MRS. GILBERT *and puts his hands on her shoulders.*)

MRS. GILBERT   Not with love at first sight. With the swing doors of our hotel bar. So of course then he apologized and . . . (ANDREW *turns and faces into the room.*)

GILBERT   (*brisquely*)   Darling. The Crocker-Harrises, I'm sure, have far more important things to do than to listen to your detailed but inaccurate account of our very sordid little encounter. Why not just say I married you for your money and leave it at that? Come on, we must go.

MRS. GILBERT   (*moving above the settee; to* MILLIE)   Isn't he awful to me?

MILLIE   (*moving round the* R. *end of the settee to the door up* R.) Men have no souls, my dear. My husband is just as bad.

MRS. GILBERT   Good-bye, Mr. Crocker-Harris.

ANDREW   (*with a slight bow*)   Good-bye.

MRS. GILBERT   (*moving to the door up* R.; *to* MILLIE)   I think your idea about the dining-room is awfully good—if only I can get the permit . . . (MILLIE *and* MRS. GILBERT *go out.* GILBERT *has dallied to say good-bye alone to* ANDREW.)

GILBERT   Good-bye, sir.

ANDREW (*crossing* C. *to* L. *of* GILBERT) Er—you will, I know, respect the confidences I have just made to you.

GILBERT I should hate you to think I wouldn't.

ANDREW I am sorry to have embarrassed you. I don't know what came over me. I have not been very well, you know. Good-bye, my dear fellow, and my best wishes.

GILBERT Thank you. The very best of good luck to you too, sir, in your future career.

ANDREW My future career? Yes. Thank you.

GILBERT Well, good-bye, sir. (*He crosses up* R. *and goes out.* ANDREW *moves to the chair* R., *of the desk and sits. He picks up a book and looks at it.* MILLIE *enters up* R. *She crosses above the table* C., *picks up the box of chocolates and eats one as she speaks.*)

MILLIE Good-looking couple.

ANDREW Very.

MILLIE He looks as if he'd got what it takes. I should think he'll be a success all right.

ANDREW That's what I thought.

MILLIE I don't think it's much of a career, though—a schoolmaster—for a likely young chap like that.

ANDREW I know you don't.

MILLIE (*crossing down to the desk and picking up the luggage labels*) Still, I bet when he leaves this place it won't be without a pension. It'll be roses, roses all the way, and tears and cheers and good-bye, Mr. Chips.

ANDREW I expect so.

MILLIE What's the matter with you?

ANDREW Nothing.

MILLIE You're not going to have another of your attacks, are you? You look dreadful.

ANDREW I'm perfectly all right.

MILLIE (*indifferently*) You know best. Your medicine's there, anyway, if you want it. (*She goes out up* C. ANDREW, *left alone, continues for a time staring at the text he has been pretending to read. Then he puts one hand over his eyes. There is a knock on the door up* R.)

ANDREW Come in. (TAPLOW *enters up* R. *and appears timidly from behind the screen. He is carrying a small book behind his back. Sharply*) Yes, Taplow? What is it?

TAPLOW   Nothing, sir.

ANDREW   What do you mean, nothing?

TAPLOW (*timidly*)   I just came back to say good-bye, sir.

ANDREW   Oh. (*He puts down the book and rises.*)

TAPLOW (*moving* C.)   I didn't have a chance with the head here. I rather dashed out, I'm afraid. I thought I'd just come back and—wish you luck, sir.

ANDREW   Thank you, Taplow. That's good of you.

TAPLOW   I—er—thought this might interest you, sir. (*He quickly thrusts the small book towards* ANDREW.)

ANDREW (*taking out his glasses and putting them on*)   What is it?

TAPLOW   Verse translation of *The Agamemnon*, sir. The Browning version. It's not much good. I've been reading it in the Chapel gardens.

ANDREW (*taking the book*)   Very interesting, Taplow. (*He seems to have a little difficulty in speaking. He clears his throat and then goes on in his level, gentle voice*). I know the translation, of course. It has its faults, I agree, but I think you will enjoy it more when you get used to the metre he employs. (*He hands the book to* TAPLOW.)

TAPLOW (*brusquely thrusting the book back to* ANDREW)   It's for you, sir.

ANDREW   For me?

TAPLOW   Yes, sir. I've written in it. (ANDREW *opens the fly-leaf and reads whatever is written there.*)

ANDREW   Did you buy this?

TAPLOW   Yes, sir. It was only second-hand.

ANDREW   You shouldn't have spent your pocket-money this way.

TAPLOW   That's all right, sir. It wasn't very much. (*Suddenly appalled*). The price isn't still inside, is it? (ANDREW *carefully wipes his glasses and puts them on again*).

ANDREW (*at length*)   No. Just what you've written. Nothing else.

TAPLOW   Good. I'm scrry you've got it already. I thought you probably would have.

ANDREW   I haven't got it already. I may have had it once. I can't remember. But I haven't got it now.

TAPLOW   That's all right, then. (ANDREW *continues to stare at* TAPLOW's *inscription on the fly-leaf. Suspiciously*). What's the matter, sir? Have I got the accent wrong on "eumenose"?

ANDREW   No. The perispomenon is perfectly correct. (*His hands are shaking. He lowers the book and turns away above the chair* R. *of the desk*). Taplow, would you be good enough to take that bottle of medicine, which you so kindly brought in, and pour me out one dose in a glass which you will find in the bathroom?

TAPLOW (*seeing something is wrong*) Yes, sir. (*He moves up to the sideboard and picks up the bottle.*)

ANDREW The doses are clearly marked on the bottle. I usually put a little water with it.

TAPLOW Yes, sir. (*He darts out up* C. ANDREW, *the moment he is gone, breaks down and begins to sob uncontrollably. He sits in the chair* L., *of the desk and makes a desperate attempt, after a moment, to control himself, but when* TAPLOW *comes back his emotion is still apparent.* TAPLOW *re-enters with the bottle and a glass, comes to the upstage end of the desk and holds out the glass.*)

ANDREW (*taking the glass*) Thank you. (*He drinks, turning his back on* TAPLOW *as he does so*). You must forgive this exhibition of weakness, Taplow. The truth is I have been going through rather a strain lately.

TAPLOW (*putting the bottle on the desk*) Of course, sir. I quite understand. (*He eases towards* C. *There is a knock on the door upper* L.)

FRANK Oh, sorry. I though you'd be finished by now. (*He moves to* L. *of* TAPLOW.)

ANDREW Come in, Hunter, do. It's perfectly all right. Our lesson was over some time ago, but Taplow most kindly came back to say good-bye. (FRANK, *taking in* TAPLOW's *rather startled face and* ANDREW's *obvious emotion, looks a little puzzled.*)

FRANK Are you sure I'm not intruding?

ANDREW No, no. I want you to see this book that Taplow has given me, Hunter. Look. A translation of *The Agamemnon*, by Robert Browning. (*He rises*). Do you see the inscription he has put into it? (*He hands the book open to* FRANK *across the desk.*)

FRANK (*glancing at the book*) Yes, but it's no use to me, I'm afraid. I never learnt Greek.

ANDREW Then we'll have to translate it for him, won't we, Taplow? (*He recites by heart*). "ton kratownta malthecose theos prosothen eumenose prosdirkati." That means—in a rough translation: "God from afar looks graciously upon a gentle master." It comes from a speech of Agamemnon's to Clytaemnestra.

FRANK I see. Very pleasant and very apt. (*He hands the book back to* ANDREW).

ANDREW Very pleasant. But perhaps not, after all, so very apt.

(*He turns quickly away from both of them as emotion once more seems about to overcome him.* FRANK *brusquely jerks his head to the bewildered* TAPLOW *to get out.* TAPLOW *nods.*)

TAPLOW   Good-bye, sir, and the best of luck.

ANDREW   Good-bye, Taplow, and thank you very much. (TAPLOW *flees quickly up* R. *and goes out.* FRANK *watches* ANDREW's *back with a mixture of embarrassment and sympathy.*)

ANDREW (*turning at length, slightly recovered*)   Dear me, what a fool I made of myself in front of that boy. And in front of you, Hunter. (*He moves in to the desk*). I can't imagine what you must think of me.

FRANK   Nonsense.

ANDREW   I am not a very emotional person, as you know, but there was something so very touching and kindly about his action, and coming as it did just after . . . (*He stops, then glances at the book in his hand*). This is a very delightful thing to have, don't you think?

FRANK   Delightful.

ANDREW   The quotation, of course, he didn't find entirely by himself. I happened to make some little joke about the line in form the other day. But he must have remembered it all the same to have found it so readily—and perhaps he means it.

FRANK   I'm sure he does, or he wouldn't have written it. (MILLIE *enters up* C. *with a tray of supper things. She puts the tray on the sideboard. She puts table napkins, mats and bread on the table.* ANDREW *turns and looks out of the window.*)

MILLIE   Hullo, Frank. I'm glad you're in time. Lend me a cigarette. I've been gasping for one for an hour. (FRANK *moves up* L. *of the table* C. *and once more extends his case.* MILLIE *takes a cigarette.*)

FRANK   Your husband has just had a very nice present.

MILLIE   Oh? Who from?

FRANK   Taplow. (*He comes down* L. *of the table.*)

MILLIE (*coming down* R. *of the table; smiling*)   Oh, Taplow. (FRANK *lights* MILLIE's *cigarette.*)

ANDREW (*moving above the desk to the chair* R. *of it*).   He bought it with his own pocket-money, Millie, and wrote a very charming inscription inside.

FRANK   "God looks kindly upon a gracious master."

ANDREW No—not gracious—gentle, I think. "ton kratownta malthecose"—yes, I think gentle is the better translation. I would rather have had this present, I think, than almost anything I can think of. (*There is a pause.* MILLIE *laughs suddenly.*)

MILLIE (*holding out her hand*) Let's see it. The artful little beast. (ANDREW *hands the book across to* MILLIE. MILLIE *opens it.*)

FRANK (*urgently*) Millie. (MILLIE *looks at* ANDREW.)

ANDREW Artful? (MILLIE *looks at* FRANK). Why artful? (FRANK *stares meaningly at* MILLIE. MILLIE *looks at* ANDREW). Why artful, Millie? (MILLIE *laughs again, quite lightly.*)

MILLIE My dear, because I came into this room this afternoon to find him giving an imitation of you to Frank here. Obviously he was scared stiff I was going to tell you, and you'd ditch his remove or something. I don't blame him for trying a few bobs' worth of appeasement. (*She gives the book to* ANDREW, *then moves up* R. *of the table to the sideboard, where she stubs out her cigarette, picks up some cutlery and starts to lay the table.* ANDREW *stands quite still, looking down at the book.*)

ANDREW (*after a pause, nodding*) I see. (*He puts the book gently on the desk, pick up the bottle of medicine and moves up* L. *of the table to the door up* C.)

MILLIE Where are you going, dear? Dinner's nearly ready.

ANDREW (*opening the door*) Only to my room for a moment. I won't be long.

MILLIE You've just had a dose of that, dear. I shouldn't have another, if I were you.

ANDREW I am allowed two at a time.

MILLIE Well, see it is two and no more, won't you? (ANDREW *meets her eye for a moment, then goes out quietly.* MILLIE *moves to* L. *of the table and lays the last knife and fork. She looks at* FRANK *with an expression half defiant and half ashamed.*)

FRANK (*with a note of real repulsion in his voice*) Millie! My God! How could you?

MILLIE Well, why not? (*She crosses above the table and comes down* L. *of the settee*). Why should he be allowed his comforting little illusions? I'm not.

FRANK (*advancing on her*) Listen. You're to go to his room now and tell him that was a lie.

MILLIE Certainly not. It wasn't a lie.

FRANK If you don't, I will.

MILLIE I shouldn't, if I were you. It'll only make things worse. He won't believe you.

FRANK (*moving up* R. *of the table* C.) We'll see about that.

MILLIE Go ahead. See what happens. He knows I don't lie to him. He knows what I told him was the truth, and he won't like your sympathy. He'll think you're making fun of him, like Taplow. (FRANK *hesitates, then comes slowly down* C. *again.* MILLIE *watches him, a little frightened.*)

FRANK (*after a pause*) We're finished, Millie—you and I.

MILLIE (*laughing*) Frank, really! Don't be hysterical.

FRANK I'm not. I mean it.

MILLIE (*lightly*) Oh yes, you mean it. Of course you mean it. Now just sit down, dear, and relax and forget all about artful little boys and their five bob presents, and talk to me. (*She pulls at his coat.*)

FRANK (*pulling away*) Forget? If I live to be a hundred I shall never forget that little glimpse you've just given me of yourself.

MILLIE Frank—you're making a frightening mountain out of an absurd little molehill.

FRANK Of course, but the mountain I'm making in my imagination is so frightening that I'd rather try to forget both it and the repulsive little molehill that gave it birth. But as I know I never can, I tell you, Millie—from this moment you and I are finished.

MILLIE (*quietly*) You can't scare me, Frank. (*She turns away towards the fireplace*). I know that's what you're trying to do, but you can't do it.

FRANK (*quietly*) I'm not trying to scare you, Millie. I'm telling you the simple truth. I'm not coming to Bradford. (*There is a pause.*)

MILLIE (*turning to face* FRANK; *with an attempt at bravado*) All right, my dear, if that's the way you feel about it. Don't come to Bradford.

FRANK Right. Now I think you ought to go to your room and look after Andrew. (*He crosses towards the door up* L.). I'm leaving.

MILLIE (*following* FRANK) What is this? Frank, I don't understand, really I don't. What have I done?

FRANK I think you know what you've done, Millie. Go and look after Andrew.

MILLIE (*moving to the* L. *end of the settee*) Andrew? Why this sudden concern for Andrew?

FRANK   Because I think he's just been about as badly hurt as a human being can be; and as he's a sick man and in a rather hysterical state it might be a good plan to go and see how he is.

MILLIE   (*scornfully*)   Hurt? Andrew hurt? You can't hurt Andrew. He's dead.

FRANK   (*moving to* R. *of* MILLIE)   Why do you hate him so much, Millie?

MILLIE   Because he keeps me from you.

FRANK   That isn't true.

MILLIE   Because he's not a man at all.

FRANK   He's a human being.

MILLIE   You've got a fine right to be so noble about him, after deceiving him for six months.

FRANK   Twice in six months—at your urgent invitation. (MILLIE *slaps his face, in a violent paroxysm of rage*). Thank you for that. I deserved it. (*He crosses to the chair* R. *of the desk*). I deserve a lot worse than that, too.

MILLIE   (*running to him*)   Frank, forgive me—I didn't mean it.

FRANK   (*quietly*)   You'd better have the truth, Millie, it had to come some time. (*He turns to face* MILLIE). I've never loved you. I've never told you I loved you.

MILLIE   I know, Frank, I know. (*She backs away slightly*). I've always accepted that.

FRANK   You asked me just now if I was running away from you. Well, I was.

MILLIE   I knew that, too.

FRANK   But I was coming to Bradford. It was going to be the very last time I was ever going to see you and at Bradford I would have told you that.

MILLIE   You wouldn't. You wouldn't. You've tried to tell me that so often before—(*she crosses to the fireplace*) and I've always stopped you somehow—somehow. I would have stopped you again.

FRANK   (*quietly*)   I don't think so, Millie. Not this time.

MILLIE   (*crossing to* R. *of the table* C.)   Frank, I don't care what humiliations you heap on me. I know you don't give two hoots for me as a person. I've always known that. I've never minded so long as you cared for me as a woman. And you do, Frank. You do. You do, don't you? (FRANK *is silent. He crosses slowly to the fireplace*). It'll be all right at Bradford, you see. It'll be all right, there.

FRANK   I'm not coming to Bradford, Millie. (*The door up* C.

opens slowly and ANDREW *enters. He is carrying the bottle of medicine. He hands it to* MILLIE *and passes on crossing down* L. *below the desk.* MILLIE *holds the bottle up to the light.*)

ANDREW (*gently*) You should know me well enough by now, my dear, to realize how unlikely it is that I should ever take an overdose. (MILLIE, *without a word, puts the bottle on the sideboard and goes out up* C. ANDREW *goes to the cupboard down* L. *and takes out the sherry and one glass.*)

FRANK I'm not staying to dinner, I'm afraid.

ANDREW Indeed? I'm sorry to hear that. You'll have a glass of sherry?

FRANK No, thank you.

ANDREW You will forgive me if I do.

FRANK Of course. Perhaps I'll change my mind. (*He crosses to* C. ANDREW *takes out a second glass and fills both of them*). About Taplow . . .

ANDREW Oh yes?

FRANK It *is* perfectly true that he was imitating you. I, of course, was mostly to blame in that, and I'm very sorry.

ANDREW That is perfectly all right. Was it a good imitation?

FRANK No.

ANDREW I expect it was. Boys are often very clever mimics.

FRANK We talked about you, of course, before that. (*He moves in to* R. *of the desk*). He said—you probably won't believe this, but I thought I ought to tell you—he said he liked you very much. (ANDREW *smiles slightly.*)

ANDREW Indeed? (*He drinks.*)

FRANK I can remember very clearly his exact words. He said: "He doesn't seem to like people to like him—but in spite of that, I do—very much." (*Lightly*). So you see it looks after all as if the book might not have been a mere question of—appeasement.

ANDREW The book? (*He picks it up*). Dear me! What a lot of fuss about a little book—and a not very good little book at that. (*He drops it on the desk.*)

FRANK I would like you to believe me.

ANDREW Possibly you would, my dear Hunter; but I can assure you I am not particularly concerned about Taplow's views of my character: or about yours either, if it comes to that.

FRANK (*hopelessly*) I think you should keep that book all the same. You may find it'll mean something to you after all.

ANDREW (*turning to the cupboard and pouring himself another sherry*) Exactly. It will mean a perpetual reminder to myself of the story with which Taplow is at this very moment regaling his friends in the House. "I gave the Crock a book, to buy him off, and he blubbed. The Crock blubbed. I tell you I was there. I saw it. The Crock blubbed." My mimicry is not as good as his, I fear. Forgive me. (*He moves up* L. *of the desk*). And now let us leave this idiotic subject and talk of more pleasant things. Do you like this sherry? I got it on my last visit to London.

FRANK If Taplow ever breathes a word of that story to anyone at all, I'll murder him. But he won't. And if you think I will you greatly underestimate my character as well as his. (*He drains his glass and puts it on the desk. He moves to the door up* L. ANDREW *comes down* L., *puts his glass on the cupboard, and stands facing down stage*). Good-bye.

ANDREW Are you leaving so soon? Good-bye, my dear fellow. (FRANK *stops. He takes out his cigarette case and places it on the* L. *end of the table* C.)

FRANK As this is the last time I shall probably ever see you, I'm going to offer you a word of advice.

ANDREW (*politely*) I shall be glad to listen to it.

FRANK Leave your wife. (*There is a pause.* ANDREW *looks out of the window.*)

ANDREW So that you may the more easily carry on your intrigue with her?

FRANK (*moving in to the upstage end of the desk*) How long have you known that?

ANDREW Since it first began.

FRANK How did you find out?

ANDREW By information.

FRANK By whose information?

ANDREW By someone's whose word I could hardly discredit. (*There is a pause.*)

FRANK (*slowly, with repulsion*) No! That's too horrible to think of.

ANDREW (*turning to* FRANK) Nothing is ever too horrible to think of, Hunter. It is simply a question of facing facts.

FRANK She might have told you a lie. Have you faced that fact?

ANDREW She never tells me a lie. In twenty years she has never told me a lie. Only the truth.

FRANK   This was a lie.

ANDREW   (*moving up* L. *of* FRANK)   No, my dear Hunter. Do you wish me to quote you dates?

FRANK   (*still unable to believe it*)   And she told you six months ago?

ANDREW   (*moving down* L.)   Isn't it seven?

FRANK   (*savagely*)   Then why have you allowed me inside your home? Why haven't you done something—reported me to the governors—anything—made a scene, knocked me down?

ANDREW   Knocked you down?

FRANK   You didn't have to invite me to dinner.

ANDREW   My dear Hunter, if, over the last twenty years, I had allowed such petty considerations to influence my choice of dinner guests I would have found it increasingly hard to remember which master to invite and which to refuse. You see, Hunter, you mustn't flatter yourself you are the first. My information is a good deal better than yours, you understand. It's authentic. (*There is a pause.*)

FRANK   She's evil.

ANDREW   That's hardly a kindly epithet to apply to a lady whom, I gather, you have asked to marry.

FRANK   Did she tell you that?

ANDREW   She's a dutiful wife. She tells me everything.

FRANK   That, at least, was a lie.

ANDREW   She never lies.

FRANK   (*leaning on the desk*)   That was a lie. Do you want the truth? Can you bear the truth?

ANDREW   I can bear anything. (*He crosses to the fireplace.*)

FRANK   (*turning to face* ANDREW)   What I did I did coldbloodedly out of weakness and ignorance and crass stupidity. I'm bitterly, bitterly ashamed of myself, but, in a sense, I'm glad you know (*he moves* C.) though I'd rather a thousand times that you'd heard it from me than from your wife. I won't ask you to forgive me. I can only tell you, with complete truth, that the only emotion she has ever succeeded in arousing in me she aroused in me for the first time ten minutes ago— an intense and passionate disgust.

ANDREW   What a delightfully chivalrous statement.

FRANK   (*moving below the settee*)   Forget chivalry, Crock, for God's sake. Forget all your fine mosaic scruples. You must leave her —it's your only chance.

ANDREW She's my wife, Hunter. You seem to forget that. As long as she wishes to remain my wife, she may.

FRANK She's out to kill you.

ANDREW My dear Hunter, if that was indeed her purpose, you should know by now that she fulfilled it long ago.

FRANK Why won't you leave her?

ANDREW Because I wouldn't wish to add another grave wrong to one I have already done her.

FRANK What wrong have you done her?

ANDREW To marry her. (*There is a pause.* FRANK *stares at him in silence*). You see, my dear Hunter, she is really quite as much to be pitied as I. We are both of us interesting subjects for your microscope. (*He sits on the fender*). Both of us needing from the other something that would make life supportable for us, and neither of us able to give it. Two kinds of love. Hers and mine. Worlds apart as I know now, though when I married her I didn't think they were incompatible. In those days I hadn't thought that her kind of love—the love she requires and which I was unable to give her—was so important that its absence would drive out the other kind of love the kind of love that I require and which I thought, in my folly, was by far the greater part of love. (*He rises*). I may have been, you see, Hunter, a brilliant classical scholar, but I was woefully ignorant of the facts of life. I know better now, of course. I know that in both of us, the love that we should have borne each other has turned to bitter hatred. That's all the problem is. Not a very unusual one, I venture to think—nor nearly as tragic as you seem to imagine. Merely the problem of an unsatisfied wife and a henpecked husband. You'll find it all over the world. It is usually, I believe, a subject for farce. (*He turns to the mantelpiece and adjusts the hands of the clock*). And now, if you have to leave us, my dear fellow, please don't let me detain you any longer. (FRANK *makes no move to go.*)

FRANK Don't go to Bradford. Stay here, until you take up your new job.

ANDREW I think I've already told you I'm not interested in your advice.

FRANK Leave her. It's the only way.

ANDREW (*violently*) Will you please go!

FRANK All right. I'd just like you to say good-bye to me, properly, though. Will you? I shan't see you again. I know you don't want my pity, but, I would like to be of some help. (ANDREW *turns and face* FRANK.)

ANDREW If you think, by this expression of kindness, Hunter, that you can get me to repeat the shameful exhibition of emotion I made to Taplow a moment ago, I must tell you that you have no chance. My hysteria over that book just now was no more than a sort of reflex action of the spirit. The muscular twitchings of a corpse. It can never happen again.

FRANK A corpse can be revived.

ANDREW I don't believe in miracles.

FRANK Don't you? Funnily enough, as a scientist, I do.

ANDREW (*turning to the fireplace*) Your faith would be touching, if I were capable of being touched by it.

FRANK You are, I think. (*He moves behind* ANDREW. *After a pause*). I'd like to come and visit you at this crammer's.

ANDREW That is an absurd suggestion.

FRANK I suppose it is rather, but all the same I'd like to do it. May I?

ANDREW Of course not.

FRANK (*sitting on the settee*) Your term begins on the first of September, doesn't it? (*He takes out a pocket diary.*)

ANDREW I tell you the idea is quite childish.

FRANK I could come about the second week.

ANDREW You would be bored to death. So, probably, would I.

FRANK (*glancing at his diary*) Let's say Monday the twelfth, then.

ANDREW (*turning to face* FRANK, *his hands beginning to tremble*). Say anything you like, only please go. Please go, Hunter.

FRANK (*writing in his book and not looking at* ANDREW) That's fixed, then. Monday, September the twelfth. Will you remember that?

ANDREW (*after a pause; with difficulty*) I suppose I'm at least as likely to remember it as you are.

FRANK That's fixed, then. (*He rises, slips the book into his pocket and puts out his hand*). Good-bye, until then. (*He moves in to* AN-DREW. ANDREW *hesitates, then shakes his hand.*)

ANDREW Good-bye.

FRANK May I go out through your garden? (*He crosses to* C.)

ANDREW (*nodding*) Of course.

FRANK I'm off to have a quick word with Taplow. By the way, may I take him a message from you?

ANDREW What message?

FRANK Has he or has he not got his remove?

ANDREW He has.

FRANK May I tell him?

ANDREW It is highly irregular. Yes, you may.

FRANK Good. (*He turns to go, then turns back*). Oh, by the way, I'd better have the address of that crammer's. (*He moves below the settee, takes out his diary, and points his pencil, ready to write.* MILLIE *enters up* C. *She carries a casserole on three plates.*)

MILLIE (*coming above the table* C.) Dinner's ready. You're staying, Frank, aren't you? (*She puts the casserole and plates on the table.*)

FRANK (*politely*) No. I'm afraid not. (*To* ANDREW). What's that address?

ANDREW (*after great hesitation*) The Old Deanery, Malcombe, Dorset.

FRANK I'll write to you and you can let me know about trains. Good-bye. (*To* MILLIE). Good-bye. (*He crosses to the door up* L. *and goes out.* MILLIE *is silent for a moment. Then she laughs.*)

MILLIE That's a laugh, I must say.

ANDREW What's a laugh, my dear?

MILLIE You inviting him to stay with you.

ANDREW I didn't. He suggested it.

MILLIE (*moving to the* L. *end of the settee*) He's coming to Bradford.

ANDREW Yes. I remember your telling me so.

MILLIE He's coming to Bradford. He's not going to you.

ANDREW The likeliest contingency is, that he's not going to either of us.

MILLIE He's coming to Bradford.

ANDREW I expect so. Oh, by the way, I'm not. I shall be staying here until I go to Dorset.

MILLIE (*indifferently*) Suit yourself. What makes you think I'll join you there?

ANDREW I don't.

MILLIE You needn't expect me.

ANDREW I don't think either of us has the right to expect anything further from the other. (*The telephone rings*). Excuse me. (*He moves to the table down* R. *and lifts the receiver*). Hullo . . . (*While he is speaking* MILLIE *crosses to* L. *of the table* C. *About to sit, she sees the cigarette case. She picks it up, fingers it for a moment, and finally drops it into her pocket*). Yes, Headmaster . . . The time-table? . . . It's perfectly simple. The middle fourth B division will take a ten-minute break on Tuesdays and a fifteen-minute break on alternate Wednesdays; while exactly the reverse procedure will apply to the lower Shell, C division. I thought I had sufficiently explained that on my chart . . . Oh, I see . . . Thank you, that is very good of you . . . Yes. I think you will find it will work out quite satisfactorily . . . Oh by the way, Headmaster. I have changed my mind about the prize-giving ceremony. I intend to speak after, instead of before, Fletcher, as is my privilege . . . Yes, I quite understand, but I am now seeing the matter in a different light . . . I know, but I am of opinion that occasionally an anti-climax can be surprisingly effective. Good-bye. (*He replaces the receiver, crosses to* R. *of the table* C., *and sits*). Come along, my dear. We mustn't let our dinner get cold. (*He unrolls his table napkin.* MILLIE *sits* L. *of the table and unrolls her table napkin.* ANDREW *offers her the bread. She ignores it. He takes a piece. She removes the lid of the casserole as—*

CURTAIN

DISCUSSION

1. Show how the following occurrences foreshadow the conflict of of the play:
   (a) Frank Hunter gives golf instruction in the center of Crocker-Harris's living room, tears the carpet, and then assures Taplow, "That was there already."
   (b) Taplow and Hunter discuss *The Agamemnon*, its theme, and the manner in which the play is taught by Crocker-Harris.
2. What are the earliest indications that Crocker-Harris is not like the other masters? How does he differ?
3. How does Taplow's admission that "in spite of everything I rather like him" help to make later developments in the play understandable?
4. How do Millie's references to a cigarette lighter clarify her relationship with Frank Hunter? What proof can you offer that this relationship has become strained? In what connection does Rattigan reintroduce the cigarette lighter at the end of the play?

5. By the time of his arrival on stage, you are already well-acquainted with Crocker-Harris. What have you learned about his teaching career? About his marriage? Does his first appearance confirm your advance impressions?

6. What is self-revealing in Crocker-Harris's admission that a play he once wrote is now "lost—like so many other things . . ."?

7. Considering Crocker-Harris's position as a husband and as a teacher, how is it ironic that the school administrators "couldn't make an exception to the rule" regarding pension benefits? How does Frobisher's later request that Crocker-Harris speak out of his rightful turn at the prize-giving ceremony heighten the irony?

8. What does the Buller incident confirm about the policies of the school administrators? Why is such confirmation necessary?

9. Why is it significant that while Millie is scolding her husband for not standing up to Frobisher, he is busy "turning the pages of *The Agamemnon*, and not looking at her"? How does their subsequent discussion of money reveal a basic difference between Millie's sense of values and Andrew's?

10. Explain the dramatic purpose of the Gilberts' visit to the Crocker-Harris apartment. Can you think of a reason, other than the one that Crocker-Harris provides, for the ease with which he unburdens himself to Gilbert?

11. What is Taplow's motive in offering Crocker-Harris a farewell gift? Are Crocker-Harris's reactions understandable? In evaluating these reactions, why is it necessary to consider Crocker-Harris's admission that the Browning version "has its faults"?

12. What incident prompts Millie's remark about "comforting little illusions"? How is Millie's behavior during this incident a commentary on her character? How is Frank Hunter's rejection of Millie a commentary on his? Why are these decisive turning points in the action?

13. Why does Rattigan refer repeatedly to Crocker-Harris's heart condition? Explain the double meaning, and hence the irony, of Crocker-Harris's reminder to Millie: "You should know me well enough by now, my dear, to realize how unlikely it is that I should ever take an overdose."

14. What explains Hunter's sudden concern for a man whose welfare he had previously disregarded? Why does he feel that Crocker-Harris's "only chance" is to leave Millie? Why does Crocker-Harris disagree? How realistically does he appraise his own marriage?

15. How does Rattigan suggest Crocker-Harris's change of outlook

during the final portions of the play? Does the change in
Crocker-Harris seem plausible, in view of the circumstances of
the play and his own character? Has any other character changed
as much as he? Justify your answers.
16. What do you predict for Crocker-Harris in his future as a husband
and as a teacher?

TOPICS FOR WRITING

According to the Greek tragedy, Clytemnestra murdered her husband,
Agamemnon, because she was in love with another man. Discuss the
applicability of this story to the conflict in *The Browning Version*.
Discuss similarities *or* differences in personality and viewpoint
between
    (a) Crocker-Harris and Frank Hunter
    (b) Crocker-Harris and Frobisher
    (c) Frobisher and Millie
In many respects *The Browning Version* is a typical one-act play, in
some respects it is not. Comment on this.

NOTES

p. 367   remove: (British): a promotion of a student from one school
           grade or division to another.
p. 373   *bonhomie* (French): simple good-heartedness
p. 378   queue (Chiefly British): a line of people
p. 379   digs (British): lodgings
p. 382   gaffe (British): rudeness or thoughtlessness of speech
p. 388   swank: swagger in behavior, show off
p. 393   Mr. Chips: hero of a sentimental novel by James Hilton.
           "Chips" was a teacher dearly beloved by almost all of
           his students and colleagues.

THE SHELTER

Rod Serling

CHARACTERS

Dr. Stockton
Grace Stockton
Paul Stockton
Harlowe
Mrs. Harlowe
Marty Weiss
Mrs. Weiss

Mr. Henderson
Mrs. Henderson
Man #1
Woman #1
Announcer
Narrator

Rod Serling (1924-   )

Rod Serling was born in 1924 in Syracuse, New York. He is the orig-
inator of The Twilight Zone, the popular television series, featured
on the CBS Television Network for several seasons, on which The
Shelter first appeared in 1961. Almost unknown as a writer fifteen
years ago, Serling is today firmly established as one of the nation's
leading television playwrights. In addition to The Twilight Zone series,
he has written such successful television plays as Patterns, Requiem
for a Heavyweight, and The Comedian, all of which earned for him
the coveted "Emmy" award.

   In The Shelter Serling offers a fresh perspective to a time-old
question: Am I my brother's keeper?

THE SHELTER

SETS

EXT. RESIDENTIAL STREET AND STOCKTON
HOUSE

INT. STOCKTON LIVING ROOM, DINING ROOM,
HALLWAY, AND KITCHEN

INT. STOCKTON CELLAR, SHELTER AND STAIRS
FROM MAIN PART OF HOUSE

ACT ONE

FADE ON:

1. STANDARD ROAD OPENING
*With vehicle smashing into letters, propulsion into starry
night then* PAN DOWN TO OPENING SHOT OF PLAY.

2. EXT RESIDENTIAL STREET NIGHT LONG
   ANGLE SHOT LOOKING DOWN A TREE-LINED
   SMALL TOWN STREET

*On a summer evening. The lights from the big, old stately
houses that flank on either side cast warm orange glows,
intermingled with the moonlight that is streaming through
the broad-leafed trees. The CAMERA PANS DOWN THEN
ACROSS toward one house in particular. A sign in the front
yard announces that this is the home of* DR. WILLIAM STOCK-
TON. *And from inside we can hear the sound of laughter and
merry-making.*

DISSOLVE THRU TO:

3. INT DINING ROOM HOUSE NIGHT
There are four couples there gathered around the table. The
HENDERSONS, *the* WEISS's, DR. STOCKTON *and his* WIFE *and* JERRY
and MARTHA HARLOWE. *The latter is standing at his place at
the table and knocking a glass with a spoon, calling for
quiet. We see the remnant of a dinner and also one half of
large cake with candles. The CAMERA MOVES OVER for
a medium close shot of* HARLOWE *as he holds up his hand,
throws the glass down.*

HARLOWE   Ladies and gentlemen . . . may I have your attention,
please!

*The laughter and talk subsides and they all stare up smiling
at* HARLOWE

HARLOWE   No birthday celebration is complete without an after-dinner speech!

> *More laughter and applause at this, then* HARLOWE *looks toward the guest of honor,* DR. STOCKTON.

HARLOWE   And to get to the business at hand and the honoring of one Dr. William Stockton who's grown one year older and will admit to being over twenty-one!

> *More laughter and the doctor's wife leans over to hug him.*

HARLOWE   And who in the short space of twenty years has taken care of us, our kids . . . even our grandkids! And I doubt if there's a single person in this room who still doesn't owe the good doctor for a visit or two!

> *Again laughter, humorous protests, et al.*

A VOICE (*shouts out*)   What about this hammering at all hours of the night? That's another thing we owe him for.

> *There's laughter at this.*

HARLOWE (*joins in the laughter then holds up his hand*)   Oh, yes, the good doctor's bomb shelter. I think we might as well forgive him for this. Despite the fact that what he thinks of as far-sightedness on his part is a pain in the neck to all the rest of us with the concrete trucks and the nocturnal hammering and all the rest of it.

> *There's some joshing and more good natured cat-calls at this.*

HARLOWE   Anyway . . . when Grace— (*he points toward the woman sitting next to Stockton*) mentioned that it was your birthday —we took it on ourselves to handle the proceedings. And just as a little personal aside let me conclude this way.

> *The CAMERA MOVES IN for an extremely tight close shot of* HARLOWE, *whose smile fades.*

HARLOWE   You're a very beloved fellah . . . and rightfully so. And you may not have the biggest practice in the history of medicine . . . but there isn't a sawbones in any one of the fifty states whose patients have such a regard . . . an affection . . . a respect for the man with the black bag . . . as we do for ours!

4. OUT

5. MED SHOT   TABLE

There's applause and laughter. GRACE STOCKTON *leans over to kiss her husband who returns the kiss, then stands and holds out his hand to* HARLOWE *who grips it with both of his.*

STOCKTON (*with a grin*)   You dirty dog, you! First a surprise party—which I abhor. And then that sloppy sentimental speech!

But the two men continue to stand there and grip their hands together.

                                                                          CUT TO:

6. ENTRANCE TO THE DINING ROOM

As the Stockton's twelve year old boy enters.

BOY   Hey, Pop . . . Pop?

                                                                          CUT TO:

7. DIFFERENT ANGLE   THE GROUP

As STOCKTON *looks over toward the youngster.*

STOCKTON   What is it, Paul?
PAUL   The picture went out on the television set. Then there was some kind of goofey announcement. Something about—

The boy continues to speak, but he's drowned out by one of the women laughing.

8. CLOSE SHOT WEISS

Whose face suddenly looks serious. He rises and crosses the room and then in a loud voice—

WEISS   Hold it, everybody.

There's a gradual silence.

9. TWO SHOT WEISS AND THE BOY

WEISS   What did you say, Paul?
PAUL   The announcer said something about turning to the Conelrad station on the radio.

10. PAN SHOT AROUND THE ROOM

As the people suddenly become deadly still and faces take on a sudden tight, grim cast.

STOCKTON   You must have heard it wrong, Paul—
PAUL   I didn't hear it wrong, Pop. That's what he said. Turn on your Conelrad station, then everything went blank completely.

11. DIFFERENT ANGLE LOOKING TOWARD DINING ROOM FROM LIVING ROOM

As STOCKTON *comes out on the run over to a small table radio. He flicks it on then whirls the dials around. After a moment we hear an announcer's voice.*

ANNOUNCER'S VOICE   . . . direct from Washington, D. C. Repeating that. Four minutes ago the President of the United States made the following announcement. I quote: "At 11:04 PM Eastern Standard Time both our Distant Early Warning line and Ballistics Early Warning line reported radar evidence of unidentified flying objects flying due south east. As of this moment we have been unable to determine the nature of these objects, but for the time being in the interest of national safety we are declaring a state of Yellow Alert.

(*a pause*)

The Civil Defense authorities request that if you have a shelter already prepared go there at once. If you do not have a shelter use your time to move supplies of food, water, medicine and other supplies to a central place. Keep all windows and doors closed. We repeat: if you're in your home go to your prepared shelters or to your basement . . .

> *His voice fades.*

12. DIFFERENT ANGLE   THE ROOM

As after a stunned moment of sheer inarticulate horror, the people in the room start toward the front door and outside.

CUT TO:

13. EXT HOUSE   NIGHT

As they come out, cross the porch and then start down the steps in a mad, frenetic exodus toward each of their houses. As they arrive outside a siren starts to blare out its dissonant, shrieking scream and the sound of it stops them in their tracks.

14. SERIES OF CLOSE SHOTS   FACES OF THE
thru   MEN AND WOMEN
17.

As they each stare toward the sky. The voice of the Conelrad radio announcer continues underneath from the house. Then they each break off and head in different directions toward their homes.

NARRATOR   What you're about to watch is a nightmare. It is not meant to be prophetic. It need not happen. It is the fervent and urgent prayer of all men of good will that it shall never happen.

> (*a pause*)

But in this place . . . in this moment . . . it does happen.

FADE TO BLACK:

FADE ON:

18. INT CELLAR STOCKTON'S HOUSE NIGHT

At the far end of the room is a concrete wall with a heavy steel door, now open, revealing a small, perhaps ten by ten shelter encased by reinforced concrete walls. Three cots, a shelf full of canned goods and a portable radio which is on.

ANNOUNCER'S VOICE This is Conelrad your emergency broadcasting station. You will find Conelrad at either 640 or 1240 on your dial. Remain tuned to this frequency. We repeat our previous announcement. We are in a state of Yellow Alert. If you have a shelter already prepared go there at once. If you do not have a shelter use your time to move supplies of food, water, medicine and other supplies to a central place. Keep all windows and doors closed. We repeat: if you're in your home go to your prepared shelters or to your basement . . .

CUT TO:

19. EXTREMELY TIGHT CLOSE SHOT FAUCET

PULL BACK FOR FULL SHOT STOCKTON KITCHEN NIGHT. The water is just dribbling out of the tap. GRACE STOCKTON *has collected several jugs and vases and is filling them.* PAUL *hurries through the kitchen carrying a box full of canned goods, followed by his father who goes over toward the sink and hoists up two of the jugs.*

STOCKTON Fill up as many as you can, Grace. I'm going to start the generator up in the shelter in case the power goes off.

(*looking up toward dimming lights*)

And that may happen any moment now.
    GRACE And there's hardly any water coming through the tap—

STOCKTON   That's because everybody and his brother is doing the same thing we are. Keep it on full force until it stops.

20. MED CLOSE SHOT   GRACE

As she picks up a jug that's partially filled, shoves another one under the tap in its place. But in the process of moving the filled one onto the sink counter, it slips and smashes on the floor. She lets out a gasp and puts her hands to the sides of her head.

STOCKTON (*gentle, but firm*)   Easy, honey, easy. Make believe it's perfume and it costs a hundred bucks an ounce. Maybe in an hour or so it'll be worth even more than that—

PAUL (*enters from the basement*)   What else, Pop?

STOCKTON   All the canned goods down?

PAUL   All that I could find.

GRACE   How about the fruit cellar?

PAUL   I put all those in too.

STOCKTON   Get my bag from the bedroom. Put that in there too.

PAUL   What about books and stuff?

GRACE (*close to hysteria*)   Your father told you to get his bag—!

STOCKTON (*reaches out and holds Grace's arm*)   There's time, Grace. There's plenty of time. And we'll need books and things. Who knows how long we'll have to stay down there.

PAUL (*crossing the room and heading out into the dining room*) I'll get your bag, Pop.

STOCKTON   What about light bulbs. Where do you keep the light bulbs?

GRACE (*points*)   Top shelf in that cupboard there. (*then closes her eyes tightly and clenching her fists*) We don't have any. I ran out yesterday. I was going to buy some at the store. There was a sale on— (*she lets out one sob*) Oh, my dear God, I'm talking like an idiot. (*then even more frightened*) How much time do we have?

STOCKTON   There's no telling. Seems to me I remember reading someplace from the first alarm we might have anywhere from fifteen minutes to half an hour.

GRACE (*her eyes going wide*)   Fifteen minutes!

STOCKTON   I'm winging it, Grace. I don't know for sure. I don't think anyone does. (*he heads toward the door to dining room*) Keep pouring the water.

CUT TO:

21. INT DINING ROOM

As STOCKTON *enters, goes through and then into the front hall. He calls.*

STOCKTON   Paul? You get my bag?

22. DIFFERENT ANGLE   PAUL

As he comes down the steps carrying a bag and an armful of books and magazines.

PAUL   I got everything, Pop.

STOCKTON *takes the things from his arms at the foot of the steps.*

STOCKTON   Lemmee give you a hand.

CUT TO:

23. KITCHEN

As the water in the tap drips . . . drips . . . and finally stops altogether. Grace whirls around from the sink and shouts.

GRACE   Bill, there's no more water.

24. MED CLOSE SHOT   DOOR LEADING TO DINING ROOM

As STOCKTON *and* PAUL *enter the kitchen and head toward the basement door.*

STOCKTON It doesn't make any difference. I think we've got enough now anyway. Bring a jug with you, Grace. Paul and I'll get the rest in a minute.

25. ANGLE SHOT   LOOKING DOWN THE BASEMENT STEPS

As all three head down them.

CUT TO:

26. INT SHELTER

Now loaded down with boxes, jugs, et al, as the three of them enter and deposit their loads.

STOCKTON You two stay here. I'll get the rest of the water. (*he suddenly snaps his fingers*) There's a five gallon can of gasoline in the garage. Paul, you run out and get that. We'll need it for the generator.
PAUL Right, Pop.

He goes out past his father. GRACE *sits down on the cot, her fist clenched, staring out at nothing.*

STOCKTON I'll get the rest of the water.

GRACE nods. He makes a move to leave, then looks at her intently, crosses over to her and kneels down in front of her. He takes both her hands in his.

STOCKTON If it's a bomb there's no assurance that it'll land near us. And if it doesn't—
GRACE (*interrupting, pulling her hands away*) But if it does . . . we're forty miles from New York. And New York's going to get it. We know that, And then we'll get it too. All of it. The poison, the radiation, the whole thing. We'll get it too.
STOCKTON We'll be in a shelter, Grace. And with any luck at all, we'll survive. We've got enough food and water to last us at least two weeks. Maybe even longer if we use it wisely.
GRACE And then what? Then what, Bill? We crawl out of here

like gophers to tip toe through all the rubble up above. The rubble and the ruins and the bodies of our friends—

> (*she gives him a long, queer look, composite of horror and a building panic*)

Why is it so necessary that we survive? What's the good of it, Bill?

> (*she suddenly breaks, grabbing him, her voice a long drawn out sob*)

Bill, wouldn't it be better . . . wouldn't it be quicker and easier if we just—

> *At this moment there's the sound of Paul's voice from up above calling down to them.*

PAUL'S VOICE   I got the gasoline, Pop. Is that all you need from out there?

STOCKTON (*turns toward his wife, evenly*)   That's why we have to survive. *That's* the reason. He may inherit just rubble now, but he's twelve years old.

> (*he turns away thoughtfully*)

He's twelve years old, Grace . . .

> (*then he rises and calls out*)

Paul!

PAUL'S VOICE (*nearer*)   I got the gas, Pop.

> *The boy appears at the door to the shelter.*

STOCKTON   Lay it down there next to the generator. I'll go up and get the rest of the water.

27. TRACK SHOT WITH HIM

> *As he walks through the basement and starts up the steps toward the kitchen.*

28. INT KITCHEN

As he goes over to the sink, starts to collect the last of the jugs. There's a sudden knock on the back door and through the window and the semi-parted curtains we see the face of JERRY HARLOWE. STOCKTON *crosses over, unlocks the door and opens it.*

HARLOWE   How you doing, Bill?

STOCKTON   Collecting water which is what you should be doing.

HARLOWE   We've got about thirty gallons and the water stopped. Did yours stop too?

STOCKTON   (*nods*) You better get on home, Jerry. Get into your shel— (*he stops abruptly, wets his lips*) Into your basement. I'd board up the windows if I were you. And if you've got any wood putty or anything I'd seal the corners.

29. CLOSE SHOT HARLOWE

His voice is very gentle.

HARLOWE   We don't have a cellar, Bill. Remember?

(*then a lopsided grin*)

The benefits of modern architecture. We've got the one brand new house on the street. Everything at your beck and call. Everything at your fingertips. And a nice electrical laundry room right off the kitchen.

(*his voice shakes slightly*)

Every wonder of modern science taken into account except the one that's heading for us now.

(*there's a silence and* HARLOWE *tries to keep the supplication out of his voice*)

Bill, can I bring Martha and the kids over here?

STOCKTON   Over *here?*

HARLOWE   We're sitting ducks over there. Sitting ducks. We don't have any protection at all.

STOCKTON   (*after a moment's hesitation*)   You can use our basement.

HARLOWE   Your basement? What about your shelter? That's the only place anyone can survive! We've got to get into a shelter.

STOCKTON   (*after a pause*)   I don't have any room, Jerry. I don't have near enough room. Or supplies or anything. It's designed for three people.

HARLOWE   We'll bring our own water and our own food. We'll sleep on top of one another if necessary. Please . . . Bill. We've got to use your shelter. I've got to keep my family alive. We won't use any of your stuff.

STOCKTON   What about your own air? Will you bring your own air? That's a ten by ten room, Jerry.

HARLOWE   (*momentarily taken aback and having to recover*)   Just let us stay in there the first forty-eight hours or so, then we'll get out. Just so we can have a chance during the rough time.

STOCKTON   When that door gets closed and locked—it *stays* closed and locked. There'll be radiation and heaven knows what else. (*and now his face torn by anguish*) I'm sorry, Jerry. As God is my witness, I'm sorry. But I built that for *my* family.

HARLOWE   (*grabbing him, his voice high, shrill and unsteady*) And what about *mine?* What do *we* do? Just rock on the front porch until we get burned into cinders?

STOCKTON   (*breaks away from him*)   That's not my concern. Right at this given moment it's my family I have to worry about.

> *He picks up the water jugs and starts toward the basement door.* HARLOWE *runs toward him, whirls him around, grabs him.*

HARLOWE   I am not going to sit by and watch my wife and children die in agony. I'm not going to do that. Do you understand me, Bill? (*he shakes Stockton*) I am not going to do—

> *In the process and as* STOCKTON *tries to pull away, he trips and falls through the cellar door opening.*

ANGLE SHOT DOWN THE STEPS

As one of the jugs rolls down one step at a time, miraculously not breaking. STOCKTON *slowly rises to his feet.*

31. CLOSE TWO SHOT THE TWO MEN

HARLOWE *closes his eyes and lowers his head.*

HARLOWE I'm sorry, Bill. Please forgive me.

STOCKTON (*guiltily averts his eyes then looks up, in a very soft and gentle voice*) I kept telling you. All of you. Build a shelter. Get ready. Forget the card parties and the barbecues for maybe two hours a week. And make an admission to yourself that the worst is possible.

(*he shakes his head*)

But you didn't want to listen, Jerry. None of you wanted to listen. To build a shelter was admitting the kind of age we lived in and none of you had the guts to face that. So now, Jerry, now you've got to find some guts to face something far worse. Not just the possibility . . . that was easy to live with. Now you've got to face the reality. God protect you, Jerry. It's out of my hands now. It's simply out of my hands. It's got to be God.

He turns and starts down the basement steps as we take an

ABRUPT CUT TO:

32. FRONT DOOR

It's flung open and in walks MARTY WEISS, *his* WIFE, *a tiny sleepy little boy in a pair of Dr. Denton's, rubbing his eyes, and an infant in his arms. He barges into the dining room, calling.*

WEISS Bill? Bill, where are you?

MRS. WEISS (*coming up close to him, her face pale with terror*) They're already in the shelter. I told you they'd be in the shelter. They've locked themselves in.

> At this moment HARLOWE *comes out from the kitchen. He looks at them briefly.*

HARLOWE It's no use, Marty. He won't let anyone in.

WEISS (*close to hysteria*) He's *got* to let us in. We don't even have any windows in half the basement. I don't have anything to plug them up either. And a basement wouldn't be any help anyway. (*he starts to push his way past* HARLOWE) Where is he? Is he downstairs? Is he in the shelter?

CUT TO:

33. ANGLE SHOT LOOKING UP THE STEPS AT WEISS

> *As he appears at the top, shouting down.*

WEISS Bill? Bill, it's Marty. We've got the kids with us. (*he frantically stumbles half way down the cellar steps*) Bill? Bill?

34. DIFFERENT ANGLE OF HIM

> *As he goes down the rest of the steps, turns and starts across the basement toward the shelter which has now been closed and locked. Halfway across the room the lights suddenly go out and once again the sirens can be heard.*

35. DIFFERENT ANGLE THE DOOR

> *As Weiss gropes his way over to it, stumbles, reaches out to clutch at it for support.*

WEISS Bill? Bill, please. Please—

> *Above him we hear the sound of his little boy suddenly screaming in fear, then his wife's voice.*

MRS. WEISS'S VOICE Marty? Marty, where are you? The lights are out. Marty, please . . . come back and get us—

36. DIFFERENT CLOSER ANGLE WEISS

As he presses his cheek against the shelter door.

WEISS Bill. Please, Bill, please let us in. Please.

CUT TO:

37. EXTREMELY TIGHT CLOSE SHOT STOCKTON

On the other side of the door. Weiss's voice can be heard, muffled.

WEISS'S VOICE Please, Bill. Please let us in.

38. EXTREMELY TIGHT CLOSE SHOT GRACE

As she closes her eyes as if by this act she could blot out the voices.

39. DIFFERENT ANGLE STOCKTON

As he crosses over, manipulates a few buttons, then pulls a small starter knob attached to the tiny generator. It starts up after a few preliminary coughs and then hums into action. At this moment the lights go on in the shelter.

40. CLOSE SHOT STOCKTON

His face suddenly illuminated by the lights. It's creased, lined, furrowed with the results of this massive attack on first his conscience, his beliefs, the habit pattern of a lifetime which he must suddenly simply turn aside. He takes a hesitant step toward the door, facing it. His lips move for a moment and finally speech comes.

STOCKTON Marty, I would if I could. Do you understand? I swear to you, I would.

WEISS'S VOICE Bill, please. Please. You've got to. You've got to let us in.

41. CLOSE SHOT STOCKTON

As he drops to his knees and presses his face against the side of the door. His lips tremble.

STOCKTON I can't, Marty. Don't stay there asking me. Because I can't. I can't and I won't.

CUT TO:

42. CLOSE SHOT WEISS

In the shadowed darkness on the other side of the door.

WEISS (*his voice breaking perceptibly*) I feel sorry for you then, Bill. I really do. You probably will survive—but you're going to have blood on your hands. Do you hear me, Bill? You'll have blood on your hands!

CUT TO:

43. CLOSE SHOT PAUL

His young face white with the terror of it, of the sudden exposure to naked emotions of adults set against a background of terror that he cannot even assimilate.

44. CLOSE SHOT GRACE

As she closes her eyes tightly and leans her head against her fists.

45. CLOSE SHOT STOCKTON

As he slowly turns away from the door. At this moment he can hear the sound of the child crying again and Mrs. Weiss's forlorn, lost cry for her husband.

46. DIFFERENT ANGLE STOCKTON

STOCKTON (*very softly*) That was a million years ago. A million years ago. (*he whirls around, slams himself against the door*) Marty, get out of here! Do you hear me? *Get out of here.*

> *Then he closes his eyes tightly and lets his head sink forward as the sound of the radio intermingles with the cry of a small child.*

FADE TO BLACK:

END ACT ONE

Act Two

FADE ON:

47. INT DINING ROOM STOCKTON HOUSE NIGHT

> MARTY WEISS, HIS WIFE *and* CHILDREN *feel their way through the kitchen toward the dining table where the burned down candles of the birthday banquet give them some light.* MARTY *takes the candles and assists his wife through the dining room toward the living room as we hear and see* MRS. HARLOWE *and* CHILDREN:

MRS. HARLOWE Well, go back!
HARLOWE, *standing in front doorway.*
HARLOWE Wouldn't help.
MRS. HARLOWE Jerry, ask again.
> *By the time* WEISS *and his* WIFE *reach the front door beside* HARLOWE:

CUT TO:

47A. EXT STREET POV STREET OUTSIDE
STOCKTON HOME

> *Pan* HENDERSON *and* MRS. HENDERSON *into front door of* STOCKTON *house as* HENDERSON *is saying:*

HENDERSON It'll land any minute. I just know it. It's going to land any minute—

MRS. HENDERSON (*grabs hold of him*) What are we going to do, Frank? What are we going to do?

Throughout above and following dialogue, a portable radio carried by one of the children carries the following dialogue:

ANNOUNCER'S VOICE This is Conelrad. This is Conelrad. We are still in a state of Yellow Alert. If you are a public official or government employee with an emergency assignment, or a civil defense worker, you should report to your post immediately. If you are a public official or government employee . . .

HARLOWE Don't waste your time. He won't let anyone in.

MRS. HENDERSON What'll we do?

HARLOWE Maybe we ought to pick out just one basement and go to work on it. Pool all our stuff. Food, water, everything.

MARTHA HARLOWE It isn't fair. (*she points toward Stockton house*) He's down there in a bomb shelter completely safe. And *our* kids have to just wait around for a bomb to drop and—

HENDERSON Let's just go down into his basement and break down the door?

A chorus of voices greet this with assent.

CUT TO:

47B. INT DINING ROOM

As HENDERSON *streaks through toward the basement entrance.* HARLOWE *over-takes him saying:*

HARLOWE Wait a minute, wait a minute. All of us couldn't fit in there. That would be crazy to even try.

WEISS Why don't we draw lots? Pick out *one* family?

HARLOWE What difference would it make? He won't let us in.

HENDERSON We can all march down there and tell him he's got the whole street against him. We could do that.

HARLOWE What good would that do? I keep telling you. Even if we were to break down the door, it couldn't accommodate all of us. We'd just be killing everybody and for no reason.

MRS. HENDERSON   If it saves even one of these kids out here—I call that a reason.

The voice comes up again.

WEISS   Jerry, you know him better than any of us. You're his best friend. Why don't you go down again. Try to talk to him. Plead with him. Tell him to pick out one family—Draw lots or something—

HENDERSON   One family, meaning yours, Weiss, huh?

WEISS (*whirls around to him*)   Why not? I've got a three month old infant—

MRS. HENDERSON   What difference does that make? Is your baby's life any more precious than our kids?

WEISS (*shouting at her*)   I never said that. If you're going to start trying to argue about who deserves to live more than the next one—

HENDERSON   Why don't you shut your mouth, Weiss? (*with a wild, illogical anger*) That's the way it is when the foreigners come over here. Pushy, grabby, semi-Americans—

48. CLOSE SHOT   WEISS

His face goes white.

WEISS   Why you garbage-brained idiot you—

MRS. HENDERSON   It still goes, Weiss! For my dough you're at the bottom of the list—

49. DIFFERENT ANGLE   THE GROUP

As WEISS *suddenly flings himself through the crowd toward the man and there's a brief, inexpert grappling between them broken up by Harlowe who stands between them breathless.*

HARLOWE   Keep it up, both of you. Just keep it up. We won't need a bomb. We can slaughter each other.

MRS. WEISS (*pleading*)   Marty, go down to Bill's shelter again. Ask him—

WEISS   I've already asked him. It wouldn't do any good.

Once again the siren sounds and the people seem to move closer together, staring up toward the night sky. Off in the distance we see searchlights.

HARLOWE   Searchlights. It must be coming closer. (*then to the man with the portable*)

CUT TO:

49A. EXT POV OVER HARLOWE'S SHOULDER

HARLOWE   Anything *new* on the radio?
MAN #1 (*listens for a moment*)   No . . .

CUT TO:

50. INT DIFFERENT ANGLE   ON GROUP

HENDERSON (*as he suddenly pushes* HARLOWE *aside and heads for the steps*)   I'm going down there and get him to open up that door. I don't care what the rest of you think. That's the only thing left to do.
MAN #1   He's right. Come on, let's do it.

51. INT SHELTER

GRACE *is holding tight to* PAUL. STOCKTON *stands close to the door listening to the noises from outside as they approach. There's a pounding on the shelter door that reverberates. We hear* MAN ONE's *Voice.*

HENDERSON   Bill? Bill Stockton? You've got a bunch of your neighbors out here who want to stay alive. Now you can open the door and talk to us and figure out with us how many can come in there. Or else you can just keep doing what you're doing—and we'll bust our way in there.

CUT TO:

52. INT BASEMENT THE OTHER SIDE OF THE SHELTER DOOR

HARLOWE *appears and pushes his way through the group and goes over to the shelter door.*

HARLOWE Bill. This is Jerry. They mean business out here.

STOCKTON'S VOICE And I mean business in *here*. I've already told you, Jerry. You're wasting your time. You're wasting precious time that could be used for something else . . . like figuring out how you can survive.

MAN #1 Why don't we get some kind of battering ram?

HENDERSON We could go over to Bennett Avenue. Phil Kline has a bunch of two by fours in his basement. I've seen them.

MAN #1 That would get him into the act then and who cares about saving *him*? The minute we do that then we let all those people know that there's a shelter on this street. We'd have a whole mob to contend with. A whole bunch of outsiders.

MRS. HENDERSON Sure and what right have they got to come over here. This isn't *their* street. This isn't their shelter.

53. CLOSE SHOT HARLOWE

He's been listening to all of this and he slowly shakes his head, clenching and unclenching his fists. He suddenly pushes himself through to the shelter door and turns with his back against it.

HARLOWE This is *our* shelter, huh? And on the next street—that's a different country. Patronize home industries. You idiots. You fools. You're insane now, all of you.

MRS. WEISS Maybe you don't want to live, Jerry. Maybe you don't care.

HARLOWE I care. Believe me, I care. I'd like to see the morning come too. But you're becoming a mob now. And a mob doesn't have any brains and that's what you're proving.

HENDERSON I say let's get the battering ram. And we'll just tell Kline to keep his mouth shut as to why we want it.

WEISS I agree with Jerry. Let's get hold of ourselves. Let's stop and think for a minute—

HENDERSON (*turning to face* WEISS) Nobody cares what you think. You or your kind. I thought I made that clear upstairs. I think the first order of business is to get you out of here.

> *With this he lashes out, smashing his fist into* WEISS's *face in a blow so unexpected and so wild that* WEISS, *totally unprepared, is battered against the wall. His wife screams and, still holding the baby, rushes to him. There's a commotion as several men try to grab the neighbor and* HARLOWE *is immediately at* WEISS's *side trying to help him to his feet. Once again the sirens blast and it's almost as if it were some kind of a signal reigniting the panic.*

HENDERSON (*shouts over the noise and commotion*) Come on, let's get something to smash this door down.

54. DIFFERENT ANGLE AS THEY START OUT OF THE CELLAR

Toward the steps.

55. ANGLE SHOT OF NEIGHBOR ONE

As he shouts over his shoulder.

HENDERSON You had your chance, Stockton. Just remember that. You had your chance—

CUT TO:

56. INT SHELTER

As STOCKTON *slowly turns to face his wife. The angry screaming cries of the people ring in their ears even as they depart.*

57. CLOSE SHOT GRACE

As she looks up.

GRACE Bill? Who were those people?

58. CLOSE SHOT STOCKTON

As he turns to stare toward the door.

STOCKTON "Those people"? Those are our neighbors, Grace. Our friends. The people we've lived with and alongside for twenty years. (*then in a different fixed expression and in a different tone*) Come on, Paul. Let's put stuff up against this door. Everything we can.

The man and boy then start to pile up a barricade, using furniture, the generator, books, any movable object they can get their hands on.

DISSOLVE TO:

59. THE MOB

As they march down the street carrying a giant two by four that is perhaps fifteen feet long.

60. DIFFERENT ANGLE OF THE MARCHERS

As their own shouts mix with the sound of the intermittent siren and with the voice of the announcer on the Conelrad station.

ANNOUNCER'S VOICE We've been asked to once again remind the population that they are to remain calm, stay off the streets. This is urgent. *Please remain off the streets.* Everything possible is being done in the way of protection. But the military and important civil defense vehicles must have the streets clear. So you're once again reminded to remain off the streets. *Remain off the streets!*

61. DIFFERENT ANGLE   THE STOCKTON HOUSE

As the mob converges on it.

CUT TO:

62. INT THE HOUSE

As they smash into it, carrying the battering ram.

63. DIFFERENT ANGLES
thru
65.

As they move down the cellar steps.

CUT TO:

66. SHELTER DOOR

As the board smashes into it. The siren goes up louder and more piercing and it is at this moment that we see both WEISS *and* HARLOWE *join the men on the battering ram to lend their support to it.*

CUT TO:

67. INT THE SHELTER

As STOCKTON *and* PAUL *lean against it as it starts to give under the weight, under the pressure. The air is filled with angry shouts, the intermittent siren, the cries of women and children.*

68. SEVERAL SHOTS INTERSPERSING THE AREAS
thru
71. INSIDE AND OUTSIDE OF THE SHELTER

And it all reaches one vast pitch just as the door buckles and is forced open. PAUL *and* STOCKTON *are pushed back into the shelter and just at this moment the lights go on in the basement. The siren also reaches its pinnacle and then suddenly goes off and there is absolute dead silence for a long moment. The CAMERA PANS past the faces of the people including the occupants of the shelter to the portable radio in the corner.*

ANNOUNCER'S VOICE   This is Conelrad. This is Conelrad. Remain tuned for an important message. Remain tuned for an important message. (*a pause*) The President of the United States has just announced that the previously unidentified objects have now been definitely ascertained as being satellites. Repeat. There are no enemy missiles approaching. Repeat. There are no enemy missiles approaching. The objects have been identified as satellites. They are harmless and we are in no danger. Repeat. We are in no danger. The state of emergency has officially been called off. We are in no danger. Repeat. There is no enemy attack. There is no enemy attack.

72. PAN SHOT ACROSS THE FACES OF THE PEOPLE

As this news registers and sinks in.

MRS. WEISS (*her eyes closed and crying softly*)   Thank God. Oh, thank God.

PAN SHOT over to Weiss, his face bruised and blood clotted.

WEISS (*in a whisper*)   Amen to that.

PAN SHOT over to MAN ONE *who doesn't seem to know whether to smile or cry or what. And finally he turns to* WEISS, *cups his face in his hands.*

HENDERSON   Hey, Marty . . . Marty . . . I went off my rocker. You understand that, don't you? I just went off my rocker. I didn't mean all the things I said. (*he wets his lips, his voice shaking*) We were all of us . . . we were so scared . . . so confused. (*he holds out his hands in a gesture*) Well it's no wonder really, is it? I mean . . . well you can understand why we blew our tops a little—

There's a murmur of voices, a few perfunctory, half-hearted nods, but they're all still in a state of shock.

73. CLOSE SHOT   HARLOWE

HARLOWE   I don't think Marty's going to hold it against you. (*then turning to* STOCKTON) I just hope Bill won't hold *this*—(he *points to the wreckage and rubble around him*) against us. We'll pay for the damage, Bill. We'll take up a collection right away.

74. MOVING SHOT STOCKTON

As he walks past them across the cellar and up toward the stairs. All eyes are on him and there's an absolute dead silence.

WEISS (*his voice shaky and nervous*) We could . . . we could have a block party or something tomorrow night. A big celebration. I think we rate one now.

He looks around smiling at the others, a nervous smile born of a carry-over of fear and the realization that something has taken hold of all of them now. Something deadening in its effect and disquieting beyond words. Stockton takes a step up on the stairs then stops and turns back toward them. His face is impassive more thoughtful than anything.

HARLOWE (*with phony laughter desperately trying to relieve situation*) Block party's not a bad idea. (*looking around at the others*) anything to get back to normal.

75. CLOSE SHOT STOCKTON

As he looks from face to face and slowly shakes his head.

STOCKTON Normal? (*a pause*) I don't know. I don't know what "normal" is. I thought I did, but I don't any more.

76. GROUP SHOT

HARLOWE I told you we'd pay for the damages—
STOCKTON (*stares at him*) The damages? (*he nods*) I wonder if we realize just what those damages are? (*he looks from face to face again*) Maybe the worst of them was finding out just what we're like when we're normal. The kind of people we are. Just underneath the surface. I mean all of us. A lot of naked animals who put such a premium on staying alive that they claw their neighbors to death just for the privilege. (*he leans against the stairway wall, suddenly desperately tired, very softly as he turns away from them*) We were

spared a bomb tonight . . . but I wonder if we weren't destroyed even
without it.

> *He continues up the steps as we*

DISSOLVE TO:

77. EXT HIS HOUSE LONG ANGLE SHOT
LOOKING DOWN

> *As the people come out quietly in twos and threes and dis-*
> *appear in all directions, back to their houses. Over this shot*
> *we hear* NARRATOR'S *voice.*

NARRATOR No moral . . . no message . . . no prophetic tract. Just
a simple statement of fact. For civilization to survive . . . the human
race has to remain civilized.

FADE TO BLACK:

THE END

DISCUSSION

1. Briefly state the conflict in this play. How does the fact that
   Stockton is a doctor intensify the conflict?
2. Why does Serling begin the play with a birthday celebration at
   which many of Stockton's neighbors are present?
3. How is Mr. Harlowe's after-dinner speech to be interpreted, in
   the light of later developments?
4. How does Serling clarify Stockton's attitude toward survival
   during the scene in which the family gathers last-minute supplies?
   Is there any significance to the family's discussion of these supplies? Explain.
5. What are Stockton's reasons for refusing his neighbors shelter?
   Do you feel that he is right in refusing them?
6. What differences do you note between Stockton's behavior during
   the crisis, and his wife's? Can you account for these differences?
7. What is the meaning of Stockton's reply to Weiss, "That was a
   million years ago"?

8. What hostilities develop among Stockton's neighbors as they converse outside the shelter? Why do they reject Henderson's suggestion to seek help from a resident of Bennett Avenue? Why do they turn with such vehemence upon Mr. Weiss?

9. What moment constitutes the climax of the play? How do you know?

10. Why is it significant that both Weiss and Harlowe lend their support to the battering ram? In what sense is the battering down of the shelter door a symbolic act?

11. How do the neighbors assess their own behavior, once the crisis has passed? Why are they so eager to resume life just as it was beforehand? Do you think it will be possible for them to accomplish this?

12. What conclusions does Stockton draw from the events of the evening? Why is he in a better position than the others to pass judgment? What does Stockton mean when he comments, "We were spared a bomb tonight . . . but I wonder if we weren't destroyed even without it?"

13. What is symbolized by the fact that, during the major portion of the play, the lights are out and Stockton's neighbors move about in almost total darkness?

14. What dramatic purpose is served by the intermittent blaring of the sirens, the voice of the Conelrad announcer, and the movements of the searchlights?

15. Considering the events of this play, how would you describe Serling's attitude toward human nature?

16. Does the theme have universal application? Why?

TOPICS FOR WRITING

An appraisal of Dr. Stockton's character
Man's responsibility to his fellow man
What Price Survival?

Questions for Comparative Studies

The questions in this section are exploratory in nature, suggesting, but by no means exhausting, the possibilities for the comparative study of these short plays. Further comparative reading questions are certain to result from a productive classroom discussion of those that appear below.

1. Compare the attitudes of Captain Keeney (*Ile*) and Shirley (*Native Dancer*) toward failure and success.
2. How does their treatment of subordinates reveal the basic differences in temperament between Lincoln (*The Thinking Heart*) and Captain Keeney (*Ile*)?
3. Prove that a major problem in *Trifles, The Browning Version,* and *Ile* concerns the destruction of illusions.
4. What are the similarities between Bobolink's position (*To Bobolink, for Her Spirit*) and Mrs. Dowey's (*The Old Lady Shows Her Medals*)? What are the differences?
5. Compare the conflict in *The Shelter* with the conflict in *The Clod*, the conflict in *The Rising of the Moon* with the conflict in *Trifles*.
6. How is it a result of character as well as situation that Henry Adams (*The Million-Pound Bank Note*) has unlimited financial credit, whereas Sammy (*Sammy*) has none?
7. What is similar about the manner in which Saroyan (*The Man With the Heart in the Highlands*) and Beach (*The Clod*) use setting as an indication of character?
8. Explain why both Glaspell (*Trifles*) and Beach (*The Clod*) include moments in their plays during which the stage is left temporarily unoccupied.
9. How do Inge (*To Bobolink, for Her Spirit*) and Benét (*The Devil and Daniel Webster*) differ in their technique of introducing essential background information? How is this difference explainable?
10. Compare the basic plot structure of *Sammy* with that of *Sorry, Wrong Number*. Does your attitude toward the outcome of these two plays differ? Why?

11. What ironic contrast do you observe between Lincoln's position in *The Thinking Heart* and Mary Trask's position in *The Clod?*

12. Is it for similar or for different reasons that both Faulkner (*The Thinking Heart*) and Benét (*The Devil and Daniel Webster*) include passages of poetry in their plays? Explain.

13. What is the connection between Kaufman's use of humor (*The Still Alarm*) and that of Stern and Zelinka (*The $99,000 Answer*)?

14. For what similar purpose do Corwin (*My Client Curley*) and Shaw (*Native Dancer*) introduce minor characters into their stories?

15. How do young people exhibit maturity beyond their years in both *The Browning Version* and *The Man With the Heart in the Highlands?*

16. Contrast the effects of new-found wealth upon the lives of Henry Adams (*The Million-Pound Bank Note*) and the White family (*The Monkey's Paw*).

17. Compare the position of the County Attorney at the end of *Trifles* with the position of Policeman X at the end of *The Rising of the Moon*.

18. Contrast the outcome of Frank Hunter's relationship with a woman (*The Browning Version*) to the outcome of Kenneth Dowey's (*The Old Lady Shows Her Medals*). Does the nature of these relationships imply a difference in point of view between the two playwrights? Explain.

19. Compare the attitudes of Elbert Stevenson (*Sorry, Wrong Number*) and John Wright (*Trifles*) toward their wives.

20. Contrast the attitudes of Millie Crocker-Harris (*The Browning Version*) and Mary Stone (*The Devil and Daniel Webster*) toward their husbands.

21. How is the act of gift-giving symbolically significant in both *The Browning Version* and *The Old Lady Shows Her Medals?*

22. Are the reasons for which Macgregor (*The Man With the Heart in the Highlands*) and the hunted man (*The Rising of the Moon*) seek attention with their music in any way comparable?

23. How is the function of the narrator in *My Client Curley* similar to the function of the narrator in *The Million-Pound Bank Note?* How does it differ from the function of the narrator in *The Thinking Heart?*

24. What is similar about the manner in which the authors of *Sorry, Wrong Number* and *The Monkey's Paw* foreshadow the element of tragedy?

25. At one point in *Sammy*, in *The Thinking Heart*, and in *The Devil*

and Daniel Webster, the main character slumps, utterly dejected, into a chair. How are the reasons for this dejection similar? How do they differ?

26. What significant differences do you note between Doctor Stockton's judgment of human nature (*The Shelter*) and Daniel Webster's (*The Devil and Daniel Webster*)? With which of these judgments are you more in sympathy? Why?

27. How does the element of chance play a part in the action of both *The Million-Pound Bank Note* and *The Clod*? To what degree, if any, is your enjoyment of the plays affected?

28. Compare the function of stage lighting in *Sammy* with its function in *The Shelter.*

29. From the plays that you have read, consider *one* in which the author includes extensive stage directions, and *one* in which the author includes only a few. Evaluate the use of stage directions as a means of dramatic expression.

30. Discuss the relative merits of television and radio for short play production, referring to at least one play of each type to support your conclusions.

Glossary of Terms

AD LIB   Speech or stage business that is indicated, but not actually written out, by the playwright. The actors are supposed to improvise. The ad lib may call, for example, for a cordial exchange of greetings among several characters.

ATMOSPHERE   The overall feeling or mood that results from the writer's use of setting and special effects. The manner in which the characters react to their surroundings may contribute to the atmosphere of a story.

BLACK-OUT   The sudden disappearance of a picture from the television screen, indicating a sharp break in the action of a play.

CLIMAX   The major turning point in the story, the point at which the conflict is finally resolved. The climax may be a moment of dramatic action, or a moment of quiet decision. In either case, it usually marks a significant change in the lives of the characters involved.

CLOSE-UP   A television picture in which the full face of an actor fills the screen.

COMEDY   A play that is typically light and cheerful in feeling. In many comedies the hero triumphs over seemingly impossible odds.

CUE   Any words or sound effects in a play that signal the speech of an oncoming actor.

CUT   An interruption in the action of a television play, during which there is an abrupt shift of scene.

CONFLICT   The struggle between opposing forces, ideas, or attitudes that is usually resolved before the conclusion of the story.

DÉNOUEMENT   The portion of the story that shows how the solution to the conflict affects the main characters. It follows the climax and precedes the actual ending. Dénouement comes from the French word that means "the unraveling."

DIALOGUE   The conversation between characters in a story. Dialogue is the playwright's most useful means of revealing character motivation and character change.

DISSOLVE   The gradual fading of one picture from the television screen, and the emergence of another.

DOLLY IN   The gradual movement of a television camera toward the focal point of a scene.

DRAMATIC IRONY   A form of irony in which the reader is aware of circumstances about which a character in the story has no knowledge. If the character knew what the reader knows, he would presumably not react to a particular situation as he does. (see IRONY)

EXPOSITION   The portion of a story that presents background information necessary to the reader's understanding of the characters and their situation.

FADE IN   The gradual appearance of a television picture, or the gradual increase in sound.

FADE OUT   The reverse of "fade in."

FARCE   A story, light in mood, which mocks or ridicules a common situation. In most farces there is little attempt on the part of the author to establish full, subtly-defined characters. The situation itself is of foremost importance.

FANTASY   A story, or an element within a story, that has the quality of the imaginary and the unreal.

FIGURATIVE LANGUAGE   Language in which words are used to suggest ideas and associations that go beyond literal, dictionary meanings.

FLASHBACK   Any description, during the course of a story, of events that took place at a previous time. The flashback helps to explain how a particular situation developed.

FOIL   A minor character in a story whose main purpose is to set off, by contrast, the personality of a major character.

FORESHADOWING   The hinting by an author of events yet to come, for the purpose of arousing reader curiosity.

IRONY   A kind of humor in which the opposite of what is expected or deserved occurs. Irony may involve a single statement, or an extended situation. Sometimes the reader understands the ironic implications of a situation, while the character involved does not. (see DRAMATIC IRONY)

MELODRAMA   A play characterized by exaggerated sentiment, violence, and passion.

MONOLOGUE   A drama, or part of a drama, in which a single character speaks while entirely alone. Often during a monologue a character reveals feelings that he would find difficult to express were other characters present. (see SOLILOQUY)

PAN   The movement of a television camera up, down, or across a scene.

PLOT   The sequence of events that forms the substance of a story. These events clarify the author's underlying purpose in writing. The plot is not to be confused with the theme. (see THEME).

RISING ACTION   The portion of a story that present the conflict, and shows the steps that generally lead to its solution.

SATIRE   A type of humor devoted to exposing, ridiculing, or denouncing personal follies or social abuses.

SETTING   The time and place of a story. In most plays the setting is clearly indicated by the author in his introductory stage directions.

SOLILOQUY   A speech in which a character reveals his innermost thoughts and feelings. Unlike a monologue, a soliloquy never constitutes more than a portion of a play.

STAGE BUSINESS   Movements and gestures that a playwright indicates for his characters in the stage directions. Such movements are sometimes more effective than dialogue in quickly establishing a character's attitudes.

SYMBOL   The use of one object, action, or idea to represent another, often for the purpose of producing an emotional response in the reader, or for giving depth of meaning to a story. Common symbols are The Statue of Liberty, which represents freedom, and the handshake, which represents friendship.

THEME   The underlying idea of a story, the author's purpose in writing. (see UNIVERSAL THEME).

TURNING POINT   A moment during the course of a story when a character seems about to solve his problems, but is unsuccessful. (see CLIMAX)

TYPE   A character that can be distinguished by a few, vivid personality traits. These traits mark him as one of a kind or class: "the intellectual," for example, "the buffoon," or "the optimist." Typed characters are seldom described by the author in more than surface detail.

UNIVERSAL THEME   A theme of far-reaching significance, one that contains some truth with which almost every reader can personally identify. (see THEME).

SCRIBNER STUDENT PAPERBACKS